## Date Loaned

*THE TROLLOPE READER*

# THE
# *Trollope Reader*

SELECTED AND EDITED BY
ESTHER CLOUDMAN DUNN
AND
MARION E. DODD

NEW YORK
OXFORD UNIVERSITY PRESS
1947

Copyright 1947 by Oxford University Press, New York, Inc.

PRINTED IN THE UNITED STATES OF AMERICA

# Contents

Introduction to Trollope, vii

## TROLLOPE LOOKS AT LIFE

Portrait Gallery, 3
Where It Happened, 26
Crucial Moments, 53
Daily Life, 105
Servants, 123

## HE CONSIDERS ITS PATTERNS

'Society,' 141
Marriage, 163
Hunting and Racing, 176
Clergy, 209
Doctors, Lawyers, and Others, 235
Business, 258

## HE DISTILLS ITS IDEAS AND THEORIES

Social Ideas, 279
Women, 317
Politics, 329
The Press, 344
Education, 350
Art and Letters, 360
Life's Vagaries, 386

## HE VISITS THE UNITED STATES

He Visits the United States, 401

Books on Trollope, 429
Index, 431

# Introduction

ALMOST ANY AFTERNOON in the London winter of 1861, a stocky Victorian gentleman in steel-rimmed spectacles, with a notable graying beard, might be seen at whist 'in the little room upstairs' at the Garrick Club in King Street. 'This playing of whist before dinner,' he confessed, 'has become a habit with me, so that unless there be something special to do . . . unless there be hunting, or I am wanted to ride in the Park . . . it is "my custom always in the afternoon."'

A description, you would say, of a comfortable, middle-aged English gentleman, with plenty of leisure, a substantial bank account, some distinction (for the Garrick Club made demands before it granted membership), a taste for the country and hunting, and an equal gift for life in London, with whist at the club or riding in the park. And you would be right.

For this Victorian figure was Anthony Trollope, novel-writing contemporary of Dickens and Thackeray and creator of that famous termagent among clerical ladies, Mrs. Proudie, wife of the Bishop of Barchester.

In a frank, straightforward *Autobiography,* which came out soon after his death in the early 'eighties, Anthony Trollope maintained that writing novels was a business to be accomplished at the rate of so many words per hour, so many pages per day, with an eye on the income they would make from a rapidly growing set of readers. His career as a novelist had proved the success of his commercial point of view and method, so that already in the early 'sixties he sat at his ease in his London club, while a stable with no less than four

INTRODUCTION

hunters awaited him at his near-by country place at Waltham Cross. There, too, strawberries and cabbages, fresh butter and home-cured hams furnished delicious fare for 'suburban hospitalities.'

Now in the 1940's the formula of Trollope's novels, 'a story ... thoroughly English ... [with] a little fox-hunting and a little tuft-hunting, some Christian virtue and some Christian cant,' as he put it, works as potent magic on present-day readers as it did in Trollope's lifetime. There is a boom in Anthony Trollope. The Archbishop of York (appropriate clerical source) in the summer of 1945 'nominated Trollope for first place in wartime British reading popularity.' And at the same moment one of Manhattan's largest second-hand bookshops reported that anything by Trollope was a request made 'five times a day.' Across the continent in San Francisco the Public Library reported Trollope withdrawals to be 76 per cent greater than in the preceding years.

During World War II over the B.B.C., in England, Trollope's novels were broadcast in radio versions. To the ears of wartime England in the mid-twentieth century, his mid-nineteenth-century dialogue sounded natural; his people seemed actually to come alive on the air.

Not only during World War II but 'since 1918,' says V. S. Pritchett, 'Trollope has become one of the great air raid shelters... Barsetshire has been one of the great Never-Never Lands of our time. It has been the normal country to which we all aspire.' This may be true or it may not. It is an interesting theory. The more one reads Trollope, however, the less one is able to dismiss him with a neat label; his variety, his complexity even, defy tidy critical phrases. The twentieth-century Trollopians are various, diverse in their tastes; they must read Trollope for very different reasons. In the middle 1930's, Gertrude Stein told one of the editors of the *Reader* that Trollope was her favorite English novelist. Another sort of reader finds half the charm of Angela Thirkell in discover-

[ viii ]

## INTRODUCTION

ing his 'beloved Barchester landscape brought back to life' in her pages.

What, then, are these novels that absorbed a Victorian world and claim many readers again in our so different twentieth century? The first key to their quality lies in certain phases of Trollope's own life. There were startlingly diverse elements in his background and early years that partly account for the substance and point of view of his novels: their wide gamut of human experience; their vivid portrayal of suffering, of the disparity between appearance and reality; the air of sunny comfort in which they bathe the stable and rooted phases of society.

Trollope's parents on both sides belonged to the established English tradition. Behind them were clergymen and university people. There was a baronetcy not too far back of Trollope's father. There were material 'expectations,' property that should have descended. Trollope's mother 'loved society,' her son says. She followed what was fashionable in politics, from the rage against tyrants in her youth to those later Tory leanings that made her think 'archduchesses were sweet.'

Anthony's own early sufferings and confusion came, as he puts it, from a 'mixture of poverty and gentle standing.' There was stark poverty in his early years, arising out of the too easy assumption of his barrister father that a gentleman should have a country place as well as a house in town. To the innate assurance that privilege belonged to him, Trollope senior added confidence in his own brains; for he was a gifted lawyer. But here, too, he misjudged his situation; for his bad temper drove his associates and his clients away and left him without cases.

Against such a background, Anthony's boyhood was unhappy. His mother, whose brains and courage served her well in the financial crisis of her husband, was off to the U. S. A. when Anthony was only twelve. She spent four years over here, incidentally gathering the materials for that devastating book, *The Domestic Manners of the Americans*. It offered a

## INTRODUCTION

jaundiced view of American life. It was written out of failure, with bitterness, but with a cleverness too, which made it sell well when it first came out in 1832. It 'saved the family from ruin,' says Anthony, looking backward. But he adds that it was an unfair book to the young nation that was America; 'it had hardly recognized their energy.'

Meanwhile Trollope spent four crucial years, from twelve to sixteen, without a mother, living first in a decaying, gloomy old farmhouse with his bad-tempered, badly adjusted failure of a father, attending as a day pupil a gentleman's boarding school, Harrow. Then he migrated from school to school, with floggings, insensitive headmasters, no pocket money, not even cleanliness and neat attire. He was dragged away from Winchester just when a scholarship at Oxford was almost within his grasp. He was put down as the hobbledehoy non-college member of a family that included both an Oxford and a Cambridge brother.

The temporary recovery of both social and financial standing after Mrs. Trollope's return and the publication of her *Domestic Manners* was only a momentary check in the dreadful fall of the family. The place at Harrow was 'sold up'; the sheriff was in charge; Anthony drove his ill father, a fugitive from debt, to London and saw him on the boat for Ostend. After the usual shifts and embarrassments, the family followed to Belgium and a house outside Bruges. This 'new banishment,' Trollope called it; for all his life up to then had, indeed, been his first banishment from the well-regulated and normal world to which by birth he belonged. This lonely, put-upon, teen-age boy must have had to think long and deeply in order to puzzle out who and what he was, what life was, and why conditions were as they were. The circumstances, cruel in themselves, were nicely calculated to ripen him early and make his perception of people and events keen and deeply articulate. It was the perfect youthful training for a novelist of manners, society, and life in its widely different, multiple faces.

## INTRODUCTION

The brief period in Belgium was dogged by increasing illness and poverty. 'By degrees,' he says, 'an established sorrow was at home among us.' His mother, tending an ill son, daughter, and husband, all near to death, filled every free interval in her dreadful days with novel writing. For she had learned that writing could produce the necessary money to keep things running. The force of this lesson must have been deeply impressed upon Anthony during those haunting months. She spent time too trying to get a post for him. He taught for a few weeks in an English school in Brussels; he faced the prospect of a 'commission in an Austrian cavalry regiment' with apathetic compliance. Through a friend of his mother's came an offer of a clerkship in the General Post Office in London. He took it.

His poverty-stricken life in London as a postal clerk, beginning at the age of nineteen at £90 a year and continuing for seven years, was to yield him material that, more than twenty years later, came out as a novel, under the title of *The Three Clerks*. Although his mother, after his father's death, was near London for a brief time, she was soon off again, first into Cumberland and afterwards to Italy. He was not her favorite son; she did not know how to bring variety, affection, stability, all those things that he so badly needed, into his life. He was alone again in a third period of spiritual 'banishment.'

The desperate gaieties of young clerks 'out of hours,' the moneylenders, the hostility of London streets, where there were no friendly houses to visit, no possibility of pleasures that cost money, the grim routine of the impersonal, gloomy pile in which he spent his days, all these things he felt with a vividness that made his *Three Clerks,* to modern readers who care to understand Trollope, one of his most interesting, though one of his most sordid, novels.

As he recalled that phase of his life in his *Autobiography,* he wrote, 'I wonder how many young men fall utterly to pieces from being turned loose into London after the same

[ xi ]

fashion. Mine was, I think, of all the phases of such life the most dangerous.' That he survived these dangers as he had the earlier ones, used them in his novels, won by them and through them his established ease and reputation, all this has a positive reassuring quality. It may be one of the reasons that makes Trollope so welcome today to the uncertain, disenchanted people that we, in the mid-twentieth century, are supposed to be.

In any case, these formative years, as an unhappy child and schoolboy, as an exile in Belgium, as a government clerk in London, though they offered less concrete material for the novels than his later years, shaped the point of view, sharpened the sensitivity of the future novelist.

The events of Trollope's mature life, from which he drew most of the atmosphere, setting, milieu in its broadest sense, for his novels, are better known, more carefully considered for their place in his art than the earlier period. His ten years in Ireland, still in the service of the Post Office but now as Deputy Postal Surveyor, saw his marriage, the beginning of his passion for hunting, and the start on novel writing. Then came the transfer to the west of England where, for a little more than two years, he rode up and down the counties on a special mission, to increase the efficiency of local postal deliveries. After this, though his official home was to be Ireland for another half dozen years, the novels were mostly about England. He worked the rich vein of country life which he had observed so closely during his two years in the western counties, and which with the publication of *The Warden* (begun in England and finished in Ireland in 1853) indicated to him the line to follow, and the probability of his future success.

In this period, too, interspersed with the drudgeries and exactions of his service for the Post Office at home, began those trips abroad on postal business which produced a series of fat travel books. But, more important for his career as a novelist, these trips offered uninterrupted leisure to write. The foreign travel, too, increased that perception of the essence of English life which absence, distance from the scene one is working on, always lends.

These journeys were nicely spaced to break the routine and give the feeling of change that refreshed his imagination. There was the mission to Egypt with return via Malta, Gibraltar, and Spain in 1858; the trip to the West Indies in '58-9; the voyage to the United States in August 1861, which he saw in the midst of Civil War. In fact, that regular habit of travel, with its yield of travel books as well as its incidental contribution to the novels, became a part of Trollope's life that he never relinquished. Australia, South Africa, later trips to America, to Ireland, and the Continent, interspersed the years of prosperity to the end of his life.

A novelist is of interest first, perhaps, as the vehicle that sees and records the story. That is why Trollope's early life with its vicissitudes and their effect upon him is an essential prelude to the understanding of his work. His experience, too —what he sees as well as how he sees it—especially in Trollope's case, is the very stuff of his novels. He has left us in the honest, penetrating pages of his stalwart biography the necessary knowledge about him as a novelist; how he worked and his own notion of what his novels should be, how they should strike the reader.

Trollope was one of those beings who 'always wrote.' His thoughts and the record of events that befell him came out easily at the end of his pen. In fact, one wonders whether human beings with this writing facility can really complete the process of observing and thinking unless they set pen to paper to record what is going on in their heads. At fifteen Trollope was keeping a journal which he continued for ten years, till the very moment when novel writing supplanted the daily record. 'Rapid use of pen and ink,' he says, 'taught me to express myself with facility.' What a harvest he was to make of it: over forty novels, several collections of short stories, four travel books, three biographies, two or three sets of sketches, not to mention the *Autobiography*.

INTRODUCTION

This blessedly incurable writing habit went on in the midst of his travel. But it also went on at home along with the exacting routine of his increasingly busy life. The much-quoted passages from the *Autobiography* about the daily stint of novel writing, the working timetable that he made on beginning a new novel, his Spartan adherence to the schedule, are important. They reflect his whole attitude toward novel writing. 'I have no anxiety as to "copy,"' he writes. 'The needed pages, far ahead—very far ahead—have almost always been in the drawer beside me. And that little diary, with its dates and ruled space . . . its daily, weekly demand upon my industry, has done all that for me. . . I was once told that the surest aid to the writing of a book was a piece of cobbler's wax on my chair. I certainly believe in the cobbler's wax more than the inspiration.'

He carried on the relentless schedule not only on long voyages and at home but during train journeys. 'If I intended to make profitable business out of my writing, and at the same time do my best for the Post Office, I must turn these hours to more account. . . I made myself, therefore, a little tablet and found, after a few days of exercise, that I could write as quickly in a railway carriage as I could at my desk.'

The indefatigable character of this kind of performance and the emphasis upon financial profit as a major reason for writing came naturally to him. There were those memories of the ease from debt that his mother's writing had brought; the picture of her, during the dreadful months at Bruges, 'at her table at four in the morning,' enduring days in which 'the Doctor's vials and the ink-bottle held equal places.' Trollope's frank emphasis upon this financial gain from writing may have shocked the general reader of his *Autobiography* when it came out after his death. Perhaps the reading public in the 1880's wanted to believe that writing was something inspired and that writers were beings who produced their work in a mysterious fashion, quite different from the working methods of ordinary mortals. It is the fashion nowadays,

INTRODUCTION

at any rate, to say that the public's disapproval of Trollope's revelation of his methodical writing habits accounted for the falling off in popularity of his novels in the late 'eighties and 'nineties.

But it is easy to overemphasize the systematic phases of his work. The *Autobiography* itself gives many evidences that Trollope, beard, spectacles, timetable, and all, was not merely pedestrian, not merely a writer by the clock. He relied heavily upon his imagination, deliberately nursed it into productivity.

He not only early developed the 'writing habit'; he early was possessed of the 'imagining habit.' From the time he was twelve or thirteen, 'for weeks, for months, I would carry on the same tale [in my head],' he says. As his novel writing grew into the major activity of his life, he would seek periods of time in which to imagine and particular localities in which his fancy would burgeon; 'some quiet spot among the mountains . . . circumstances which have enabled me to give all my thoughts to the book I have been writing . . . I have wandered alone among the rocks and woods, crying at their [my characters] grief, laughing at their absurdities and thoroughly enjoying their joy . . . till it has been my only excitement to sit with pen in hand and drive my team before me at as quick a pace as I could make them travel.' Here surely Trollope is 'inspired author' enough to please the most demanding reader.

But, granting the imaginative growth, the creative process, Trollope never forgets that the imagined people, places, and events of a novel must spring from life as it has been experienced, observed. He exhorts the young author 'to give his mind to that work of observation and reception.' From these he says 'comes his power. . . In his walks abroad, in all his movements through the world, in all his intercourse with his fellow creatures [the novelist must be] drawing matter from all that he has seen and heard.'

Trollope's own material was drawn into his novels in just this way. His activities, his wide-ranging business of riding

[ xv ]

INTRODUCTION

on horseback up and down England and Ireland, moving in and out of the many cities that London itself is—from Mayfair to the law courts, from mean lodgings to spacious town houses, from moneylenders' dingy quarters up alleyways to the high-ceiled, half-hushed, dim interior of the Houses of Parliament—all this experience was laid under contribution.

No wonder Trollope liked Hawthorne's comment on the world he had created. It is the much-quoted passage that praises his novels for being 'just as real as if some giant had hewn a great lump out of the earth and put it under a glass case, with all its inhabitants going about their daily business, and not suspecting they were being made a show of.' Trollope quotes this passage of Hawthorne's about his own novels with the deepest pleasure. Hawthorne has here described, says Trollope, 'with wonderful accuracy the purpose that I have ever had in view of my writing. I have always desired to "hew out some lump of the earth" and to make men and women walk upon it just as they do walk here among us.'

To the reader of Trollope, consequently, it is a pleasure to discover in his *Autobiography* those vivid, real moments, poignant actual experiences, which turn up again, slightly altered in their passage through the author's imagination, in his novels.

Scenes in lawyers' offices, for instance, appear again and again in his stories, where the grim setting is always a potent factor in the whole effect. He must have remembered his barrister father's offices. They were 'dingy, almost suicidal,' he says in his *Autobiography*. In them he had spent a desperately lonely, midsummer school holiday, as an unwanted child, in the way. The vivid moneylenders in his novels must have had their prototype in that 'man who lived in a little street near Mecklenburgh Square' who had loaned to Trollope while he was a young postal clerk and 'who became so attached to me as to visit me every day at my office.'

His own unsuccessful experience in standing for Parliament is reflected in the great election scenes in *Ralph the Heir*.

## INTRODUCTION

When he failed to secure a seat, yet still wanted to write novels about political figures with a background of Parliament, 'I had humbly to crave the Speaker permission for a seat in the gallery. . . He gave me a running order for, I think, a couple of months. . . It was enough . . . to enable me . . . to talk of the proceedings about as well as though Fortune had enabled me to fall asleep within the House itself.'

In the work of a man of such active habits, wide experience, and power of observing, both natural and deliberately cultivated, no wonder Hawthorne saw novels that were miraculously real creations. Henry James, then in his early forties, felt their 'spacious, geographical quality.'

Trollope's passion for hunting enriched his novels with some of the best hunting scenes to be found in English literature. 'I have always felt myself deprived of a legitimate joy,' he confesses, 'when the nature of the tale has not allowed me a hunting chapter.' The knowledge of English country, too, county towns, cathedral closes, country houses and churches, which probably more than any other single quality has endeared Trollope's novels to his myriad readers, was based, of course, upon intimate first-hand knowledge. Those two years in the western counties of England, from the spring of 1851 to the autumn of 1853, while he evolved for the Post Office a plan 'for extending the rural delivery of letters,' were the rich material from which he worked. 'I had an opportunity of seeing a considerable portion of Great Britain with a minuteness which few have enjoyed. . . I went almost everywhere on horseback. . . I saw almost every house . . . I think I may say every house of importance . . . in this large district. . . It was my special delight to take them by all short cuts. . . I would ride up to the farmhouses of parsonages or other lone residences about the country and ask the people how they got their letters.' Out of this actual setting, these varied encounters, came the scenes of his most famous novels.

It was not always peaceful English countryside, however, or decorous 'county' behavior that he recorded. Life 'in the raw' was close to Trollope's experience and closely woven into the fabric of his tales. Card sharpers, promoters, 'money-riggers' with their attendant shifts, sordid marital difficulties, sexual infidelities (even the great Lady Glencora narrowly escapes running off with Burgo Fitzgerald), all these things are present in the novels. Suicide by prussic acid, by flinging oneself in front of a train, garroting, imprisonment, trial scenes (including the great murder trial in *Phineas Redux*) are realistically portrayed. An element of the detective story is often present, as in *The Eustace Diamonds*. The impact of property upon human life by its descent through wills furnishes thrilling pages, notably in *Cousin Henry* and *Orley Farm*. The intrigue of election bribery is graphically reproduced and there are desperate moments in the gambling rooms at Monte Carlo. Trollope, most masculine of men, witnessed the whole range of human weakness, meanness, and crime, as well as the more decorous aspects of existence, and wrote of what he saw, whether fair or foul.

Now, in the mid-twentieth century when almost every novel seems to be used as a vehicle for conveying an idea, political, social or philosophic, it is refreshing to come upon Trollope's simple strong belief that a novel's chief business is to be a novel, to tell a story. 'No novel is anything,' he says, 'unless the reader can sympathize with the character... Let an author so tell his tale as to touch his reader's heart ... and he has, so far, done his work well.' The fancy phrases of the critics did not interest him: 'sensational,' 'anti-sensational,' 'realistic,' all these categories Trollope refuses. Criticism that announces that either the 'elucidation of character' or 'the gradual development of plot' is the important thing is, he says, 'a mistake.' A highly readable story, that was his critical goal. One wonders how well mid-twentieth-century fiction stands up to this first and essential test.

In the battle between plot and character that always goes on in fiction, Trollope naturally throws his weight on the side of character. For his peculiar gift lay in the delineation of

## INTRODUCTION

human beings: people, in their settings, doing things, that was how he saw life and in that order. 'The canvas should be crowded,' he says, 'with real portraits, not of individuals known to the world or to the author, but of created personages impregnated with traits of character which are known.' The plot through which these people move is, he says, 'but the vehicle for all this.' He sees the highest merit lying 'in perfect delineation of character rather than in plot.'

Following this emphasis in his own experience as a novelist, he confesses the reality to him of his own characters: 'There is a gallery of them and of all that gallery I may say that I know the tone of the voice and the colour of the hair, every flame of the eye and the very clothes they wear.'

To Trollope the chief business of his novels is to tell a story; the reader will not find in them either a consistent satiric point of view or a sustained argument for a specific political or social theory. He discusses labor groups, refers to communists, but his references are merely by the way. The novels are not media for social reform or political propaganda. There are satiric moments in Trollope, biting scenes, caustic figures, even specific social abuses neatly impaled upon his pages. But these are separate nuggets; they are not the main purpose of the story, the driving force by which the author hopes to arouse the reader.

'The satirist,' says Trollope, in considering his admired friend, Thackeray, 'who writes nothing but satire should write but little . . . or it will seem that his satire springs rather from his own caustic nature than from the sins of the world in which he lives.' True to the 'regular blend' of life as he had observed it, Trollope might allow a mixture of satire in the brew. But he could not admit that an overall satiric point of view was anything but a distortion of one single element. To elevate that element to chief position would be untrue to the blend that his balanced vision of existence revealed to him. Yet the 'regular blend' did not exclude a gen-

## INTRODUCTION

eral social concern. In fact, out of his experience he has developed in almost every novel a core of social implication.

In politics, too, Trollope did not see himself as a campaigner for a political program. In his series of political novels, he evokes all the phases of life of the political leader: elections, scenes in Parliament, country-house weekends. He even understands the emotions of great office holders, the weight of their responsibilities, the mixed feelings with which they take up or lay down office. He knows the function of political ladies, the indirections by which affairs of state are often shaped.

But his political novels are guiltless of a consistent effort to move his readers to take up this or that political view. Of his Prime Minister, Plantagenet Palliser ('Planty Pal') and his wife, Lady Glencora, Trollope says, 'They have been as real to me as free-trade was to Mr. Cobden or the dominion of party to Mr. Disraeli.' He adds that 'they have served me as safety-valves by which to deliver my soul.' But it is his 'soul,' his conviction, that they deliver. Instead of a philosophy of government, he offers a picture of political society, warm, authentic, magically re-created as it lived and moved in mid-nineteenth-century England.

Here, then, is Trollope the man and the author, whose interpretation of life and cross section of his own time are offered in the following pages.

To carve up a novelist whose sense of symmetry and wholeness in a novel is keen would be an act of vandalism. But the leisurely extendedness of Trollope's method allows scenes and moments, vistas and conversations, to be lifted out of their context and speak wholly for themselves. So the present editors have gone happily through the thousands of pages in which Trollope's world of men and women is presented, selecting here and there a lively figure, a ludicrous or tragic moment, an inimitable scene, a lightning flash of revelation on the way men live.

[ xx ]

## INTRODUCTION

Initiated Trollopians not only will enjoy again many selections familiar to them. They may discover that the severing from context of moments, figures, conversations, throws fresh light upon Trollope and heightens their sense of his genius for portraying life. Our insistence on having each passage a self-contained unit, not depending for its meaning on the rest of the story, has necessarily excluded some scenes that Trollopians will look for. But on the whole, the editors feel that the selections are representative of the myriad facets and the high points of Trollope's world.

We have envisaged a reader of these pages who can be as various as is his mood. If he wishes to escape into a visual Victorian England, he can read consecutively in such sections as 'Where It Happened' or 'The Portrait Gallery,' 'Society' or 'Hunting.' If he wishes to hear the old problems of government and society, business and the press, education and the arts, tossed about in Victorian drawing rooms or dingy London law offices, in town squares on election eve or along the ordered paths of a country house, he can find them. Professional men, diplomats, clergy, will discover the perennial outlines of their world set forth in Victorian guise. The more casual reader may turn here and there, leaf over, and find tense moments, trials, suicides, death in the hunting field, demagoguery, theft, gambling, and other highly colored episodes, set down by the hand of a master.

ESTHER CLOUDMAN DUNN
MARION E. DODD

*Northampton, Massachusetts*
*August* 1947

## Note

For essential books on Trollope and the arrangement of the index, see pages 429 and 431.

For the use of selections from copyright material, the editors are indebted to the following people and copyright proprietors: The University of California Press, *The Tireless Traveler,* edited by Bradford A. Booth, 1941; Charles Scribner's Sons, *The London Tradesman,* Foreword by Michael Sadleir, 1927; Edwin V. Mitchell, *Hunting Sketches,* Introduction by Cedric E. Smith, 1929.

*TROLLOPE LOOKS AT LIFE*

# Portrait Gallery

## The Fugitive Human Being

It is to be regretted that no mental method of daguerreotype or photography has yet been discovered, by which the characters of men can be reduced to writing and put into grammatical language with an unerring precision of truthful description. How often does the novelist feel, ay, and the historian also and the biographer, that he has conceived within his mind and accurately depicted on the tablet of his brain the full character and personage of a man, and that nevertheless, when he flies to pen and ink to perpetuate the portrait, his words forsake, elude, disappoint, and play the deuce with him, till at the end of a dozen pages the man described has no more resemblance to the man conceived than the sign board at the corner of the street has to the Duke of Cambridge?

And yet such mechanical descriptive skill would hardly give more satisfaction to the reader than the skill of the photographer does to the anxious mother desirous to possess an absolute duplicate of her beloved child. The likeness is indeed true; but it is a dull, dead, unfeeling, inauspicious likeness. The face is indeed there, and those looking at it will know at once whose image it is; but the owner of the face will not be proud of the resemblance.

There is no royal road to learning; no short cut to the acquirement of any valuable art. Let photographers and daguerreotypers do what they will, and improve as they may with further skill on that which skill has already done, they will never achieve a portrait of the human face divine. Let biographers, novelists, and the rest of us groan as we may under the burdens which we so often feel too heavy for our shoulders; we must either bear them up like men, or own ourselves too weak for the work we have undertaken. There is no way of writing well and also of writing easily.

## The Squire and His Foibles

WILFRED THORNE, ESQ., OF ULLATHORNE, was the squire of St. Ewold's; or rather the squire of Ullathorne; for the domain of the modern landlord was of wider notoriety than the fame of the ancient saint. He was a fair specimen of what that race has come to in our days, which a century ago was, as we are told, fairly represented by Squire Western. If that representation be a true one, few classes of men can have made faster strides in improvement. Mr. Thorne, however, was a man possessed of quite a sufficient number of foibles to lay him open to much ridicule. He was still a bachelor, being about fifty, and was not a little proud of his person. When living at home at Ullathorne there was not much room for such pride, and there therefore he always looked like a gentleman, and like that which he certainly was, the first man in his parish. But during the month or six weeks which he annually spent in London, he tried so hard to look like a great man there also, which he certainly was not, that he was put down as a fool by many at his club. He was a man of considerable literary attainment in a certain way and on certain subjects. His favourite authors were Montaigne and Burton, and he knew more perhaps than any other man in his own county, and the next to it, of the English essayists of the two last centuries. He possessed complete sets of the 'Idler,' the 'Spectator,' the 'Tatler,' the 'Guardian,' and the 'Rambler'; and would discourse by hours together on the superiority of such publications to anything which has since been produced in our Edinburghs and Quarterlies. He was a great proficient in all questions of genealogy, and knew enough of almost every gentleman's family in England to say of what blood and lineage were descended all those who had any claim to be considered as possessors of any such luxuries.

## Mr. Thorne

Mr. Thorne was a gentleman usually precise in his dress, and prone to make the most of himself in an unpretending way. The grey hairs in his whiskers were eliminated perhaps once a month; those on his head were softened by a mixture which we will not call a dye; it was only a wash. His tailor lived in St. James's Street, and his bootmaker at the corner of that street and Piccadilly. He was particular in the article of gloves, and the getting up of his shirts was a matter not lightly thought of in the Ullathorne laundry.

## Mrs. Greenow

'Omnibus;—no, indeed. Jeannette, get me a fly.' These were the first words Mrs. Greenow spoke as she put her foot upon the platform at the Yarmouth station. Her maid's name was Jenny; but Kate had already found, somewhat to her dismay, that orders had been issued before they left London that the girl was henceforth to be called Jeannette. Kate had also already found that her aunt could be imperious; but this taste for masterdom had not shown itself so plainly in London as it did from the moment that the train had left the station at Shoreditch. In London Mrs. Greenow had been among Londoners, and her career had hitherto been provincial. Her spirit, no doubt, had been somewhat cowed by the novelty of her position. But when she felt herself to be once beyond the stones, as the saying used to be, she was herself again; and at Ipswich she had ordered Jeannette to get her a glass of sherry with an air that had created a good deal of attention among the guards and porters.

The fly was procured; and with considerable exertion all Mrs. Greenow's boxes, together with the more moderate belongings of her niece and maid, were stowed on the top of it, round upon the driver's body on the coach box, on the maid's lap, and I fear in Kate's also, and upon the vacant seat.

'The large house in Montpelier Parade,' said Mrs. Greenow.

'They is all large, ma'am,' said the driver.

'The largest,' said Mrs. Greenow.

'They're much of a muchness,' said the driver.

'Then Mrs. Jones's,' said Mrs. Greenow. 'But I was particularly told it was the largest in the row.'

'I know Mrs. Jones's well,' said the driver, and away they went.

Mrs. Jones's house was handsome and comfortable; but I fear Mrs. Greenow's satisfaction in this respect was impaired by her disappointment in finding that it was not perceptibly bigger than those to the right and left of her. Her ambition in this and in other similar matters would have amused Kate greatly had she been a bystander, and not one of her aunt's party. Mrs. Greenow was good-natured, liberal, and not by nature selfish; but she was determined not to waste the good things which fortune had given, and desired that all the world should see that she had forty thousand pounds of her own. And in doing this she was repressed by no feeling of false shame. She never hesitated in her demands through bashfulness. She called aloud for such comfort and grandeur as Yarmouth could afford her, and was well pleased that all around should hear her calling.

## Norfolk Farmer

'He is a man of substance, and should I ever become Mrs. Cheesacre, I have reason to think that I shall not be left in want. We went up to his place on a visit the other day. Oileymead is the name. . . And we had such a time there! We reached the place at ten and left it at four, and he managed to give us three meals. I'm sure we had before our eyes at different times every bit of china, delf, glass, and plate in the establishment. He made us go into the cellar, and told us how much wine he had got there, and how much beer. "It's all paid for, Mrs. Greenow, every bottle of it," he said, turning round to my aunt, with a pathetic earnestness, for which I had hardly given him credit. "Everything in this house is my own; it's all paid for. I don't call anything a man's own till it's paid for." . . . He took us into every bedroom, and disclosed to us all the glories of his upper chambers. It would have done you good to see him lifting the counterpanes, and bidding my aunt feel the texture of the blankets! And then to see her turn round to me and say:—"Kate, it's simply the best-furnished house I ever went over in my life!"—"It does seem very comfortable," said I. "Comfortable!" said he. "Yes, I don't think there's anybody can say that Oileymead isn't comfortable." . . . But when we got to the farmyard his eloquence reached the highest pitch. "Mrs. Greenow," said he, "look at that," and he pointed to heaps of manure raised like the streets of a little city. "Look at that!" "There's a great deal," said my aunt. "I believe you," said he. "I've more muck upon this place here than any farmer in Norfolk, gentle or simple; I don't care who the other is." Only fancy, Alice; it may all be mine; the blankets, the wine, the muck, and the rest of it. So my aunt assured me when we got home that evening.'

## Morning After

BURGO WENT ON, and made his way into the house in Grosvenor Square, by some means probably unknown to his aunt, and certainly unknown to his uncle. He emptied his pockets as he got into bed, and counted a roll of notes which he had kept in one of them. There were still a hundred and thirty pounds left. . .

He breakfasted upstairs in his bedroom,—in his bed, indeed, eating a small paté de foie gras from the supper-table, as he read a French novel. There he was still reading his French novel in bed when his aunt's maid came to him, saying that his aunt wished to see him before she went out. 'Tell me, Lucy,' said he, 'how is the old girl?'

'She's as cross as cross, Mr. Burgo. Indeed, I shan't;—not a minute longer. Don't, now; will you? I tell you she's waiting for me.' From which it may be seen that Lucy shared the general feminine feeling in favour of poor Burgo.

Thus summoned Burgo applied himself to his toilet; but as he did so, he recruited his energies from time to time by a few pages of the French novel, and also by small doses from a bottle of curaçao which he had in his bedroom. He was utterly a pauper. There was no pauper poorer than he in London that day. But, nevertheless, he breakfasted on pâté de foie gras and curaçao, and regarded those dainties very much as other men regard bread and cheese and beer.

## Widow's Weeds

The widow was almost gorgeous in her weeds. I believe that she had not sinned in her dress against any of those canons which the semi-ecclesiastical authorities on widowhood have laid down as to the outward garments fitted for gentlemen's relicts. The materials were those which are devoted to the deepest conjugal grief. As regarded every item of the written law her suttee worship was carried out to the letter. There was the widow's cap, generally so hideous, so well known to the eyes of all men, so odious to womanhood. Let us hope that such headgear may have some assuaging effect on the departed spirits of husbands. There was the dress of deep, clinging, melancholy crape,—of crape which becomes so brown and so rusty, and which makes the six months' widow seem so much more afflicted a creature than she whose husband is just gone, and whose crape is therefore new. There were the trailing weepers, and the widow's kerchief pinned close round her neck and somewhat tightly over her bosom. But there was that of genius about Mrs. Greenow, that she had turned every seeming disadvantage to some special profit, and had so dressed herself that though she had obeyed the law to the letter, she had thrown the spirit of it to the winds. Her cap sat jauntily on her head, and showed just so much of her rich brown hair as to give her the appearance of youth which she desired. Cheesacre had blamed her in his heart for her private carriage, but she spent more money, I think, on new crape than she did on her brougham. It never became brown and rusty with her, or formed itself into old lumpy folds, or shaped itself round her like a grave cloth. The written law had not interdicted crinoline, and she loomed as large with weeds, which with her were not sombre, as she would do with her silks when the period of her probation should be over. Her weepers were bright with newness, and she would waft them aside from her shoulder with an air which turned even them into auxiliaries. Her kerchief was fastened close round her neck and close over her bosom; but Jeannette well knew what she was doing as she fastened it,—and so did Jeannette's mistress.

## City Woman at the Seaside

LONDON WAS HER SPHERE, as she herself had understood when declaiming against those husbands who keep their wives in the country. And she had no love for the sea specially, regarding all winds as nuisances excepting such as had been raised by her own efforts, and thinking that salt from a saltcellar was more convenient than that brought to her on the breezes. It was now near the end of May, but she had not been half an hour at the inn before she was loud in demanding a fire,—and when the fire came she was unwilling to leave it. Her gesture was magnificent when Lady Ongar proposed to her that she should bathe. What,—put her own dear little dry body, by her own will, into the cold sea! She shrugged herself, and shook herself, and without speaking a word declined with so much eloquence that it was impossible not to admire her. Nor would she walk. On the first day, during the warmest part of the day, she allowed herself to be taken out in a carriage belonging to the inn; but after her drive she clung to the fire, and consumed her time with a French novel.

## Scatcherd, the Stone-Mason

Roger Scatcherd had also a reputation, but not for beauty or propriety of conduct. He was known for the best stone-mason in the four counties, and as the man who could, on occasions, drink the most alcohol in a given time in the same localities. As a workman, indeed, he had higher repute even than this: he was not only a good and very quick stone-mason, but he had also a capacity of turning other men into good stone-masons: he had a gift of knowing what a man could and should do; and, by degrees, he taught himself what five, and ten, and twenty—latterly, what a thousand and two thousand men might accomplish among them: this, also, he did with very little aid from pen and paper, with which he was not, and never became, very conversant. He had also other gifts and other propensities. He could talk in a manner dangerous to himself and others; he could persuade without knowing that he did so; and being himself an extreme demagogue, in those noisy times just prior to the Reform Bill, he created a hubbub in Barchester of which he himself had had no previous conception.

## The Venomous Lady Linlithgow

Lady Linlithgow was worldly, stingy, ill-tempered, selfish, and mean. Lady Linlithgow would cheat a butcher out of a mutton-chop, or a cook out of a month's wages, if she could do so with some slant of legal wind in her favour. She would tell any number of lies to carry a point in what she believed to be social success. It was said of her that she cheated at cards. In backbiting no venomous old woman between Bond Street and Park Lane could beat her,—or, more wonderful still, no venomous old man at the clubs. But nevertheless she recognized certain duties,—and performed them, though she hated them. She went to church, not merely that people might see her there,—as to which in truth she cared nothing,—but because she thought it was right. And she took in Lizzie Greystock, whom she hated almost as much as she did sermons, because the admiral's wife had been her sister, and she recognized a duty. But, having thus bound herself to Lizzie,—who was a beauty,—of course it became the first object of her life to get rid of Lizzie by a marriage. And, though she would have liked to think that Lizzie would be tormented all her days, though she thoroughly believed that Lizzie deserved to be tormented, she set her heart upon a splendid match. She would at any rate be able to throw it daily in her niece's teeth that the splendour was of her doing.

## Mrs. Carbuncle

Mrs. Carbuncle was a wonderful woman. She was the wife of a man with whom she was very rarely seen, whom nobody knew, who was something in the City, but somebody who never succeeded in making money; and yet she went everywhere. She had at least the reputation of going everywhere, and did go to a great many places. Carbuncle had no money,—so it was said; and she had none. She was the daughter of a man who had gone to New York and had failed there. Of her own parentage no more was known. She had a small house in one of the very small Mayfair streets, to which she was wont to invite her friends for five o'clock tea. Other receptions she never attempted. During the London seasons she always kept a carriage, and during the winters she always had hunters. Who paid for them no one knew or cared. Her dress was always perfect,—as far as fit and performance went. As to approving Mrs. Carbuncle's manner of dress,—that was a question of taste. Audacity may, perhaps, be said to have been the ruling principle of her toilet;—not the audacity of indecency, which, let the satirists say what they may, is not efficacious in England, but audacity in colour, audacity in design, and audacity in construction. She would ride in the park in a black and yellow habit, and appear at the opera in white velvet without a speck of colour. Though certainly turned thirty, and probably nearer to forty, she would wear her jet-black hair streaming down her back, and when June came would drive about London in a straw hat. But yet it was always admitted that she was well dressed. And then would arise that question, Who paid the bills?

Mrs. Carbuncle was certainly a handsome woman. She was full-faced,—with bold eyes, rather far apart, perfect black eyebrows, a well-formed broad nose, thick lips, and regular teeth. Her chin was round and short, with, perhaps, a little bearing towards a double chin. But though her face was plump and round, there was a power in it, and a look of command of which it was, perhaps, difficult to say in what features was the seat. But in truth the mind will lend a tone to every feature, and it was the desire of Mrs. Carbuncle's heart to command. But perhaps the wonder of her face was its complexion. People said,—before they knew her, that, as a matter of course, she had been made beautiful for ever. But, though that too brilliant colour was almost always there, covering the cheeks but never touching the forehead or the neck, it would at certain moments shift, change, and even depart. When she was angry, it would vanish for a moment and then return intensified. There was no chemistry on Mrs. Carbuncle's cheek; and yet it was a tint so brilliant and so little transparent, as almost to justify a conviction that it could not be genuine. There were those who declared that nothing in the way of complexion so beautiful as that of Mrs. Carbuncle's had been seen on the face of any other woman in this age, and there were others who called her an exaggerated milk-maid. She was tall, too, and had learned so to walk as though half the world belonged to her.

## The Soft Sadness of Age

IN A FEW MINUTES he was shown into the library, and had hardly time, while looking at the shelves, to remember what Mr. Crawley had said of his anger at the beautiful bindings, before an old man, very thin and very pale, shuffled into the room. He stooped a good deal, and his black clothes were very loose about his shrunken limbs. He was not decrepit, nor did he seem to be one who had advanced to extreme old age; but yet he shuffled rather than walked, hardly raising his feet from the ground. Mr. Toogood, as he came forward to meet him, thought that he had never seen a sweeter face. There was very much of melancholy in it, of that soft sadness of age which seems to acknowledge, and in some sort to regret, the waning oil of life; but the regret to be read in such faces has in it nothing of the bitterness of grief; there is no repining that the end has come, but simply a touch of sorrow that so much that is dear must be left behind.

## Mr. Prettyman, Wine Merchant

MR. PRETTYMAN IS ALSO a wine merchant. He is a handsome old gentleman with grey hair, always well dressed, who goes about London in a pill-box brougham, by which he is well known to all men who know anything, and to dine with whom is, according to our ideas, the acme of human bliss. It is a great thing to get Prettyman to dine with you; but it is glorious to have to dine with Prettyman. How is it that he has his wine in such condition that no one else can approach it? You might no doubt buy the same wine from his house, or have bought it in some previous stage of its, and of your, existence. He does not have a special tipple made for his own drinking. And then he talks about his wine with a modest humour, but with a gentle sarcasm. He is always the fine gentleman though he never drops the wine merchant. What stories he can tell of the past history of London gourmets! He knows the whole history of the wine trade for fifty years, and speaks of the good old time when men laid down great cellars. The drinkers of wine now send to him for six dozen, for three, or even for a dozen at a time, and wisely impose upon him the duty of keeping the wine, and charging for the capital required. Chance circumstances have brought us to know Prettyman. But he lives chiefly with men of fashion and with men of wealth. He is very decided in his own opinion but presses it on no one. I should as soon think of asking the collector of income-tax to take less than his due as of proposing to Prettyman any diminution of his prices. Did any customer ever suggest discount to him? Once a year his bill comes, and it may remain unpaid for another without remark.

## Mr. Neefit, Breeches-Maker

Mr. Neefit was a breeches-maker in Conduit Street, of such repute that no hunting man could be said to go decently into the hunting-field unless decorated by a garment made in Mr. Neefit's establishment. His manipulation of leather was something marvellous; and in latter years he had added to his original art,—an art which had at first been perfect rather than comprehensive,—an exquisite skill in cords, buckskins, and such like materials. When his trade was becoming prosperous, he had thought of degenerating into a tailor, adding largely to his premises, and of compensating his pride by the prospects of great increase to his fortune; but an angel of glory had whispered to him to let well alone, and he was still able to boast that all his measurements had been confined to the legs of sportsmen. Instead of extending his business, he had simply extended his price, and had boldly clapped on an extra half-guinea to every pair that he supplied. The experiment was altogether successful, and when it was heard by the riding-men of the City that Mr. Neefit's prices were undoubtedly higher than those of any other breeches-maker in London, and that he had refused to supply breeches for the grooms of a Marquis because the Marquis was not a hunting man, the riding-men of the City flocked to him in such numbers, that it became quite a common thing for them to give their orders in June and July, so that they might not be disappointed when November came round. Mr. Neefit was a prosperous man, but he had his troubles. Now, it was a great trouble to him that some sporting men would be so very slow in paying for the breeches in which they took pride!

Mr. Neefit's fortune had not been rapid in early life. He had begun with a small capital and a small establishment, and even now his place of business was very limited in size. He had been clever enough to make profit even out of its smallness,—and had contrived that it should be understood that the little back room in which men were measured was so diminutive because it did not suit his special business to welcome a crowd. It was his pride, he said, to wait upon hunting men,—but with the garments of the world at large he wished to have no concern whatever. In the outer shop, looking into Conduit Street, there was a long counter on which goods were unrolled for inspection; and on which an artist, the solemnity of whose brow and whose rigid silence betokened the nature of his great employment, was always cutting out leather. This grave man was a German, and there was a rumour among young sportsmen that old Neefit paid this highly-skilled operator £600 a year for his services! Nobody knew as he did how each morsel of leather would behave itself under the needle, or could come within two hairbreadths of him in accuracy across the kneepan. As for measuring, Mr. Neefit did that himself,—almost always. To be measured by Mr. Neefit was as essential to perfection as to be cut out for by the German. There were rumours, indeed, that from certain classes of customers Mr. Neefit and the great foreigner kept themselves personally aloof. It was believed that Mr. Neefit would not condescend to measure a retail tradesman. . .

Mr. Neefit was a stout little man, with a bald head and somewhat protrusive eyes, whose manners to his customers contained a combination of dictatorial assurance and subservience, which he had found to be efficacious in his peculiar business. On general subjects he would rub his hands, and bow his head, and agree most humbly with every word that was uttered. In the same day he would be a Radical and a Conservative, devoted to the Church and a scoffer at parsons, animated on behalf of staghounds and a loud censurer of aught in the way of hunting other than the orthodox fox. On all trivial outside subjects he considered it to be his duty as a tradesman simply to ingratiate himself; but in a matter of breeches he gave way to no man, let his custom be what it might. He knew his business, and was not going to be told by any man whether the garments which he made did or did not fit. It was the duty of a gentleman to come and allow him to see them on while still in a half-embryo condition. If gentlemen did their duty, he was sure that he could do his. He would take back anything that was not approved without a murmur;—but after that he must decline further transactions. It was, moreover, quite understood that to complain of his materials was so to insult him that he would condescend to make no civil reply. An elderly gentleman from Essex once told him that his buttons were given to breaking. 'If you have your breeches,—washed,—by an old woman,—in the country,'—said Mr. Neefit, very slowly, looking into the elderly gentleman's face, 'and then run through the mangle,—the buttons will break.' The elderly gentleman never dared even to enter the shop again.

Mr. Neefit was perhaps somewhat over-imperious in matters relating to his own business; but, in excuse for him, it must be stated that he was, in truth, an honest tradesman;— he was honest at least so far, that he did make his breeches as well as he knew how. He had made up his mind that the best way to make his fortune was to send out good articles,— and he did his best. Whether or no he was honest in adding on that additional half-guinea to the price because he found that the men with whom he dealt were fools enough to be attracted by a high price, shall be left to advanced moralists to decide. In that universal agreement with diverse opinions there must, we fear, have been something of dishonesty. But he made the best of breeches, put no shoddy or cheap stitching into them, and was, upon the whole, an honest tradesman.

From 9.30 to 5.15 were Mr. Neefit's hours; but it had come to be understood by those who knew the establishment well, that from half-past twelve to half-past one the master was always absent. The young man who sat at the high desk, and seemed to spend all his time in contemplating the bad debts in the ledger, would tell gentlemen who called up to one that Mr. Neefit was in the City. After one it was always said that Mr. Neefit was lunching at the Restaurong. The truth was that Mr. Neefit always dined in the middle of the day at a public-house round the corner, having a chop and a 'follow chop,' a pint of beer, a penny newspaper and a pipe.

## The Duke of Omnium's Heir

Mr. Plantagenet Palliser was the Duke of Omnium's heir —heir to that nobleman's title and to his enormous wealth; and, therefore, was a man of mark in the world. He sat in the House of Commons, of course. He was about five-and-twenty years of age, and was, as yet, unmarried. He did not hunt or shoot or keep a yacht, and had been heard to say that he had never put a foot upon a race-course in his life. He dressed very quietly, never changing the colour or form of his garments; and in society was quiet, reserved, and very often silent. He was tall, slight, and not ill-looking; but more than this cannot be said for his personal appearance—except, indeed, this, that no one could mistake him for other than a gentleman. With his uncle, the duke, he was on good terms —that is to say, they had never quarrelled. A very liberal allowance had been made to the nephew; but the two relatives had no tastes in common, and did not often meet. Once a year Mr. Palliser visited the duke at his great country seat for two or three days, and usually dined with him two or three times during the season in London. Mr. Palliser sat for a borough which was absolutely under the duke's command; but had accepted his seat under the distinct understanding that he was to take whatever part in politics might seem good to himself. Under these well-understood arrangements, the duke and his heir showed to the world quite a pattern of a happy family. 'So different to the earl and Lord Porlock!' the people of West Barsetshire used to say. For the estates, both of the duke and of the earl, were situated in the western division of that county.

Mr. Palliser was chiefly known to the world as a rising politician. We may say that he had everything at his command, in the way of pleasure, that the world could offer him. He had wealth, position, power, and the certainty of attaining the highest rank among, perhaps, the most brilliant nobility in the world. He was courted by all who could get near enough to court him. It is hardly too much to say that he might have selected a bride from all that was most beautiful and best among English women. If he would have bought race-horses, and have expended thousands on the turf, he would have gratified his uncle by doing so. He might have been the master of hounds, or the slaughterer of hecatombs of birds. But to none of these things would be devote himself. He had chosen to be a politician, and in that pursuit he laboured with a zeal and perseverance which would have made his fortune at any profession or in any trade. He was constant in committee-rooms up to the very middle of August. He was rarely absent from any debate of importance, and never from any important division. Though he seldom spoke, he was always ready to speak if his purpose required it. No man gave him credit for any great genius—few even considered that he could become either an orator or a mighty statesman. But the world said that he was a rising man, and old Nestor of the Cabinet looked on him as one who would be able, at some far future day, to come among them as a younger brother. Hitherto he had declined such inferior offices as had been offered to him, biding his time carefully; and he was as yet tied hand and neck to no party, though known to be Liberal in all his political tendencies. He was a great reader—not taking up a book here, and another there, as chance brought books before him, but working through an enormous course of books, getting up the great subject of the world's history—filling himself full of facts—though perhaps not destined to acquire the power of using those facts otherwise than as precedents. He strove also diligently to become a linguist—not without success, as far as a competent understanding of various languages. He was a thin-minded, plodding, respectable man, willing to devote all his youth to work, in order that in old age he might be allowed to sit among the Councillors of the State.

## The Earl at the Cattle Show

The show of fat beasts in London took place this year on the twentieth day of December, and I have always understood that a certain bullock exhibited by Lord De Guest was declared by the metropolitan butchers to have realized all the possible excellences of breeding, feeding, and condition. No doubt the butchers of the next half-century will have learned much better, and the Guestwick beast, could it be embalmed and then produced, would excite only ridicule at the agricultural ignorance of the present age; but Lord De Guest took the praise that was offered to him, and found himself in a seventh heaven of delight. He was never so happy as when surrounded by butchers, graziers, and salesmen who were able to appreciate the work of his life, and who regarded him as a model nobleman. 'Look at that fellow,' he said to Eames, pointing to the prize bullock. Eames had joined his patron at the show after his office hours, looking on upon the living beef by gaslight. 'Isn't he like his sire? He was got by Lambkin, you know.'

'Lambkin,' said Johnny, who had not as yet been able to learn much about the Guestwick stock.

'Yes, Lambkin. The bull that we had the trouble with. He has just got his sire's back and forequarters. Don't you see?'

'I daresay,' said Johnny, who looked very hard, but could not see.

## The Countess

When he first called he was shown into the great family dining-room, which looked out towards the back of the house. The front windows were, of course, closed, as the family was not supposed to be in London. Here he remained in the room for some quarter of an hour, and then the countess descended upon him in all her grandeur. Perhaps he had never before seen her so grand. Her dress was very large, and rustled through the broad doorway, as if demanding even a broader passage. She had on a wonder of a bonnet, and a velvet mantle that was nearly as expansive as her petticoats. She threw her head a little back as she accosted him, and he instantly perceived that he was enveloped in the fumes of an affectionate, but somewhat contemptuous patronage. In old days he had liked the countess, because her manner to him had always been flattering. In his intercourse with her he had been able to feel that he gave quite as much as he got, and that the countess was aware of the fact. In all the circumstances of their acquaintance the ascendancy had been with him, and therefore the acquaintance had been a pleasant one. The countess had been a good-natured, agreeable woman, whose rank and position had made her house pleasant to him; and therefore he had consented to shine upon her with such light as he had to give. Why was it that the matter was reversed, now that there was so much stronger a cause for good feeling between them? He knew that there was such change, and with bitter internal upbraidings he acknowledged to himself that this woman was getting the mastery over him. As the friend of the countess he had been a great man in her eyes;—in all her little words and looks she had acknowledged his power; but now, as her son-in-law, he was to become a very little man.

## VICTOIRE

THE HAPPY VICTOIRE was dressed up to his eyes. That, perhaps, is not saying much, for he was only a few feet high; but what he wanted in quantity he fully made up in quality. He was a well-made, shining, jaunty little Frenchman, who seemed to be perfectly at ease with himself and all the world. He had the smallest little pair of moustaches imaginable, the smallest little imperial, the smallest possible pair of boots, and the smallest possible pair of gloves. Nothing on earth could be nicer, or sweeter, or finer, than he was. But he did not carry his finery like a hog in armour, as an Englishman so often does when an Englishman stoops to be fine. It sat as naturally on Victoire as though he had been born in it. He jumped about in his best patent leather boots, apparently quite heedless whether he spoilt them or not; and when he picked up Miss Golightly's parasol from the gravel, he seemed to suffer no anxiety about his gloves.

He handed out the ladies one after another, as though his life had been passed in handing out ladies, as, indeed, it probably had—in handing them out and handing them in; and when Mrs. Val's 'private' carriage passed on, he was just as courteous to the Misses Neverbend and Katie in their cab, as he had been to the greater ladies who had descended from the more ambitious vehicle. As Katie said afterwards to Linda, when she found the free use of her voice in their own bedroom, 'he was a darling little duck of a man, only he smelt so strongly of tobacco.'

But when they were once in the garden, Victoire had no time for anyone but Mrs. Val and Clementina. He had done his duty by the Misses Neverbend and those other two insipid young English girls, and now he had his own affairs to look after. He also knew that Miss Golightly had £20,000 of her own!

He was one of those butterfly beings who seem to have been created that they may flutter about from flower to flower in the summer hours of such gala times as those now going on at Chiswick, just as other butterflies do. What the butterflies were last winter, or what will become of them next winter, no one but the naturalist thinks of inquiring. How they may feed themselves on flower-juice, or on insects small enough to be their prey, is matter of no moment to the general world. It is sufficient that they flit about in the sunbeams, and add bright glancing spangles to the beauty of the summer day.

And so it was with Victoire Jaquêtanàpe. He did no work. He made no honey. He appeared to no one in the more serious moments of life. He was the reverse of Shylock; he would neither buy with you nor sell with you, but he would eat with you and drink with you; as for praying, he did little of that either with or without company. He was clothed in purple and fine linen, as butterflies should be clothed, and fared sumptuously every day; but whence came his gay colours, or why people fed him with *pâté* and champagne, nobody knew and nobody asked.

Like most Frenchmen of his class, he never talked about himself. He understood life, and the art of pleasing, and the necessity that he should please, too well to do so. All that his companions knew of him was that he came from France, and that when the gloomy months came on in England, the months so unfitted for a French butterfly, he packed up his azure wings and sought some more genial climate, certain to return and be seen again when the world of London became habitable.

If he had means of living no one knew it; if he was in debt no one ever heard of it; if he had a care in the world he concealed it. He abounded in acquaintances who were always glad to see him, and would have regarded it as quite *de trop* to have a friend. Nevertheless time was flying on with him as with others; and, butterfly as he was, the idea of Miss Golightly's £20,000 struck him with delightful amazement—500,000 francs! 500,000 francs! and so he resolved to dance his very best, warm as the weather undoubtedly was at the present moment.

## Tourists

THE UNITED ENGLISH TOURIST batters his hat, and twists it, and sits on it, and rumples and crumples it, till it is manifestly and undeniably of its owner. And having so completed its manufacture he obtrudes it upon the world with a remarkable ingenuity. In a picture gallery he will put it on the head of a bust of Apollo; in a church he will lay it down on the railing of the altar, or he will carry it on high on the top of his stick, so that all men may see it and know its owner by the sign. Sitting in public places he will chuck it up and catch it, and at German beer-gardens he will spread it carefully in the middle of the little table intended for the glasses. He never keeps it on his head when he should take it off,—because he is a gentleman; but he rarely keeps it on his head when that is the proper place for it,—because he is a United Englishman who travels for fun. He wears a suit of grey clothes, the coat being a shooting coat, and the trousers, if he be loud in his vocation, being exchanged for knickerbockers. And it is remarkable that the suit in which you will see him will always strike you as that which he had procured for last year's tour, and that he is economically wearing it to shreds on the present occasion. But this is not so. The clothes were new when he left London; but he has been assiduous with his rumpling and crumpling here as he has been with his hat, and at the expiration of his first week out he is able to boast to himself that he has, at any rate, got rid of the gloss. He wears flannel shirts, and in warm weather goes about without a cravat. He carries in his portmanteau a dress-coat, waistcoat, and trousers, which are of no use to him, as who would think of asking such a man to dinner? But, as he abhors the extra package which a decent hat would make needful, he is to be seen in Paris, Vienna, or Florence with that easily-recognized covering for his head which I have above described. He has a bludgeon usually in his hand, and often a pipe in his mouth. He knows nothing of gloves, but is very particular as to the breadth and strength of his shoes. He often looks to be very dirty; but his morning tub is a religious ceremony, and, besides that, he bathes whenever he comes across a spot which, from its peculiar difficulties, is more than ordinarily inappropriate for the exercise.

### Mr. Jay, Ironmonger

Mr. Jay was a slight man, of middle height, with very respectable iron-gray hair that stood almost upright upon his head, but with a poor, inexpressive, thin face below it. He was given to bowing a good deal, rubbing his hands together, smiling courteously, and to the making of many civil little speeches; but his strength as a leading man in Warminster lay in his hair, and in the suit of orderly well-brushed black clothes which he wore on all occasions. He was, too, a man fairly prosperous, who went always to church, paid his way, attended sedulously to his business, and hung his bells, and sold his pots in such a manner as not actually to drive his old customers away by default of work. 'Jay is respectable, and I don't like to leave him,' men would say, when their wives declared that the backs of his grates fell out, and that his nails never would stand hammering. So he prospered; but, perhaps, he owed his prosperity mainly to his hair.

### A 'Great' Man

Sir Walter Wanless was one of those great men who never do anything great, but achieve their greatness partly by their tailors, partly by a breadth of eyebrow and carriage of the body,—what we may call deportment,—and partly by the outside gifts of fortune. Taking his career altogether we must say that he had been unfortunate. He was a baronet with a fine house and park,—and with an income hardly sufficient for the place. He had contested the county four times on old Whig principles, and had once been in Parliament for two years. There he had never opened his mouth; but in his struggle to get there had greatly embarrassed his finances. His tailor had been well chosen, and had always turned him out as the best dressed old baronet in England. His eyebrow was all his own, and certainly commanded respect from those with whom eyebrows are efficacious. He never read; he eschewed farming, by which he had lost money in early life; and had, so to say, no visible occupation at all. But he was Sir Walter Wanless, and what with his tailor and what with his eyebrow he did command a great deal of respect in the country round Beetham. He had, too, certain good gifts for which people were thankful as coming from so great a man. He paid his bills, he went to church, he was well behaved, and still maintained certain old-fashioned family charities, though money was not plentiful with him.

# Where It Happened

### ULLATHORNE COURT

WHILE WE ARE ON THE SUBJECT of the Thornes, one word must be said of the house they lived in. It was not a large house, nor a fine house, nor perhaps to modern ideas a very commodious house; but by those who love the peculiar colour and peculiar ornaments of genuine Tudor architecture it was considered a perfect gem. We beg to own ourselves among the number, and therefore take this opportunity to express our surprise that so little is known by English men and women of the beauties of English architecture. The ruins of the Colosseum, the Campanile at Florence, St. Mark's, Cologne, the Bourse and Notre Dame, are with our tourists as familiar as household words; but they know nothing of the glories of Wiltshire, Dorsetshire, and Somersetshire. Nay, we much question whether many noted travellers, men who have pitched their tents perhaps under Mount Sinai, are not still ignorant that there are glories in Wiltshire, Dorsetshire, and Somersetshire. We beg that they will go and see.

Mr. Thorne's house was called Ullathorne Court, and was properly so called; for the house itself formed two sides of a quadrangle, which was completed on the other two sides by a wall about twenty feet high. This wall was built of cut stone, rudely cut indeed, and now much worn, but of a beautiful rich tawny yellow colour, the effect of that stonecrop of minute growth, which it had taken three centuries to produce. The top of this wall was ornamented by huge round stone balls of the same colour as the wall itself. Entrance into the court was had through a pair of iron gates, so massive that no one could comfortably open or close them, consequently they were rarely disturbed. From the gateway two paths led obliquely across the court; that to the left reaching the hall-door, which was in the corner made by the angle of the house, and that to the right leading to the back entrance, which was at the further end of the longer portion of the building. . .

The hall was hung round with family female insipidities by Lely, and unprepossessing male Thornes in red coats by Kneller; each Thorne having been let into a panel in the wainscoting, in the proper manner. At the further end of the room was a huge fire-place, which afforded much ground of difference between the brother and sister. An antiquated grate that would hold about a hundred weight of coal, had been stuck on to the hearth, by Mr. Thorne's father. This hearth had of course been intended for the consumption of wood fagots, and the iron dogs for the purpose were still standing, though half buried in the masonry of the grate. Miss Thorne was very anxious to revert to the dogs. The dear good old creature was always glad to revert to anything, and had she been systematically indulged, would doubtless in time have reflected that fingers were made before forks, and have reverted accordingly. But in the affairs of the fire-place, Mr. Thorne would not revert. Country gentlemen around him, all had comfortable grates in their dining-rooms. He was not exactly the man to have suggested a modern usage; but he was not so far prejudiced as to banish those which his father had prepared for his use. . .

At the end of the hall opposite to the fire-place a door led into the drawing-room, which was of equal size, and lighted with precisely similar windows. But yet the aspect of the room was very different. It was papered, and the ceiling, which in the hall showed the old rafters, was whitened and finished with a modern cornice. Miss Thorne's drawing-room, or, as she always called it, withdrawing-room, was a beautiful apartment. The windows opened on to the full extent of the lovely trim garden; immediately before the windows were plots of flowers in stiff, stately, stubborn little beds, each bed surrounded by a stone coping of its own; beyond, there was a low parapet wall, on which stood urns and images, fawns, nymphs, satyrs, and a whole tribe of Pan's followers; and then again, beyond that, a beautiful lawn sloped away to a sunk fence which divided the garden from the park. Mr. Thorne's study was at the end of the drawing-room, and beyond that were the kitchen and the offices. Doors opened into both Miss Thorne's withdrawing-room and Mr. Thorne's sanctum from the passage above alluded to; which, as it came to the latter room, widened itself so as to make space for the huge black oak stairs, which led to the upper regions.

Such was the interior of Ullathorne Court. . .

It is the colour of Ullathorne that is so remarkable. It is all of that delicious tawny hue which no stone can give, unless it has on it the vegetable richness of centuries. Strike the wall with your hand, and you will think that the stone has on it no covering, but rub it carefully, and you will find that the colour comes off upon your finger. No colourist that ever yet worked from a palette has been able to come up to this rich colouring of years crowding themselves on years.

## Jerusalem

At last the two mountains more and the two go-downs were performed, and George was informed that the wall he saw rising sharp from the rocky ground was Jerusalem. There is something very peculiar in the first appearance of a walled city that has no suburbs or extramural adjuncts. It is like that of a fortress of cards built craftily on a table. With us in England it is always difficult to say where the country ends and where the town begins; and even with the walled towns of the Continent, one rarely comes upon them so as to see the sharp angles of a grey stone wall rising in the sun, as they do in the old pictures of the cities in 'Pilgrim's Progress.'

But so it is with Jerusalem. One rides up to the gate feeling that one is still in the desert; and yet a moment more, with the permission of those very dirty-looking Turkish soldiers at the gate, will place one in the city. One rides up to the gate, and as every one now has a matured opinion as to the taking of casemated batteries and the inefficiency of granite bastions, one's first idea is how delightfully easy it would be to take Jerusalem. It is, at any rate, easy enough to enter it, for the dirty Turkish soldiers do not even look at you, and you soon become pleasantly aware that you are beyond the region of passports.

George Bertram had promised himself that the moment in which he first saw Jerusalem should be one of intense mental interest; and when, riding away from the orange-gardens at Jaffa, he had endeavoured to urge his Arab steed into that enduring gallop which was to carry him up to the city of the sepulchre, his heart was ready to melt into ecstatic pathos as soon as that gallop should have been achieved. But the time for ecstatic pathos had altogether passed away before he rode in at that portal. He was then swearing vehemently at his floundering jade, and giving up to all the fiends of Tartarus the accursed saddle which had been specially contrived with the view of lacerating the nether Christian man.

'Where on earth is this d—d hotel?' said he, when he and his dragoman and portmanteau had been floundering for about five minutes down a steep, narrow, ill-paved lane, with a half-formed gully in the middle, very slippery with orange-peel and old vegetables, and crowded with the turbans of all the Eastern races. 'Do you call this a street?' After all his sentiment, all his emotions, all his pious resolves, it was thus that our hero entered Jerusalem! But what piety can withstand the wear and tear of twelve hours in a Turkish saddle?

'Is this a street?' said he. It was the main street in Jerusalem. The first, or among the first in grandeur of those sacred ways which he had intended hardly to venture to pass with shoes on his feet. His horse, turning a corner as he followed the dragoman, again slipped and almost fell; whereupon Bertram again cursed. But then he was not only tired and sore, but very hungry also. Our finer emotions should always be encouraged with a stomach moderately full.

At last they stopped at a door in a wall, which the dragoman pronounced to be the entrance of Z——'s hotel. In fact, they had not yet been full ten minutes within the town; but the streets certainly were not well paved. In five minutes more George was in his room, strewing sofas and chairs with the contents of his portmanteau, and inquiring with much energy what was the hour fixed for the table d'hôte. He found, with much inward satisfaction, that he had just twenty minutes to prepare himself. At Jerusalem, as elsewhere, these, after all, are the traveller's first main questions. When is the table d'hôte? Where is the cathedral? At what hour does the train start to-morrow morning? It will be some years yet, but not very many, before the latter question is asked at Jerusalem.

## Nethercoats

THE HOUSE ITSELF was as excellent a residence for a country gentleman of small means as taste and skill together could construct. I doubt whether prettier rooms were ever seen than the drawing-room, the library, and the dining-room at Nethercoats. They were all on the ground-floor, and all opened out on to the garden and lawn. The library, which was the largest of the three, was a handsome chamber, and so filled as to make it well known in the University as one of the best private collections in that part of England. But perhaps the gardens of Nethercoats constituted its greatest glory. They were spacious and excellently kept up, and had been originally laid out with that knowledge of gardening without which no garden, merely as a garden, can be effective. And such, of necessity, was the garden of Nethercoats. Fine single forest trees there were none there, nor was it possible that there should have been any such. Nor could there be a clear rippling stream with steep green banks, and broken rocks lying about its bed. Such beauties are beauties of landscape, and do not of their nature belong to a garden. But the shrubs of Nethercoats were of the rarest kind, and had been long enough in their present places to have reached the period of their beauty. Nothing had been spared that a garden could want. The fruit-trees were perfect in their kind, and the glass-houses were so good and so extensive that John Grey in his prudence was sometimes tempted to think that he had too much of them.

It must be understood that there were no grounds, according to the meaning usually given to that word, belonging to the house at Nethercoats. Between the garden and the public road there was a paddock belonging to the house, along the side of which, but divided from it by a hedge and shrubbery, ran the private carriage-way up to the house. This swept through the small front flower-garden, dividing it equally; but the lawns and indeed the whole of that which made the beauty of the place lay on the back of the house, on which side opened the windows from the three sitting-rooms. Down on the public road there stood a lodge at which lived one of the gardeners. There was another field of some six or seven acres, to which there was a gate from the corner of the front paddock, and which went round two sides of the garden. This was Nethercoats, and the whole estate covered about twelve acres.

## Gatherum Castle

In the course of that afternoon Lady Glencora took Alice all over the house. It was a castle of enormous size, quite new,—having been built by the present proprietor,—very cold, very handsome, and very dull. 'What an immense place!' said Alice, as she stood looking round her in the grand hall, which was never used as an entrance except on very grand occasions. 'Is it not? And it cost—oh, I can't tell you how much it cost. A hundred thousand pounds or more. Well;—that would be nothing, as the Duke no doubt had the money in his pocket to do what he liked with at the time. But the joke is, nobody ever thinks of living here. Who'd live in such a great, overgrown place such as this, if they could get a comfortable house like Matching? Do you remember Longroyston and the hot-water pipes? I always think of the poor Duchess when I come through here. Nobody ever lives here, or ever will. The Duke comes for one week in the year, and Plantagenet says he hates to do that. As for me, nothing on earth shall ever make me live here.'

## Residence in Ireland

All the world must have heard of Desmond Court. It is the largest inhabited residence known in that part of the world, where rumours are afloat of how it covers ten acres of ground; how in hewing the stones for it a whole mountain was cut away; how it should have cost hundreds of thousands of pounds, only that the money was never paid by the rapacious, wicked, bloodthirsty old earl who caused it to be erected;— and how the cement was thickened with human blood. So goes rumour with the more romantic of the Celtic tale-bearers.

It is a huge place—huge, ungainly, and uselessly extensive; built at a time when, at any rate in Ireland, men considered neither beauty, aptitude, nor economy. It is three stories high, and stands round a quadrangle, in which there are two entrances opposite to each other. Nothing can well be uglier than that great paved court, in which there is not a spot of anything green, except where the damp has produced an unwholesome growth upon the stones; nothing can well be more desolate. And on the outside of the building matters are not much better. There are no gardens close up to the house, no flower-beds in the nooks and corners, no sweet shrubs peeping in at the square windows. Gardens there are, but they are away, half a mile off; and the great hall door opens out upon a flat, bleak park, with hardly a scrap around it which courtesy can call a lawn. . .

Desmond Court stood in a bleak, unadorned region, almost

among the mountains, half way between Kanturk and Maccoom, and the family had some claim to possession of the land for miles around. The earl of the day was still the head landlord of a huge district extending over the whole barony of Desmond, and half the adjacent baronies of Muskerry and Duhallow; but the head landlord's rent in many cases hardly amounted to sixpence an acre, and even those sixpences did not always find their way into the earl's pocket. When the late earl had attained his sceptre, he might probably have been entitled to spend some ten thousand a year; but when he died, and during the years just previous to that, he had hardly been entitled to spend anything.

## Barsetshire

THERE IS A COUNTY in the west of England not so full of life, indeed, nor so widely spoken of as some of its manufacturing leviathan brethren in the north, but which is, nevertheless, very dear to those who know it well. Its green pastures, its waving wheat, its deep and shady and—let us add—dirty lanes, its paths and stiles, its tawny-coloured, well-built rural churches, its avenues of beeches, and frequent Tudor mansions, its constant county hunt, its social graces, and the general air of clanship which pervades it, has made it to its own inhabitants a favoured land of Goshen. It is purely agricultural; agricultural in its produce, agricultural in its poor, and agricultural in its pleasures. There are towns in it, of course; dépôts from whence are brought seeds and groceries, ribbons and fire-shovels; in which markets are held and county balls are carried on; which return members to Parliament, generally—in spite of Reform Bills, past, present, and coming—in accordance with the dictates of some neighbouring land magnate: from whence emanate the country postmen, and where is located the supply of post-horses necessary for county visitings. But these towns add nothing to the importance of the county; they consist, with the expection of the assize town, of dull, all but death-like single streets. Each possesses two pumps, three hotels, ten shops, fifteen beer-houses, a beadle, and a market-place.

Indeed, the town population of the county reckons for nothing when the importance of the county is discussed, with the exception, as before said, of the assize town, which is also a cathedral city. Herein is a clerical aristocracy, which is certainly not without its due weight. A resident bishop, a resident dean, an archdeacon, three or four resident prebendaries, and all their numerous chaplains, vicars, and ecclesiastical satellites, do make up a society sufficiently powerful to be counted as something by the county squirearchy. In other respects the greatness of Barsetshire depends wholly on the landed powers.

## Killancodlem

Killancodlem, though it had the name of a shooting-place, certainly was not so. Men going there took their guns. Gamekeepers were provided and gillies,—and, in a moderate quantity, game. On certain grand days a deer or two might be shot,—and would be very much talked about afterwards. But a glance at the place would suffice to show that Killancodlem was not intended for sport. It was a fine castellated mansion, with beautiful though narrow grounds, standing in the valley of the Archay River, with a mountain behind and the river in front. Between the gates and the river there was a public road on which a stagecoach ran, with loud-blown horns and the noise of many tourists. A mile beyond the Castle was the famous Killancodlem hotel which made up a hundred and twenty beds, and at which half as many more guests would sleep on occasions under the tables. And there was the Killancodlem post-office halfway between the two. At Crummie-Toddie they had to send nine miles for their letters and newspapers. At Killancodlem there was lawn-tennis and a billiard-room and dancing every night. The costumes of the ladies were lovely, and those of the gentlemen, who were wonderful in knickerbockers, picturesque hats and variegated stockings, hardly less so. And then there were carriages and saddle-horses, and paths had been made hither and thither through the rocks and hills for the sake of the scenery.

## The 'Rising Sun'

LATE ON THE AFTERNOON of the same day, when London had already been given over to the gaslights, Mr. Gager, having dressed himself especially for the occasion of the friendly visit which he intended to make, sauntered into a small public-house at the corner of Meek Street and Pineapple Court, which locality,—as all men well versed with London are aware,—lies within one minute's walk of the top of Gray's Inn Lane. Gager, during his conference with his colleague Bunfit, had been dressed in plain black clothes; but in spite of his plain clothes he looked every inch a policeman. There was a stiffness about his limbs, and, at the same time, a sharpness in his eyes, which, in the conjunction with the locality in which he was placed, declared his profession beyond the possibility of mistake. Nor, in that locality, would he have desired to be taken for anything else. But as he entered the 'Rising Sun' in Meek Street, there was nothing of the policeman about him. He might probably have been taken for a betting man, with whom the world had latterly gone well enough to enable him to maintain that sleek, easy, greasy appearance, which seems to be the beau-ideal of a betting man's personal ambition. 'Well, Mr. Howard,' said the lady at the bar, 'a sight of you is good for sore eyes.'

'Six penn'orth of brandy,—warm, if you please, my dear,' said the pseudo-Howard, as he strolled easily into an inner room, with which he seemed to be quite familiar. He seated himself in an old-fashioned wooden arm-chair, gazed up at the gas lamp, and stirred his liquor slowly. Occasionally he raised the glass to his lips, but he did not seem to be at all intent upon his drinking. When he entered the room, there had been a gentleman and a lady there, whose festive moments seemed to be disturbed by some slight disagreement; but Howard, as he gazed at the lamp, paid no attention to them whatever. They soon left the room, their quarrel and their drink finished together, and others dropped in and out. Mr. Howard's 'warm' must almost have become cold, so long did he sit there, gazing at the gas lamps, rather than attending to his brandy and water. Not a word did he speak to any one for more than an hour, and not a sign did he show of impatience. At last he was alone;—but had not been so for above a minute when in stepped a jaunty little man, certainly not more than five feet high, about three or four and twenty years of age, dressed with great care, with his trousers sticking to his legs, with a French chimney-pot hat on his head, very much peeked fore and aft and closely turned up at the sides. He had a bright-coloured silk handkerchief round his neck, and a white shirt, of which the collar and wristbands were rather larger and longer than suited the small dimensions of the man. He wore a white greatcoat tight buttoned round his waist, but so arranged as to show the glories of the coloured handkerchief; and in his hand he carried a diminutive cane with a little silver knob. He stepped airily into the room, and as he did so he addressed our friend the policeman with much cordiality. 'My dear Mr. 'Oward,' he said, 'this is a pleasure. This is a pleasure. This is a pleasure.'

'What is it to be?' asked Gager.

'Well;—ay, what? Shall I say a little port wine negus, with the nutmeg in it rayther strong?' This suggestion he made to a young lady from the bar, who had followed him into the room. The negus was brought and paid for by Gager, who then requested that they might be left there undisturbed for five minutes. The young lady promised to do her best, and then closed the door. 'And now, Mr. 'Oward, what can I do for you?' said Mr. Cann, the burglar.

# WHERE IT HAPPENED

## Chaldicotes

Chaldicotes is a house of much more pretension than Framley Court. Indeed, if one looks at the ancient marks about it, rather than at those of the present day, it is a place of very considerable pretension. There is an old forest, not altogether belonging to the property, but attached to it, called the Chase of Chaldicotes. A portion of this forest comes up close behind the mansion, and of itself gives a character and celebrity to the place. The Chase of Chaldicotes—the greater part of it, at least—is, as all the world knows, Crown property, and now, in these utilitarian days, is to be disforested. In former times it was a great forest, stretching half across the country, almost as far as Silverbridge; and there are bits of it, here and there, still to be seen at intervals throughout the whole distance; but the larger remaining portion, consisting of aged hollow oaks, centuries old, and wide-spreading withered beeches, stands in the two parishes of Chaldicotes and Uffley. People still come from afar to see the oaks of Chaldicotes, and to hear their feet rustle among the thick autumn leaves. But they will soon come no longer. The giants of past ages are to give way to wheat and turnips; a ruthless Chancellor of the Exchequer, disregarding old associations and rural beauty, requires money returns from the lands; and the Chase of Chaldicotes is to vanish from the earth's surface. . .

The house of Chaldicotes is a large stone building, probably of the time of Charles the Second. It is approached on both fronts by a heavy double flight of stone steps. In the front of the house a long, solemn, straight avenue through a double row of lime-trees, leads away to lodge-gates, which stand in the centre of the village of Chaldicotes; but to the rear the windows open upon four different vistas, which run down through the forest: four open green rides, which all converge together at a large iron gateway, the barrier which divides the private grounds from the Chase.

## The Coffee House

Poulter's Alley is a narrow dark passage somewhere behind the Mansion House; and the Bremen Coffee House,—why so called no one can now tell,—is one of those strange houses of public resort in the City at which the guests seem never to eat, never to drink, never to sleep, but to come in and out after a mysterious and almost ghostly fashion, seeing their friends,—or perhaps their enemies,—in nooks and corners, and carrying on their conferences in low melancholy whispers. There is an aged waiter at the Bremen Coffee House; and there is certainly one private sitting-room up-stairs. It was a dingy, ill-furnished room, with an old large mahogany table, an old horse-hair sofa, six horse-hair chairs, two old round mirrors, and an old mahogany press in a corner. It was a chamber so sad in its appearance that no wholesome useful work could have been done within it; nor could men have eaten there with any appetite, or have drained the flowing bowl with any touch of joviality. It was generally used for such purposes as that to which it was now appropriated, and no doubt had been taken by Bozzle on more than one previous occasion. Here Lady Rowley arrived precisely at the hour fixed, and was told that the gentleman was waiting up-stairs for her.

## Manor Cross

'It is an old house, and we shall have great pleasure in showing you what the people call the state-rooms. We never use them. Of course you know the house belongs to my brother, and we only live here because it suits him to stay in Italy.'

'That's the young Marquis, my lady?'

'Yes; my elder brother is Marquis of Brotherton, but I cannot say that he is very young. He is two years my senior, and ten years older than George.'

'But I think he's not married yet?' asked Miss Tallowax. . . .

'No,' said Lady Sarah, with stately gravity; 'my elder brother is not yet married. If you would like to see the rooms, Miss Tallowax, I shall have pleasure in showing you the way.'

The Dean had seen the rooms before, and remained with the old lady. Lord George, who thought very much of everything affecting his own family, joined the party, and Mary felt herself compelled to follow her husband and her aunt. The two younger sisters also accompanied Lady Sarah.

'This is the room in which Queen Elizabeth slept,' said Lady Sarah, entering a large chamber on the ground floor, in which there was a four-post bedstead, almost as high as the ceiling, and looking as though no human body had profaned it for the last three centuries.

'Dear me,' said Miss Tallowax, almost afraid to press such sacred boards with her feet. 'Queen Elizabeth! Did she really now?'

'Some people say she never did actually come to Manor Cross at all,' said the conscientious Lady Amelia; 'but there is no doubt that the room was prepared for her.'

'Laws!' said Miss Tallowax, who began to be less afraid of distant royalty now that a doubt was cast on its absolute presence.

'Examining the evidence as closely as we can,' said Lady Sarah, with a savage glance at her sister, 'I am inclined to think that she certainly did come. We know that she was at Brotherton in 1582, and there exists the letter in which Sir Humphrey Germaine, as he was then, is desired to prepare rooms for her. I myself have no doubt on the subject.'

'After all it does not make much difference,' said Mary.

'I think it makes all the difference in the world,' said Lady Susanna. 'That piece of furniture will always be sacred to me, because I believe it did once afford rest and sleep to the gracious majesty of England.'

'It do make a difference, certainly,' said Miss Tallowax, looking at the bed with all her eyes. 'Does anybody ever go to bed here now?'

'Nobody, ever,' said Lady Sarah. 'Now we will go through to the great dining-room. That's the portrait of the first earl.'

'Painted by Kneller,' said Lady Amelia, proudly.

'Oh, indeed,' said Miss Tallowax.

'There is some doubt as to that,' said Lady Sarah. 'I have found out that Sir Godfrey Kneller was only born in 1648, and as the first earl died a year or two after the restoration, I don't know that he could have done it.'

'It was always said that it was painted by Kneller,' said Lady Amelia.

'There has been a mistake, I fear,' said Lady Sarah.

'Oh, indeed,' said Miss Tallowax, looking up with intense admiration at a very ill-drawn old gentleman in armour. Then they entered the state dining-room or hall, and Miss Tallowax was informed that the room had not been used for any purpose whatever for very many years. 'And such a beautiful room!' said Miss Tallowax, with much regret.

'The fact is, I believe, that the chimney smokes horribly,' said Lord George.

'I never remember a fire here,' said Lady Sarah. 'In very cold weather we have a portable stove brought in, just to preserve the furniture. This is called the old ball-room.'

'Dear me!' ejaculated Miss Tallowax, looking round at the faded yellow hangings.

'We did have a ball here once,' said Lady Amelia, 'when Brotherton came of age. I can just remember it.'

'Has it never been used since?' asked Mary.

'Never,' said Lady Sarah. 'Sometimes when it's rainy we walk up and down for exercise. It is a fine old house, but I often wish that it were smaller. I don't think people want rooms of this sort now as much as they used to do. Perhaps a time may come when my brother will make Manor Cross gay again, but it is not very gay now. I think that is all, Miss Tallowax.'

'It's very fine—very fine indeed,' said Miss Tallowax, shivering. Then they all trooped back into the morning-room which they used for their daily life.

The old lady when she had got back into the brougham with her nephew, the Dean, was able to express her mind freely. 'I wouldn't live in that house, Henry, not if they was to give it me for nothing.'

## On Board Ship

THERE IS NO PECULIAR LIFE more thoroughly apart from life in general, more unlike our usual life, more completely a life of itself, governed by its own rules and having its own roughness and amenities, than life on board ship. What tender friendship it produces, and what bitter enmities! How completely the society has formed itself into separate sets after the three or four first days! How thoroughly it is acknowledged that this is the aristocratic set, and that the plebeian! How determined are the aristocrats to admit no intrusion, and how anxious are the plebeians to intrude! Then there arises the great demagogue, who heads a party, having probably been disappointed in early life,—that is, in his first endeavours on board the ship. And the women have to acknowledge all their weaknesses, and to exercise all their strength. It is a bad time for them on board ship if they cannot secure the attention of the men,—as it is in the other world; but in order that they may secure it, they assume indifference. They assume indifference, but are hard at work with their usual weapons. The men can do very well by themselves. For them there is drinking, smoking, cards, and various games; but the potency of female spells soon works upon them, and all who are worth anything are more or less in love by the end of the first week. Of course it must all come to an end when the port is reached. That is understood, though there may sometimes be mistakes. Most pathetic secrets are told with the consciousness that they will be forgotten as soon as the ship is left. And there is the whole day for these occupations.

No work is required from any one. The lawyer does not go to his court, nor the merchant to his desk. Pater-familias receives no bills; mater-familias orders no dinners. The daughter has no household linen to disturb her. The son is never recalled to his books. There is no parliament, no municipality, no vestry. There are neither rates nor taxes nor rents to be paid. The government is the softest despotism under which subjects were ever allowed to do almost just as they please. That the captain has a power is known, but hardly felt. He smiles on all, is responsible for everything, really rules the world submitted to him, from the setting of the sails down to the frying of the chops, and makes one fancy that there must be something wrong with men on shore because first-class nations cannot be governed like first-class ships.

## An Irish Inn

The difference of the English and Irish character is nowhere more plainly discerned than in their respective kitchens. With the former, this apartment is probably the cleanest, and certainly the most orderly, in the house. It is rarely intruded into by those unconnected, in some way, with its business. Everything it contains is under the vigilant eye of its chief occupant, who would imagine it quite impossible to carry on her business, whether of an humble or important nature, if her apparatus was subjected to the hands of the unauthorised. An Irish kitchen is devoted to hospitality in every sense of the word. Its doors are open to almost all loungers and idlers; and the chances are that Billy Bawn, the cripple, or Judy Molloy, the deaf old hag, are more likely to know where to find the required utensil than the cook herself. It is usually a temple dedicated to the goddess of disorder; and, too often joined with her, is the potent deity of dirt. It is not that things are out of their place, for they have no place. It isn't that the floor is not scoured, for you cannot scour dry mud into anything but wet mud. It isn't that the chairs and tables look filthy, for there are none. It isn't that the pots, and plates, and pans don't shine, for you see none to shine. All you see is a grimy, black ceiling, an uneven clay floor, a small darkened window, one or two unearthly-looking recesses, a heap of potatoes in the corner, a pile of turf against the wall, two pigs and a dog under the single dresser, three or four chickens on the window-sill, an old cock moaning on the top of a rickety press, and a crowd of ragged garments, squatting, standing, kneeling, and crouching, round the fire, from which issues a babel of strange tongues, not one word of which is at first intelligible to ears unaccustomed to such eloquence.

And yet, out of these unfathomable, unintelligible dens, proceed in due time dinners, of which the appearance of them gives no promise. Such a kitchen was Mrs. Kelly's; and yet, it was well known and attested by those who had often tried the experiment, that a man need think it no misfortune to have to get his dinner, his punch, and his bed, at the widow's.

Above stairs were two sitting-rooms and a colony of bedrooms, occupied indiscriminately by the family, or by such customers as might require them. If you came back to dine at the inn, after a day's shooting on the bogs, you would probably find Miss Jane's work-box on the table, or Miss Meg's album on the sofa; and, when a little accustomed to sojourn at such places, you would feel no surprise at discovering their dresses turned inside out, and hanging on the pegs in your bed-room; or at seeing their side-combs and black pins in the drawer of your dressing-table.

## In Nuremberg

THE WINDOWS from these apartments all looked out on to the slow-flowing but clear stream, which ran so close below them that the town-clerk might have sat and fished from his windows had he been so minded; for there was no road there —only the narrow slip of a garden no broader than a balcony. And opposite, beyond the river, where the road ran, there was a broad place,—the Ruden Platz; and every house surrounding this was picturesque with different colours, and with many gables, and the points of the houses rose up in sharp pyramids, of which every brick and every tile was in its place, sharp, clear, well formed, and appropriate, in those very inches of space which each was called upon to fill. For in Nuremberg it is the religion of the community that no house shall fall into decay, that no form of city beauty shall be allowed to vanish, that nothing of picturesque antiquity shall be changed.

## Irish Shebeen Shop

IN THIS LANE at the time to which we allude the widow Mulready kept the shebeen shop. . .

In her business Mrs. Mulready acquired much more profit than respectability, for, whether well or ill-deserved, she had but a bad name in the country; in spite of this, however, to the company assembled here on Wednesday evening,—the same evening that Thady dined with Father John,—we must introduce our readers.

The house, or rather cabin, consisted only of two rooms, both on the ground, and both without flooring or ceiling; the black rafters on which the thatch was lying was above, and the uneven soil below; still this place of entertainment was not like the cabins of the very poor: the rooms were both long, and as they ran lengthways down the street, each was the full breadth of the house: in the first sat the widow Mulready, a strong, red-faced, indomitable-looking woman about fifty. She sat on a large wooden seat with a back, capable of containing two persons; there was an immense blazing fire of turf, on which water was boiling in a great potato pot, should any of her guests be able to treat themselves to the expensive luxury of punch. A remarkably dirty small deal-table was beside her, on which were placed a large jar, containing a quantity of the only merchandize in which she dealt, and an old battered pewter measure, in which she gave it out; in a corner of the table away from the fire was cut a hole through the board, in which was stuck a small flickering candle. No further implements appeared necessary to Mrs. Mulready in the business which she conducted. A barefooted girl with unwashed hands and face, and unbrushed head, crouched in the corner of the fire, ready to obey the behests of Mrs. Mulready, and attend to the numerous calls of her customers. This Hebe rejoiced in the musical name of Kathleen.

The Mohill resort of the wicked, the desperate, and the drunken, was not certainly so grand, nor so conspicuous, as the gas-lighted, mahogany-fitted, pilastered gin-palaces of London; but the freedom from decent restraint, and the power of inebriety at a cheap rate, were the same in each.

There was a door at the further end of the room, which opened into the one where Mrs. Mulready's more known and regular visitors were accustomed to sit and drink, and here rumour said a Ribbon lodge was held; there was a fire also here, at the further end, and a long narrow table ran nearly the whole length of the room under the two windows, with a form on each side of it. Opposite this was Mrs. Mulready's own bed, which proved that whatever improprieties might be perpetrated in the house, the careful widow herself never retired to rest till they were all over.

## Attorney's Chambers

There is, I think, no sadder place in the world than the waiting-room attached to an attorney's chambers in London. In this instance it was a three-cornered room, which had got itself wedged in between the house which fronted to Lincoln's Inn Fields, and some buildings in a narrow lane that ran at the back of the row. There was no carpet in it, and hardly any need of one, as the greater part of the floor was strewed with bundles of dusty papers. There was a window in it, which looked out from the point of the further angle against the wall of the opposite building. The dreariness of this aspect had been thought to be too much for the minds of those who waited, and therefore the bottom panes had been clouded, so that there was in fact no power of looking out at all. Over the fireplace there was a table of descents and relationship, showing how heirship went; and the table was very complicated, describing not only the heirship of ordinary real and personal property, but also explaining the wonderful difficulties of gavelkind, and other mysteriously traditional laws. But the table was as dirty as it was complicated, and the ordinary waiting reader could make nothing of it. There was a small table in the room, near the window, which was always covered with loose papers; but these loose papers were on this occasion again covered with sheets of parchment, and a pale-faced man, of about thirty, whose beard had never yet attained power to do more than sprout, was sitting at the table, and poring over the parchments. Round the room, on shelves, there was a variety of iron boxes, on which were written the names of Mr. Slow's clients—of those clients whose property justified them in having special boxes of their own. But these boxes were there, it must be supposed, for temporary purposes—purposes which might be described as almost permanently temporary—for those boxes which were allowed to exist in absolute permanence of retirement, were kept in an iron room down-stairs, the trap-door into which had yawned upon Miss Mackenzie as she was shown into the waiting-room. There was, however, one such box open, on the middle of the floor, and sundry of the parchments which had been taken from it were lying around it.

There were but two chairs in the room besides the one occupied by the man at the table, and these were taken by John Ball and his cousin. She sat herself down, armed with patience, indifferent to the delay and indifferent to the dusty ugliness of everything around her, as women are on such occasions. He, thinking much of his time, and somewhat annoyed at being called upon to wait, sat with his chin resting on his umbrella between his legs, and as he did so he allowed his eyes to roam around among the names upon the boxes. There was nothing on any one of those up on the shelves that attracted him. There was the Marquis of B——, and Sir C. D. ——, and the Dowager Countess of E——. Seeing this, he speculated mildly whether Mr. Slow put forward the boxes of his aristocratic customers to show how well he was doing in the world.

## The Colonial Office

When Phineas received Lady Laura Kennedy's letter, he was sitting in his gorgeous apartment in the Colonial Office. It was gorgeous in comparison with the very dingy room at Mr. Low's to which he had been accustomed in his early days,—and somewhat gorgeous also as compared with the lodgings he had so long inhabited in Mr. Bunce's house. The room was large and square, and looked out from three windows on to St. James's Park. There were in it two very comfortable arm-chairs and a comfortable sofa. And the office table at which he sat was of old mahogany, shining brightly, and seemed to be fitted up with every possible appliance for official comfort. This stood near one of the windows, so that he could sit and look down upon the park. And there was a large round table covered with books and newspapers. And the walls of the room were bright with maps of all the colonies. And there was one very interesting map,—but not very bright,—showing the American colonies, as they used to be. And there was a little inner closet in which he could brush his hair and wash his hands; and in the room adjoining there sat,—or ought to have sat, for he was often absent, vexing the mind of Phineas,—the Earl's nephew, his private secretary. And it was all very gorgeous. Often as he looked round upon it, thinking of his old bedroom at Killaloe, of his little garrets at Trinity, of the dingy chambers in Lincoln's Inn, he would tell himself that it was very gorgeous. He would wonder that anything so grand had fallen to his lot.

## Old Church

It was a church such as there are, I think, thousands in England—low, incommodious, kept with difficulty in repair, too often pervious to the wet, and yet strangely picturesque, and correct too, according to great rules of architecture. It was built with a nave and aisles, visibly in the form of a cross, though with its arms clipped down to the trunk, with a separate chancel, with a large square short tower, and with a bell-shaped spire, covered with lead and irregular in its proportions. Who does not know the low porch, the perpendicular Gothic window, the flat-roofed aisles, and the noble old gray tower of such a church as this? As regards its interior, it was dusty; it was blocked up with high-backed ugly pews; the gallery in which the children sat at the end of the church, and in which two ancient musicians blew their bassoons, was all awry, and looked as though it would fall; the pulpit was an ugly useless edifice, as high nearly as the roof would allow, and the reading-desk under it hardly permitted the parson to keep his head free from the dangling tassels of the cushion above him. A clerk also was there beneath him, holding a third position somewhat elevated; and upon the whole things there were not quite as I would have had them. But, nevertheless, the place looked like a church, and I can hardly say so much for all the modern edifices which have been built in my days towards the glory of God. It looked like a church, and not the less so because in walking up the passage between the pews, the visitor trod upon the brass plates which dignified the resting-places of the departed Dales of old.

## WHERE IT HAPPENED

### SARATOGA

THAT SARATOGA is a gay place in July, August, and September the world knows well enough. To girls who go there with trunks full of muslin and crinoline, for whom a carriage and pair of horses is always waiting immediately after dinner, whose fathers' pockets are bursting with dollars, it is a very gay place. Dancing and flirtations come as a matter of course, and matrimony follows after with only too great rapidity.

### SHEPHEARD'S HOTEL, CAIRO

THE ENGLISH TONGUE in Egypt finds its centre at Shepheard's Hotel. It is here that people congregate who are looking out for parties to visit with them the Upper Nile, and who are generally all smiles and courtesy; and here also are to be found they who have just returned from this journey, and who are often in a frame of mind towards their companions that is much less amiable. From hence, during the winter, a *cortège* proceeds almost daily to the Pyramids, or to Memphis, or to the petrified forest, or to the City of the Sun. And then, again, four or five times a month the house is filled with young aspirants going out to India, male and female, full of valour and bloom; or with others coming home, no longer young, no longer aspiring, but laden with children and grievances.

### DÉJEUNER AT LE PUY

LE PUY ITSELF is a small, moderate, pleasant French town, in which the language of the people has not the pure Parisian aroma, nor is the glory of the boulevards of the capital emulated in its streets. These are crooked, narrow, steep, and intricate, forming here and there excellent sketches for a lover of street picturesque beauty; but hurtful to the feet with their small round-topped paving stones, and not always as clean as pedestrian ladies might desire.

And now I would ask my readers to join me at the morning table d'hôte at the Hôtel des Ambassadeurs. It will of course be understood that this does not mean a breakfast in the ordinary fashion of England, consisting of tea or coffee, bread and butter, and perhaps a boiled egg. It comprises all the requisites for a composite dinner, excepting soup; and as one gets further south in France, this meal is called dinner. It is, however, eaten without any prejudice to another similar and somewhat longer meal at six or seven o'clock, which, when the above name is taken up by the earlier enterprise, is styled supper.

## Hiram's Hospital

HIRAM'S HOSPITAL, as the retreat is called, is a picturesque building enough, and shows the correct taste with which the ecclesiastical architects of those days were imbued. It stands on the banks of the little river, which flows nearly round the cathedral close, being on the side furthest from the town. The London road crosses the river by a pretty one-arched bridge, and, looking from this bridge, the stranger will see the windows of the old men's rooms, each pair of windows separated by a small buttress. A broad gravel walk runs between the building and the river, which is always trim and cared for; and at the end of the walk, under the parapet of the approach to the bridge, is a large and well-worn seat, on which, in mild weather, three or four of Hiram's bedesmen are sure to be seen seated.

## Temple Gardens

HERE, ON THE CHOICEST SPOT of this choice ground, stands a lofty row of chambers, looking obliquely upon the sullied Thames; before the windows, the lawn of the Temple Gardens stretches with that dim yet delicious verdure so refreshing to the eyes of Londoners. If doomed to live within the thickest of London smoke you would surely say that that would be your chosen spot. Yes, you, you whom I now address, my dear, middle-aged bachelor friend, can nowhere be so well domiciled as here. No one here will ask whether you are out or at home; alone or with friends; here no Sabbatarian will investigate your Sundays, no censorious landlady will scrutinize your empty bottle, no valetudinarian neighbour will complain of late hours. If you love books, to what place are books so suitable? The whole spot is redolent of typography. Would you worship the Paphian goddess, the groves of Cyprus are not more taciturn than those of the Temple. Wit and wine are always here, and always together; the revels of the Temple are as those of polished Greece, where the wildest worshipper of Bacchus never forgot the dignity of the god whom he adored. Where can retirement be so complete as here? where can you be so sure of all the pleasures of society?

It was here that Tom Towers lived, and cultivated with eminent success the tenth Muse who now governs the periodical press. But let it not be supposed that his chambers were such, or so comfortless, as are frequently the gaunt abodes of legal aspirants. Four chairs, a half-filled deal book-case with hangings of dingy green baize, an old office table covered with dusty papers, which are not moved once in six months, and an older Pembroke brother with rickety legs, for all daily uses; a despatcher for the preparation of lobsters and coffee, and an apparatus for the cooking of toast and mutton chops; such utensils and luxuries as these did not suffice for the well-being of Tom Towers. He indulged in four rooms on the first floor, each of which was furnished, if not with the splendour, with probably more than the comfort of Stafford House. Every addition that science and art have lately made to the luxuries of modern life was to be found there. The room in which he usually sat was surrounded by book-shelves carefully filled; nor was there a volume there which was not entitled to its place in such a collection, both by its intrinsic worth and exterior splendour: a pretty portable set of steps in one corner of the room showed that those even on the higher shelves were intended for use. The chamber contained but two works of art—the one, an admirable bust of Sir Robert Peel, by Power, declared the individual politics of our friend; and the other, a singularly long figure of a female devotee, by Millais, told equally plainly the school of art to which he was addicted. This picture was not hung, as pictures usually are, against the wall; there was no inch of wall vacant for such a purpose: it had a stand or desk erected for its own accommodation; and there on her pedestal, framed and glazed, stood the devotional lady looking intently at a lily as no lady ever looked before.

# Crucial Moments

---

### The Senator's Arrival at Bragton

Mr. Morton asked the Senator to walk round the grounds. Mr. Gotobed, lighting an enormous cigar, of which he put half down his throat for more commodious and quick consumption, walked on to the middle of the drive, and turning back looked up at the house. 'Quite a pile,' he said, observing that the offices and outhouses extended a long way to the left till they almost joined other buildings in which were the stables and coach-house.

'It's a good-sized house,' said the owner; 'nothing very particular, as houses are built nowadays.'

'Damp, I should say?'

'I think not. I have never lived here much myself; but I have not heard that it was considered so.'

'I guess it's damp. Very lonely;—isn't it?'

'We like to have our society inside, among ourselves, in the country.'

'Keep a sort of hotel—like?' suggested Mr. Gotobed. 'Well, I don't dislike hotel life, especially when there are no charges. How many servants do you want to keep up such a house as that?'

Mr. Morton explained that at present he knew very little about it himself, then led him away by the path over the bridge, and turning to the left showed him the building which had once been the kennels of the Rufford hounds. 'All that for dogs!' exclaimed Mr. Gotobed.

'All for dogs,' said Morton. 'Hounds, we generally call them.'

[ 53 ]

'Hounds are they? Well, I'll remember; though "dogs" seems to me more civil. How many used there to be?'

'About fifty couple, I think.'

'A hundred dogs! No wonder your country gentlemen burst up so often. Wouldn't half a dozen do as well,—except for the show of the thing?'

'Half a dozen hounds couldn't hunt a fox, Mr. Gotobed.'

'I guess half a dozen would do just as well, only for the show. What strikes me, Mr. Morton, on visiting this old country is that so much is done for show.'

'What do you say to New York, Mr. Gotobed?'

'There certainly are a couple of hundred fools in New York, who, having more money than brains, amuse themselves by imitating European follies. But you won't find that through the country, Mr. Morton. You won't find a hundred dogs at an American planter's house when ten or twelve would do as well.'

'Hunting is not one of your amusements.'

'Yes, it is. I've been a hunter myself. I've had nothing to eat but what I killed for a month together. That's more than any of your hunters can say. A hundred dogs to kill one fox!'

'Not all at the same time, Mr. Gotobed.'

'And you have got none now?'

'I don't hunt myself.'

'And does nobody hunt the foxes about here at present?' Then Morton explained that on the Saturday following the U.R.U. hounds, under the mastership of that celebrated sportsman Captain Glomax, would meet at eleven o'clock exactly at the spot on which they were then standing, and that if Mr. Gotobed would walk out after breakfast he would see the whole paraphernalia, including about half a hundred 'dogs,' and perhaps a couple of hundred men on horseback. 'I shall be delighted to see any institution of this great country,' said Mr. Gotobed, 'however much opposed it may be to my opinion either of utility or rational recreation.' Then, having nearly eaten up one cigar, he lit another preparatory to eating it, and sauntered back to the house.

## Lady Glencora Gambles

'I WONDER WHETHER it would be any harm if I were to put a few pieces of money on the table, just once?' Lady Glencora said to her cousin, on the evening of the same day, in one of those gambling salons. There had been some music on that evening in one side of the building, and the Pallisers had gone to the rooms. But as neither of the two ladies would dance, they had strayed away into the other apartments.

'The greatest harm in the world!' said Alice; 'and what on earth could you gain by it? You don't really want any of those horrid people's money?'

'I'll tell you what I want,—something to live for,—some excitement. Is it not a shame that I see around me so many people getting amusement, and that I can get none? I'd go and sit out there, and drink beer and hear the music, only Plantagenet wouldn't let me. I think I'll throw one piece on to the table to see what becomes of it.'

'I shall leave you if you do,' said Alice.

'You are such a prude! It seems to me as if it must have been my special fate,—my good fate, I mean,—that has thrown me so much with you. You look after me quite as carefully as Mr. Bott and Mrs. Marsham ever did; but as I chose you myself, I can't very well complain, and I can't very well get rid of you.'

'Do you want to get rid of me, Cora?'

'Sometimes. Do you know, there are moments when I almost make up my mind to go headlong to the devil,—when I think it is the best thing to be done. It's a hard thing for a woman to do, because she has to undergo so much obloquy before she gets used to it. A man can take to drinking, and gambling and all the rest of it, and nobody despises him a bit. The domestic old fogies give him lectures if they can catch

[ 55 ]

him, but he isn't fool enough for that. All he wants is money, and he goes away and has his fling. Now I have plenty of money,—or, at any rate, I had,—and I never got my fling yet. I do feel so tempted to rebel, and go ahead, and care for nothing.'

'Throwing one piece on to the table wouldn't satisfy that longing.'

'You think I should be like the wild beast that has tasted blood, and can't be controlled. Look at all these people here. There are husbands gambling, and their wives don't know it; and wives gambling, and their husbands don't know it. I wonder whether Plantagenet ever has a fling? What a joke it would be to come and catch him!'

'I don't think you need be afraid.'

'Afraid! I should like him all the better for it. If he came to me, some morning, and told me that he had lost a hundred thousand pounds, I should be so much more at my ease with him.'

'You have no chance in that direction, I'm quite sure.'

'None the least. He'd make a calculation that the chances were nine to seven against him, and then the speculation would seem to him to be madness.'

'I don't suppose he'd wish to try, even though he were sure of winning.'

'Of course not. It would be a very vulgar kind of thing then. Look,—there's an opening there. I'll just put on one napoleon.'

'You shall not. If you do, I'll leave you at once. Look at the women who are playing. Is there one there whom it would not disgrace you to touch? Look what they are. Look at their cheeks, and their eyes, and their hands. Those men who rake about the money are bad enough, but the women look like fiends.'

'You're not going to frighten me in that hobgoblin sort of way, you know. I don't see anything the matter with any of the people.'

[56]

'What do you think of that young woman who has just got a handful of money from the man next to her?'

'I think she is very happy. I never get money given to me by handfuls, and the man to whom I belong gives me no encouragement when I want to amuse myself.' They were now standing near to one end of the table, and suddenly there came to be an opening through the crowd up to the table itself. Lady Glencora, leaving Alice's side, at once stepped up and deposited a piece of gold on one of the marked compartments. As soon as she placed it she retreated again with flushed face, and took hold of Alice's arm. 'There,' she said, 'I have done it.' Alice, in her dismay, did not know what step to take. She could not scold her friend now, as the eyes of many were turned upon them, nor could she, of course, leave her, as she had threatened. Lady Glencora laughed with her peculiar little low laughter, and stood her ground. 'I was determined you shouldn't frighten me out of it,' she said.

One of the ministers at the table had in the meantime gone on with the cards, and had called the game; and another minister had gently pushed three or four more pieces of gold up to that which Lady Glencora had flung down, and had then cunningly caught her eye, and, with all the courtesy of which he was master, had pushed them further on towards her. She had supposed herself to be unknown there in the salon, but no doubt all the croupiers and half the company knew well enough who was the new customer at the table. There was still the space open, near to which she stood, and then some one motioned to her to come and take up the money which she had won. She hesitated, and then the croupier asked her, in that low, indifferent voice which these men always use, whether she desired that her money should remain. She nodded her head to him, and he at once drew the money back again to the spot on which she had placed the first napoleon. Again the cards were turned up softly, again the game was called, and again she won. The money was dealt out to her,—on this occasion with a full hand. There were lying there between twenty and thirty napoleons, of which she was the mistress. Her face had flushed before, but now it became very red. She caught hold of Alice, who was literally trembling beside her, and tried to laugh again. But there was that in her eye which told Alice that she was really frightened. Some one then placed a chair for her at the table, and in her confusion, not knowing what she was to do, she seated herself. 'Come away,' said Alice, taking hold of her, and disregarding everything but her own purpose, in the agony of the moment. 'You must come away! You shall not sit there!' 'I must get rid of that money,' said Glencora, trying to whisper her words, 'and then I will come away.' The croupier again asked her if the money was to remain, and she again nodded her head. Everybody at the table was now looking at her. The women especially were staring at her,—those horrid women with vermilion cheeks, and loud bonnets half off their heads, and hard, shameless eyes, and white gloves, which, when taken off in the ardour of the game, disclosed dirty hands. They stared at her with that fixed stare which such women have, and Alice saw it all, and trembled.

Again she won. 'Leave it,' said Alice, 'and come away.' 'I can't leave it,' said Glencora. 'If I do, there'll be a fuss. I'll go the next time.' What she said was, of course, in English, and was probably understood by no one near her; but it was easy to be seen that she was troubled, and, of course, those around her looked at her the more because of her trouble. Again that little question and answer went on between her and the croupier, and on this occasion the money was piled up on the compartment—a heap of gold which made envious the hearts of many who stood around there. Alice had now both her hands on the back of the chair, needing support. If the devil should persist, and increase that stock of gold again, she must go and seek for Mr. Palliser. She knew not what else to do. She understood nothing of the table, or of its laws; but she supposed all those ministers of the game to be thieves, and believed that all villainous contrivances were within their capacity. She thought that they might go on adding to that heap so long as Lady Glencora would sit there, presuming that they might thus get her into their clutches. Of course, she did not sift her suspicions. Who does at such moments? 'Come away at once, and leave it,' she said, 'or I shall go.' At that moment the croupier raked it all up, and carried it all away; but Alice did not see that this had been done. A hand had been placed on her shoulder, and as she turned round her face her eyes met those of Mr. Palliser. 'It is all gone,' said Glencora, laughing. And now she, turning round, also saw her husband. 'I am so glad that you are come,' said Alice. 'Why did you bring her here?' said Mr. Palliser. There was anger in his tone, and anger in his eye. He took his wife's arm upon his own, and walked away quickly, while Alice followed them alone. He went off at once, down the front steps of the building, towards the hotel. What he said to his wife, Alice did not hear; but her heart was swelling with the ill-usage to which she herself was subjected. Though she might have to go back alone to England, she would tell him that he was ill-treating her. She followed him on, up into their drawing-room, and there he stood with the door open in his hand for her, while Lady Glencora threw herself upon a sofa, and burst out into affected laughter. 'Here's a piece of work,' she said, 'about a little accident.'

'An accident!' said Mr. Palliser.

'Yes, an accident. You don't suppose that I sat down there meaning to win all that money?' Whereupon he looked at her with scorn.

'Mr. Palliser,' said Alice, 'you have treated me this evening in a manner I did not expect from you. It is clear that you blame me.'

'I have not said a word, Miss Vavasor.'

'No; you have not said a word. You know well how to show your anger without speaking. As I do not choose to undergo your displeasure, I will return to England by myself.'

[ 59 ]

'Alice! Alice!' said Glencora, jumping up, 'that is nonsense! What is all this trumpery thing about? Leave me, because he chooses to be angry about nothing?'

'Is it nothing that I find my wife playing at a common gambling-table, surrounded by all that is wretched and vile,—established there, seated, with heaps of gold before her?'

'You wrong me, Plantagenet,' said Glencora. 'There was only one heap, and that did not remain long. Did it, Alice?'

'It is impossible to make you ashamed of anything,' he said.

'I certainly don't like being ashamed,' she answered; 'and don't feel any necessity on this occasion.'

'If you don't object, Mr. Palliser,' said Alice, 'I will go to bed. You can think over all this at night,—and so can I. Goodnight, Glencora.' Then Alice took her candle, and marched off to her own room, with all the dignity of which she was mistress.

## Good-bye to the Estate

He had spent the long evening before his last dinner in going round the whole demesne alone, so that no eye should witness what he felt. None but those who have known the charms of a country-house early in life can conceive the intimacy to which a man attains with all the various trifling objects round his own locality; how he knows the bark of every tree, and the bend of every bough; how he has marked where the rich grass grows in tufts, and where the poorer soil is always dry and bare; how he watches the nests of the rooks, and the holes of the rabbits, and has learned where the thrushes build, and can show the branch on which the linnet sits. All these things had been dear to Herbert, and they all required at his hand some last farewell. Every dog, too, he had to see, and to lay his hand on the neck of every horse. This making of his final adieu under such circumstances was melancholy enough.

And then, too, later in the evening, after dinner, all the servants were called into the parlor that he might shake hands with them. There was not one of them who had not hoped, as lately as three months since, that he or she would live to call Herbert Fitzgerald master. Indeed, he had already been their master,—their young master. All Irish servants especially love to pay respect to the 'young masther'; but Herbert now was to be their master no longer, and the probability was that he would never see one of them again.

## A Pretty Woman in Action

LIZZIE, IN HER FEARS, had been very punctual; and when the two gentlemen reached the door leading up to Mr. Camperdown's chambers, the carriage was already standing there. Lizzie had come up the stairs, and had been delighted at hearing that Mr. Camperdown was out, and would be back in a moment. She instantly resolved that it did not become her to wait. She had kept her appointment, had not found Mr. Camperdown at home, and would be off as fast as her carriage-wheels could take her. But, unfortunately, while with a gentle murmur she was explaining to the clerk how impossible it was that she should wait for a lawyer who did not keep his own appointment, John Eustace and Mr. Camperdown appeared upon the landing, and she was at once convoyed into the attorney's particular room.

Lizzie, who always dressed well, was now attired as became a lady of rank, who had four thousand a year, and was the intimate friend of Lady Glencora Palliser. When last she saw Mr. Camperdown she had been arrayed for a summer, long, dusty journey down to Scotland, and neither by her outside garniture nor by her manner had she then been able to exact much admiration. She had been taken by surprise in the street, and was frightened. Now, in difficulty though she was, she resolved that she would hold up her head and be very brave. She was a little taken aback when she saw her brother-in-law, but she strove hard to carry herself with confidence. 'Ah, John,' she said, 'I did not expect to find you with Mr. Camperdown.'

'I thought it best that I should be here,—as a friend,' he said.

'It makes it much pleasanter for me, of course,' said Lizzie. 'I am not quite sure that Mr. Camperdown will allow me to regard him as a friend.'

'You have never had any reason to regard me as your enemy, Lady Eustace,' said Mr. Camperdown. 'Will you take a seat? I understand that you wish to state the circumstances under which the Eustace family diamonds were stolen while they were in your hands.'

'My own diamonds, Mr. Camperdown.'

'I cannot admit that for a moment, my lady.'

'What does it signify?' said Eustace. 'The wretched stones are gone for ever; and whether they were of right the property of my sister-in-law, or of her son, cannot matter now.'

Mr. Camperdown was irritated, and shook his head. It cut him to the heart that everybody should take the part of the wicked, fraudulent woman who had caused him such infinite trouble. Lizzie saw her opportunity and was bolder than ever. 'You will never get me to acknowledge that they were not my own,' she said. 'My husband gave them to me, and I know that they were my own.'

'They have been stolen at any rate,' said the lawyer.

'Yes;—they have been stolen.'

'And now will you tell us how?'

Lizzie looked round upon her brother-in-law and sighed. She had never yet told the story in all its nakedness, although it had been three or four times extracted from her by admission. She paused, hoping that questions might be asked her which she could answer by easy monosyllables, but not a word was uttered to help her. 'I suppose you know all about it,' she said at last.

'I know nothing about it,' said Mr. Camperdown.

'We heard that your jewel-case was taken out of your room at Carlisle and broken open,' said Eustace.

'So it was. They broke into my room in the dead of night,

when I was in bed, fast asleep, and took the case away. When the morning came, everybody rushed into my room, and I was so frightened that I did not know what I was doing. How would your daughter bear it, if two men cut away the locks and got into her bedroom when she was asleep? You don't think about that at all.'

'And where was the necklace?' asked Eustace.

Lizzie remembered that her friend the major had specially advised her to tell the whole truth to Mr. Camperdown,—suggesting that, by doing so, she would go far towards saving herself from any prosecution. 'It was under my pillow,' she whispered.

'And why did you not tell the magistrate that it had been under your pillow?'

Mr. Camperdown's voice, as he put to her this vital question, was severe, and almost justified the little burst of sobs which came forth as a prelude to Lizzie's answer. 'I did not know what I was doing. I don't know what you expect from me. You had been persecuting me ever since Sir Florian's death about the diamonds, and I didn't know what I was to do. They were my own, and I thought I was not obliged to tell everybody where I kept them. There are things which nobody tells. If I were to ask you all your secrets, would you tell them? When Sir Walter Scott was asked whether he wrote the novels, he didn't tell.'

'He was not upon his oath, Lady Eustace.'

'He did take his oath,—ever so many times. I don't know what difference an oath makes. People ain't obliged to tell their secrets, and I wouldn't tell mine.'

'The difference is this, Lady Eustace;—that if you give false evidence upon oath, you commit perjury.'

'How was I to think of that, when I was so frightened and confused that I didn't know where I was or what I was doing? There;—now I have told you everything.'

'Not quite everything. The diamonds were not stolen at Carlisle, but they were stolen afterwards. Did you tell the police what you had lost,—or the magistrate,—after the robbery in Hertford Street?'

'Yes; I did. There was some money taken, and rings, and other jewellery.'

'Did you tell them that the diamonds had been really stolen on that occasion?'

'They never asked me, Mr. Camperdown.'

'It is all as clear as a pike-staff, John,' said the lawyer.

'Quite clear, I should say,' replied Mr. Eustace.

'And I suppose I may go,' said Lizzie, rising from her chair.

There was no reason why she should not go; and, indeed, now that the interview was over, there did not seem to be any reason why she should have come. Though they had heard so much from her own mouth, they knew no more than they had known before. The great mystery had been elucidated, and Lizzie Eustace had been found to be the intriguing villain; but it was quite clear, even to Mr. Camperdown, that nothing could be done to her. He had never really thought that it would be expedient that she should be prosecuted for perjury, and he now found that she must go utterly scatheless, although, by her obstinacy and dishonesty, she had inflicted so great a loss on the distinguished family which had taken her to its bosom. 'I have no reason for wishing to detain you, Lady Eustace,' he said. 'If I were to talk for ever, I should not, probably, make you understand the extent of the injury you have done, or teach you to look in a proper light at the position in which you have placed yourself and all those who belong to you. When your husband died, good advice was given you, and given, I think, in a very kind way. You would not listen to it, and you see the result.'

'I ain't a bit ashamed of anything,' said Lizzie.

'I suppose not,' rejoined Mr. Camperdown.

'Good-bye, John.' And Lizzie put out her hand to her brother-in-law.

'Good-bye, Lizzie.'

'Mr. Camperdown, I have the honour to wish you good

morning.' And Lizzie made a low curtsey to the lawyer, and was then attended to her carriage by the lawyer's clerk. She had certainly come forth from the interview without fresh wounds.

'The barrister who will have the cross-examining of her at the Central Criminal Court,' said Mr. Camperdown, as soon as the door was closed behind her, 'will have a job of work on his hand. There's nothing a pretty woman can't do when she has got rid of all sense of shame.'

'She is a very great woman,' said John Eustace,—'a very great woman; and, if the sex could have its rights, would make an excellent lawyer.' In the meantime Lizzie Eustace returned home to Hertford Street in triumph.

## Mrs. Proudie's Encounter

WHEN MR. THUMBLE reported himself and his failure at the palace, he strove hard to avoid seeing Mrs. Proudie, but not successfully. He knew something of the palace habits, and did manage to reach the bishop alone on the Sunday evening, justifying himself to his lordship for such an interview by the remarkable circumstances of the case and the importance of his late mission. Mrs. Proudie always went to church on Sunday evenings, making a point of hearing three services and three sermons every Sunday of her life. On week-days she seldom heard any, having an idea that week-day services were an invention of the High Church enemy, and that they should therefore be vehemently discouraged. Services on saints' days she regarded as rank papacy, and had been known to accuse a clergyman's wife, to her face, of idolatry, because the poor lady had dated a letter, St. John's Eve. Mr. Thumble, on this Sunday evening, was successful in finding the bishop at home, and alone, but he was not lucky enough to get away before Mrs. Proudie returned. The bishop, perhaps, thought that the story of the failure had better reach his wife's ears from Mr. Thumble's lips than from his own.

'Well, Mr. Thumble?' said Mrs. Proudie, walking into the study, armed in her full Sunday-evening winter panoply, in which she had just descended from her carriage. The church which Mrs. Proudie attended in the evening was nearly half a mile from the palace, and the coachman and groom never got a holiday on Sunday night. She was gorgeous in a dark brown silk dress of awful stiffness and terrible dimensions; and on her shoulders she wore a short cloak of velvet and fur, very handsome withal, but so swelling in its proportions on all sides as necessarily to create more of dismay than of admiration in the mind of any ordinary man. And her bonnet was a monstrous helmet with the beaver up, displaying the awful face of the warrior, always ready for combat, and careless to guard itself from attack. The large contorted bows which she bore were as a grisly crest upon her casque, beautiful, doubtless, but majestic and fear-compelling. In her hand she carried her armour all complete, a prayer-book, a bible, and a book of hymns. These the footman had brought for her to the study door, but she had thought fit to enter her husband's room with them in her own custody.

'Well, Mr. Thumble!' she said.

Mr. Thumble did not answer at once, thinking, probably, that the bishop might choose to explain the circumstances. But neither did the bishop say anything.

'Well, Mr. Thumble?' she said again; and then she stood looking at the man who had failed so disastrously.

'I have explained to the bishop,' said he. 'Mr. Crawley has been contumacious,—very contumacious indeed.'

'But you preached at Hogglestock?'

'No, indeed, Mrs. Proudie. Nor would it have been possible, unless I had had the police to assist me.'

'Then you should have had the police. I never heard of anything so mismanaged in all my life,—never in all my life.' And she put her books down on the study table, and turned herself round from Mr. Thumble towards the bishop. 'If things go on like this, my lord,' she said, 'your authority

[ 66 ]

in the diocese will very soon be worth nothing at all.' It was not often that Mrs. Proudie called her husband my lord, but when she did do so, it was a sign that terrible times had come; —times so terrible that the bishop would know that he must either fight or fly. He would almost endure anything rather than descend into the arena for the purpose of doing battle with his wife, but occasions would come now and again when even the alternative of flight was hardly left to him.

'But, my dear,—' began the bishop.

'Am I to understand that this man has professed himself to be altogether indifferent to the bishop's prohibition?' said Mrs. Proudie, interrupting her husband and addressing Mr. Thumble.

'Quite so. He seemed to think that the bishop had no lawful power in the matter at all,' said Mr. Thumble.

'Do you hear that, my lord?' said Mrs. Proudie.

'Nor have I any,' said the bishop, almost weeping as he spoke.

'No authority in your own diocese!'

'None to silence a man merely by my own judgment. I thought, and still think, that it was for this gentleman's own interest, as well as for the credit of the Church, that some provision should be made for his duties during his present,— present—difficulties.'

'Difficulties indeed! Everybody knows that the man has been a thief.'

'No, my dear; I do not know it.'

'You never know anything, bishop.'

'I mean to say that I do not know it officially. Of course I have heard the sad story; and, though I hope it may not be the—'

'There is no doubt about its truth. All the world knows it. He has stolen twenty pounds, and yet he is to be allowed to desecrate the Church, and imperil the souls of the people!' The bishop got up from his chair and began to walk backwards and forwards through the room with short quick steps.

[ 67 ]

'It only wants five days to Christmas Day,' continued Mrs. Proudie, 'and something must be done at once. I say nothing as to the propriety or impropriety of his being out on bail, as it is no affair of ours. When I heard that he had been bailed by a beneficed clergyman of this diocese, of course I knew where to look for the man who would act with so much impropriety. Of course I was not surprised when I found that that person belonged to Framley. But, as I have said before, that is no business of ours. I hope, Mr. Thumble, that the bishop will never be found interfering with the ordinary laws of the land. I am very sure that he will never do so by my advice. But when there comes a question of inhibiting a clergyman who has committed himself as this clergyman unfortunately has done, then I say that that clergyman ought to be inhibited.' The bishop walked up and down the room throughout the whole of this speech, but gradually his steps became quicker, and his turns became shorter. 'And now here is Christmas Day upon us, and what is to be done?' With these words Mrs. Proudie finished her speech.

'Mr. Thumble,' said the bishop, 'perhaps you had better now retire. I am very sorry that you should have had so thankless and so disagreeable a task.'

'Why should Mr. Thumble retire?' asked Mrs. Proudie.

'I think it better,' said the bishop. 'Mr. Thumble, good night.' Then Mr. Thumble did retire, and Mrs. Proudie stood forth in her full panoply of armour, silent and awful, with her helmet erect, and vouchsafed no recognition whatever of the parting salutation with which Mr. Thumble greeted her. 'My dear, the truth is, you do not understand the matter,' said the bishop as soon as the door was closed. 'You do not know how limited is my power.'

'Bishop, I understand it a great deal better than some people; and I understand also what is due to myself and the manner in which I ought to be treated by you in the presence of the subordinate clergy of the diocese. I shall not, however, remain here to be insulted either in the presence or in the absence of any one.' Then the conquered amazon collected together the weapons which she had laid upon the table, and took her departure with majestic step, and not without the clang of arms. The bishop, when he was left alone, enjoyed for a few moments the triumph of his victory.

But then he was left so very much alone! When he looked round about him upon his solitude after the departure of his wife, and remembered that he should not see her again till he should encounter her on ground that was all her own, he regretted his own success, and was tempted to follow her and to apologize. He was unable to do anything alone. He would not even know how to get his tea, as the very servants would ask questions, if he were to do so unaccustomed a thing as to order it to be brought up to him in his solitude. They would tell him that Mrs. Proudie was having tea in her little sitting-room upstairs, or else that the things were laid in the drawing-room. He did wander forth to the latter apartment, hoping that he might find his wife there; but the drawing-room was dark and deserted, and so he wandered back again. It was a grand thing certainly to have triumphed over his wife, and there was a crumb of comfort in the thought that he had vindicated himself before Mr. Thumble; but the general result was not comforting, and he knew from of old how short-lived his triumph would be.

## The Death of Mrs. Proudie

Mrs. Proudie's own maid, Mrs. Draper by name, came to him and said that she had knocked twice at Mrs. Proudie's door and would knock again. Two minutes after that she returned, running into the room with her arms extended, and exclaiming, 'Oh, heavens, sir; mistress is dead!' Mr. Thumble, hardly knowing what he was about, followed the woman into the bedroom, and there he found himself standing awe-struck before the corpse of her who had so lately been the presiding spirit of the palace.

The body was still resting on its legs, leaning against the end of the side of the bed, while one of the arms was close clasped round the bed-post. The mouth was rigidly close, but the eyes were open as though staring at him. Nevertheless there could be no doubt from the first glance that the woman was dead. He went up close to it, but did not dare to touch it. There was no one as yet there but he and Mrs. Draper;—no one else knew what had happened.

'It's her heart,' said Mrs. Draper.

'Did she suffer from heart complaint?' he asked.

'We suspected it, sir, though nobody knew it. She was very shy of talking about herself.'

'We must send for the doctor at once,' said Mr. Thumble. 'We had better touch nothing till he is here.' Then they retreated and the door was locked.

In ten minutes everybody in the house knew it except the bishop; and in twenty minutes the nearest apothecary with his assistant were in the room, and the body had been properly laid upon the bed. Even then the husband had not been told,—did not know either his relief or his loss. It was now past seven, which was the usual hour for dinner at the palace, and it was probable that he would come out of his room among the servants, if he were not summoned. When it was proposed to Mr. Thumble that he should go in to him and tell him, he positively declined, saying that the sight which he had just seen and the exertions of the day together, had so unnerved him, that he had not physical strength for the task. The apothecary, who had been summoned in a hurry, had escaped, probably being equally unwilling to be the bearer of such a communication. The duty therefore fell to Mrs. Draper, and under the pressing instance of the other servants she descended to her master's room. Had it not been that the hour of dinner had come, so that the bishop could not have been left much longer to himself, the evil time would have been still postponed.

She went very slowly along the passage, and was just going

to pause ere she reached the room, when the door was opened and the bishop stood close before her. It was easy to be seen that he was cross. His hands and face were unwashed and his face was haggard. In these days he would not even go through the ceremony of dressing himself before dinner. 'Mrs. Draper,' he said, 'why don't they tell me that dinner is ready? Are they going to give me any dinner?' She stood a moment without answering him, while the tears streamed down her face. 'What is the matter?' said he. 'Has your mistress sent you here?'

'Oh laws!' said Mrs. Draper,—and she put out her hands to support him if such support should be necessary.

'What is the matter?' he demanded angrily.

'Oh, my lord;—bear it like a Christian. Mistress isn't no more.' He leaned back against the door-post and she took hold of him by the arm. 'It was the heart, my lord. Dr. Filgrave hisself has not been yet; but that's what it was.' The bishop did not say a word, but walked back to his chair before the fire.

The bishop when he had heard the tidings of his wife's death walked back to his seat over the fire, and Mrs. Draper, the housekeeper, came and stood over him without speaking. Thus she stood for ten minutes looking down at him and listening. But there was no sound; not a word, nor a moan, nor a sob. It was as though he also were dead, but that a slight irregular movement of his fingers on the top of his bald head, told her that his mind and body were still active. 'My lord,' she said at last, 'would you wish to see the doctor when he comes?' She spoke very low and he did not answer her. Then, after another minute of silence, she asked the same question again.

'What doctor?' he said.

'Dr. Filgrave. We sent for him. Perhaps he is here now. Shall I go and see, my lord?' Mrs. Draper found that her position there was weary and she wished to escape. Anything on his behalf requiring trouble or work she would have done willingly; but she could not stand there for ever watching the motion of his fingers.

'I suppose I must see him,' said the bishop. Mrs. Draper took this as an order for her departure and crept silently out of the room, closing the door behind her with the long protracted elaborate click which is always produced by an attempt at silence on such occasions. He did not care for noise or for silence. Had she slammed the door he would not have regarded it. A wonderful silence had come upon him which for the time almost crushed him. He would never hear that well-known voice again!

He was free now. Even in his misery,—for he was very miserable,—he could not refrain from telling himself that. No one could now press uncalled-for into his study, contradict him in the presence of those before whom he was bound to be authoritative, and rob him of all his dignity. There was no one else of whom he was afraid. She had at least kept him out of the hands of other tyrants. He was now his own master, and there was a feeling,—I may not call it of relief, for as yet there was more of pain in it than of satisfaction,—a feeling as though he had escaped from an old trouble at a terrible cost of which he could not as yet calculate the amount. He knew that he might now give up all idea of writing to the archbishop.

She had in some ways, and at certain periods of his life, been very good to him. She had kept his money for him and made things go straight, when they had been poor. His interests had always been her interests. Without her he would never have been a bishop. So, at least, he told himself now, and so told himself probably with truth. She had been very careful of his children. She had never been idle. She had never been fond of pleasure. She had neglected no acknowledged duty. He did not doubt that she was now on her way to heaven. He took his hands from his head, and clasping them together, said a little prayer. It may be doubted whether he quite knew for what he was praying. The idea of praying for her soul, now that she was dead, would have scandalized him. He certainly was not praying for his own soul. I think he was praying that God might save him from being glad that his wife was dead.

But she was dead;—and, as it were, in a moment! He had not stirred out of that room since she had been there with him. Then there had been angry words between them,—perhaps more determined enmity on his part than ever had before existed; and they had parted for the last time with bitter animosity. But he told himself that he had certainly been right in what he had done then. He thought he had been right then. And so his mind went back to the Crawley and Thumble question, and he tried to alleviate the misery which that last interview with his wife now created by assuring himself that he at least had been justified in what he had done.

But yet his thoughts were very tender to her. Nothing reopens the springs of love so fully as absence, and no absence so thoroughly as that which must needs be endless. We want that which we have not; and especially that which we can never have. She had told him in the very last moments of her presence with him that he was wishing that she were dead, and he had made her no reply. At the moment he had felt, with savage anger, that such was his wish. Her words had now come to pass, and he was a widower,—and he assured himself that he would give all that he possessed in the world to bring her back again.

## The Death of Mr. Harding

ON THE MORNING of the Sunday after the dean's return Mr. Harding was lying in his bed, and Posy was sitting on the bed beside him. It was manifest to all now that he became feebler and feebler from day to day, and that he would never leave his bed again. Even the archdeacon had shaken his head, and had acknowledged to his wife that the last day for her father was near at hand. It would very soon be necessary that he should select another vicar for St. Ewold's.

'Grandpa won't play cat's-cradle,' said Posy, as Mrs. Arabin entered the room.

'No, darling,—not this morning,' said the old man. He himself well knew that he would never play cat's-cradle again. Even that was over for him now.

'She teases you, papa,' said Mrs. Arabin.

'No, indeed,' said he. 'Posy never teases me'; and he slowly moved his withered hand down outside the bed, so as to hold the child by her frock. 'Let her stay with me, my dear.'

'Dr. Filgrave is downstairs, papa. You will see him, if he comes up?' Now Dr. Filgrave was the leading physician of Barchester, and nobody of note in the city,—or for the matter of that in the eastern division of the county,—was allowed to start upon the last great journey without some assistance from him as the hour of going drew nigh. I do not know that he had much reputation for prolonging life, but he was supposed to add a grace to the hour of departure. Mr. Harding had expressed no wish to see the doctor,—had rather declared his conviction that Dr. Filgrave could be of no possible service to him. But he was not a man to persevere in his objection in opposition to the wishes of his friends around him; and as soon as the archdeacon had spoken a word on the subject he assented.

'Of course, my dear, I will see him.'

'And Posy shall come back when he has gone,' said Mrs. Arabin.

'Posy will do me more good than Dr. Filgrave I am quite sure;—but Posy shall go now.' So Posy scrambled off the bed, and the doctor was ushered into the room.

'A day or two will see the end of it, Mr. Archdeacon;—I should say a day or two,' said the doctor, as he met Dr. Grantly in the hall. 'I should say that a day or two will see the end of it. Indeed I will not undertake that twenty-four hours may not see the close of his earthly troubles. He has no suffering, no pain, no disturbing cause. Nature simply retires to rest.' Dr. Filgrave, as he said this, made a slow falling motion with his hands, which alone on various occasions had been thought to be worth all the money paid for his attendance. 'Perhaps you would wish that I should step in in the evening, Mr. Dean? As it happens, I shall be at liberty.' The dean of course said that he would take it as an additional favour. Neither the dean nor the archdeacon had the slightest belief in Dr. Filgrave, and yet they would hardly have been contented that their father-in-law should have departed without him.

'Look at that man, now,' said the archdeacon, when the doctor had gone, 'who talks so glibly about nature going to rest. I've known him all my life. He's an older man by some months than our dear old friend upstairs. And he looks as if he were going to attend death-beds in Barchester for ever.'

'I suppose he is right in what he tells us now?' said the dean.

'No doubt he is; but my belief doesn't come from his saying it.' Then there was a pause as the two church dignitaries sat together, doing nothing, feeling that the solemnity of the moment was such that it would be hardly becoming that they should even attempt to read. 'His going will make an old man of me,' said the archdeacon. 'It will be different with you.'

'It will make an old woman of Eleanor, I fear.'

'I seem to have known him all my life,' said the archdeacon. 'I have known him ever since I left college; and I have known him as one man seldom knows another. There is nothing that he has done,—as I believe, nothing that he has thought,— with which I have not been cognizant. I feel sure that he never had an impure fancy in his mind, or a faulty wish in his heart. His tenderness has surpassed the tenderness of woman; and yet, when occasion came for showing it, he had all the spirit of a hero. I shall never forget his resignation of the hospital, and all that I did and said to make him keep it.'

'But he was right?'

'As Septimus Harding he was, I think, right; but it would have been wrong in any other man. And he was right, too, about the deanery.' For promotion had once come in Mr. Harding's way, and he, too, might have been Dean of Barchester. 'The fact is, he never was wrong. He couldn't go wrong. He lacked guile, and he feared God,—and a man who does both will never go far astray. I don't think he ever coveted aught in his life,—except a new case for his violoncello and somebody to listen to him when he played it.' Then the archdeacon got up, and walked about the room in his enthusiasm; and, perhaps, as he walked, some thoughts as to the sterner ambition of his own life passed through his mind. What things had he coveted? Had he lacked guile? He told himself that he had feared God,—but he was not sure that he was telling himself true even in that.

During the whole of the morning Mrs. Arabin and Mrs. Grantly were with their father, and during the greater part of the day there was absolute silence in the room. He seemed to sleep; and they, though they knew that in truth he was not sleeping, feared to disturb him by a word. About two Mrs. Baxter brought him his dinner, and he did rouse himself, and swallowed a spoonful of soup and half a glass of wine. At this time Posy came to him, and stood at the bedside, looking at him with her great wide eyes. She seemed to be aware that life had now gone so far with her dear old friend that she must not be allowed to sit upon his bed again. But he put his hand out to her, and she held it, standing quite still and silent. When Mrs. Baxter came to take away the tray, Posy's mother got up, and whispered a word to the child. Then Posy went away, and her eyes never beheld the old man again. That was a day which Posy never forgot,—not though she should live to be much older than her grandfather was when she thus left him.

'It is so sweet to have you both here,' he said, when he had been lying silent for nearly an hour after the child had gone. Then they got up, and came and stood close to him. 'There is nothing left for me to wish, my dears;—nothing.' Not long after that he expressed a desire that the two husbands,—his two sons-in-law,—should come to him; and Mrs. Arabin went to them, and brought them to the room. As he took their hands he merely repeated the same words again. 'There is nothing left for me to wish, my dears;—nothing.' He never spoke again above his breath; but ever and anon his daughters, who watched him, could see that he was praying. The two men did not stay with him long, but returned to the gloom of the library. The gloom had almost become the darkness of night, and they were still sitting there without any light, when Mrs. Baxter entered the room. 'The dear gentleman is no more,' said Mrs. Baxter; and it seemed to the archdeacon that the very moment of his father's death had repeated itself. When Dr. Filgrave called he was told that his services could be of no further use. 'Dear, dear!' said the doctor. 'We are all dust, Mrs. Baxter; are we not?' There were people in Barchester who pretended to know how often the doctor had repeated this little formula during the last thirty years.

There was no violence of sorrow in the house that night; but there were aching hearts, and one heart so sore that it seemed that no cure for its anguish could ever reach it. 'He has always been with me,' Mrs. Arabin said to her husband, as he strove to console her. 'It was not that I loved him better than Susan, but I have felt so much more of his loving tenderness. The sweetness of his voice has been in my ears almost daily since I was born.'

They buried him in the cathedral which he had loved so well, and in which nearly all the work of his life had been done; and all Barchester was there to see him laid in his grave within the cloisters. There was no procession of coaches, no hearse, nor was there any attempt at funereal pomp. From the dean's side door, across the vaulted passage, and into the transept,—over the little step upon which he had so nearly fallen when last he made his way out of the building,—the coffin was carried on men's shoulders. It was but a short journey from his bedroom to his grave. But the bell had been tolling sadly all the morning, and the nave and the aisles and the transepts, close up to the door leading from the transept into the cloister, were crowded with those who had known the name and the figure and the voice of Mr. Harding as long as they had known anything. Up to this day no one would have said specially that Mr. Harding was a favourite in the town. He had never been forward enough in anything to become the acknowledged possessor of popularity. But, now that he was gone, men and women told each other how good he had been. They remembered the sweetness of his smile, and talked of loving little words which he had spoken to them,—either years ago or the other day, for his words had always been loving. The dean and the archdeacon came first, shoulder to shoulder, and after them came their wives. I do not know that it was the proper order for mourning, but it was a touching sight to be seen, and was long remembered in Barchester. Painful as it was for them, the two women would be there, and the two sisters would walk together;—nor would they go before their husbands. Then there were the archdeacon's two sons,—for the Rev. Charles Grantly had come to Plumstead on the occasion. And in the vaulted passage which runs between the deanery and the end of the transept all the chapter, with the choir, the prebendaries, with the fat old chancellor, the precentor, and the minor canons down to the little choristers,—they all were there, and followed in at the transept door, two by two. And in the transept they were joined by another clergyman whom no one had expected to see that day. The bishop was there, looking old and worn,—almost as though he were unconscious of what he was doing. Since his wife's death no one had seen him out of the palace or of the palace grounds till that day. But there he was,—and they made way for him into the procession behind the two ladies,—and the archdeacon, when he saw it, resolved that there should be peace in his heart, if peace might be possible.

They made their way into the cloisters where the grave had been dug,—as many as might be allowed to follow. The place indeed was open to all who chose to come; but they who had only slightly known the man, refrained from pressing upon those who had a right to stand around his coffin. But there was one other there whom the faithful chronicler of Barchester should mention. Before any other one had reached the spot, the sexton and the verger between them had led in between them, among the graves beneath the cloisters, a blind man, very old, with a wondrous stoop, but who must have owned a grand stature before extreme old age had bent him, and they placed him sitting on a stone in the corner of the archway. But as soon as the shuffling of steps reached his ears, he raised himself with the aid of his stick, and stood during the service leaning against the pillar. The blind man was so old that he might almost have been Mr. Harding's father. This was John Bunce, bedesman from Hiram's Hospital,—and none perhaps there had known Mr. Harding better than he had known him. When the earth had been thrown on to the coffin, and the service was over, and they were about to disperse, Mrs. Arabin went up to the old man, and taking his hand between hers whispered a word into his ear. 'Oh, Miss Eleanor,' he said. 'Oh, Miss Eleanor!' Within a fortnight he also was lying within the cathedral precincts.

And so they buried Mr. Septimus Harding, formerly Warden of Hiram's Hospital in the city of Barchester, of whom the chronicler may say that that city never knew a sweeter gentleman or a better Christian.

### Christmas Dinner

We will now look in for a moment at the Christmas doings of our fat friend, Mr. Moulder. Mr. Moulder was a married man living in lodgings over a wine-merchant's vaults in Great St. Helens. He was blessed—or troubled, with no children, and prided himself greatly on the material comfort with which his humble home was surrounded. 'His wife,' he often boasted, 'never wanted for plenty of the best of eating; and for linen and silks and such-like, she could show her drawers and her wardrobes with many a great lady from Russell Square, and not be ashamed, neither!' And then, as for drink, —'tipple,' as Mr. Moulder sportively was accustomed to name it among his friends, he opined that he was not altogether behind the mark in that respect. 'He had got some brandy— he didn't care what anybody might say about Cognac and eau de vie; but the brandy which he had got from Betts' private establishment seventeen years ago, for richness of flavour and fullness of strength, would beat any French article that anybody in the city could show. That at least was his idea. If anybody didn't like it, they needn't take it. There was whisky that would make your hair stand on end.' So said Mr. Moulder, and I can believe him; for it has made my hair stand on end merely to see other people drinking it. . .

On the occasion of this present Christmas-day Mr. Moulder entertained a small party. And he delighted in such occasional entertainments, taking extraordinary pains that the eatables should be of the very best; and he would maintain an hospitable good humour to the last,—unless anything went wrong in the cookery, in which case he could make himself extremely unpleasant to Mrs. M. Indeed, proper cooking for Mr. M. and the proper starching of the bands of his shirts were almost the only trials that Mrs. Moulder was doomed to suffer. 'What the d—— are you for?' he would say, almost throwing the displeasing viands at her head across the table, or tearing the rough linen from off his throat. 'It ain't much I ask of you in return for your keep'; and then he would scowl at her with bloodshot eyes till she shook in her shoes. But this did not happen often, as experiences had made her careful.

But on this present Christmas festival all went swimmingly to the end. 'Now, bear a hand, old girl,' was the harshest word he said to her; and he enjoyed himself like Duncan, shut up in measureless content. He had three guests with him on this auspicious day. There was his old friend Snengkeld, who had dined with him on every Christmas since his marriage; there was his wife's brother, of whom we will say a word or two just now;—and there was our old friend, Mr. Kantwise. Mr. Kantwise was not exactly the man whom Moulder would have chosen as his guest, for they were opposed to each other in all their modes of thought and action; but he had come across the travelling agent of the Patent Metallic Steel Furniture Company on the previous day, and finding that he was to be alone in London on this general holiday, he had asked him out of sheer good nature. Moulder could be very good natured, and full of pity when the sorrow to be pitied arose from some such source as the want of a Christmas dinner. So Mr. Kantwise had been asked, and precisely at four o'clock he made his appearance at Great St. Helens. . .

When Snengkeld and Kenneby were shown up into the room, they found nobody there but Kantwise. That Mrs. Moulder should be down stairs looking after the roast turkey was no more than natural; but why should not Moulder himself be there to receive his guests? He soon appeared, however, coming up without his coat.

'Well, Snengkeld, how are you, old fellow; many happy returns, and all that; the same to you, John. I'll tell you what, my lads; it's a prime 'un. I never saw such a bird in all my days.'

'What, the turkey?' said Snengkeld.

'You didn't think it'd be a ostrich, did you?'

'Ha, ha, ha!' laughed Snengkeld. 'No, I didn't expect nothing but a turkey here on Christmas-day.'

'And nothing but a turkey you'll have, my boys. Can you eat turkey, Kantwise?'

Mr. Kantwise declared that his only passion in the way of eating was for a turkey.

'As for John, I'm sure of him. I've seen him at the work before.' Whereupon John grinned but said nothing.

'I never see such a bird in my life, certainly.'

'From Norfolk, I suppose,' said Snengkeld, with a great appearance of interest.

'Oh, you may swear to that. It weighed twenty-four pounds, for I put it into the scales myself, and old Gibbetts let me have it for a guinea. The price marked on it was five-and-twenty, for I saw it. He's had it hanging for a fortnight, and I've been to see it wiped down with vinegar regular every morning. And now, my boys, it's done to a turn. I've been in the kitchen most of the time myself, and either I or Mrs. M. has never left it for a single moment.'

'How did you manage about divine service?' said Kantwise; and then, when he had spoken, closed his eyes and sucked his lips.

Mr. Moulder looked at him for a minute, and then said, 'Gammon.'

'Ha, ha, ha!' laughed Snengkeld. And then Mrs. Moulder appeared, bringing the turkey with her; for she would trust it to no hands less careful than her own.

'By George, it is a bird,' said Snengkeld, standing over it and eyeing it minutely.

'Uncommon nice it looks,' said Kantwise.

'All the same, I wouldn't eat none, if I were you,' said Moulder, 'seeing what sinners have been a basting it.' And then they all sat down to dinner, Moulder having first resumed his coat.

For the next three or four minutes Moulder did not speak a word. The turkey was on his mind, with the stuffing, the gravy, the liver, the breast, the wings, and the legs. He stood up to carve it, and while he was at the work he looked at it as though his two eyes were hardly sufficient. He did not help first one person and then another, so ending by himself; but he cut up artistically as much as might probably be consumed, and located the fragments in small heaps or shares in the hot gravy; and then, having made a partition of the spoils, he served it out with unerring impartiality. To have robbed any one of his or her fair slice of the breast would, in his mind, have been gross dishonesty. In his heart he did not love Kantwise, but he dealt by him with the utmost justice in the great affair of the turkey's breast. When he had done all this, and his own plate was laden, he gave a long sigh. 'I shall never cut up such another bird as that, the longest day that I have to live,' he said; and then he took out his large red silk handkerchief and wiped the perspiration from his brow.

'Deary me, M.; don't think of that now,' said the wife.

'What's the use?' said Snengkeld. 'Care killed a cat.'

'And perhaps you may,' said John Kenneby, trying to comfort him; 'who knows?'

'It's all in the hands of Providence,' said Kantwise, 'and we should look to him.'

'And how does it taste?' asked Moulder, shaking the gloomy thoughts from his mind.

'Uncommon,' said Snengkeld, with his mouth quite full. 'I never eat such a turkey in all my life.'

'Like melted diamonds,' said Mrs. Moulder, who was not without a touch of poetry.

'Ah, there's nothing like hanging of 'em long enough, and watching of 'em well. It's that vinegar as done it'; and then they went seriously to work, and there was nothing more said of any importance until the eating was nearly over.

And now Mrs. M. had taken away the cloth, and they were sitting cozily over their port wine. The very apple of the eye of the evening had not arrived even yet. That would not come till the pipes were brought out, and the brandy was put on the table, and the whisky was there that made the people's hair stand on end. It was then that the floodgates of convivial eloquence would be unloosed. In the meantime it was necessary to sacrifice something to gentility, and therefore they sat over their port wine.

## The Proposal

Two days afterwards the Duke called again. He would come generally on a Thursday,—early, so that he might be there before other visitors; and he had already quite learned that when he was there other visitors would probably be refused admittance. How Lady Glencora had made her way in, telling the servant that her uncle was there, he had not understood. That visit had been made on the Thursday, but now he came on the Saturday,—having, I regret to say, sent down some early fruit from his own hot-houses,—or from Covent Garden, —with a little note on the previous day. The grapes might have been pretty well, but the note was injudicious. There were three lines about the grapes, as to which there was some special history, the vine having been brought from the garden of some villa in which some ill-used queen had lived and died; and then there was a postscript in one line to say that the Duke would call on the following morning. I do not think that he had meant to add this when he began his note; but then children, who want the top brick, want it so badly, and cry for it so perversely!

Of course Madame Goesler was at home. But even then she had not made up her mind. She had made up her mind only to this,—that he should be made to speak plainly, and that she would take time for her reply. Not even with such a gem as the Duke's coronet before her eyes, would she jump at it. Where there was so much doubt, there need at least be no impatience.

'You ran away the other day, Duke, because you could not resist the charm of that little boy,' she said, laughing.

'He is a dear little boy,—but it was not that,' he answered.

'Then what was it? Your niece carried you off in a whirlwind. She was come and gone, taking you with her, in half a minute.'

'She had disturbed me when I was thinking of something,' said the Duke.

'Things shouldn't be thought of,—not so deeply as that.' Madame Goesler was playing with a bunch of his grapes now, eating one or two, from a small china plate which had stood upon the table, and he thought that he had never seen a woman so graceful and yet so natural. 'Will you not eat your own grapes with me? They are delicious;—flavoured with the poor queen's sorrows.' He shook his head, knowing that it did not suit his gastric juices to have to deal with fruit eaten at odd times. 'Never think, Duke. I am convinced that it does no good. It simply means doubting, and doubt always leads to error. The safest way in the world is to do nothing.'

'I believe so,' said the Duke.

'Much the safest. But if you have not sufficient command over yourself to enable you to sit in repose, always quiet, never committing yourself to the chance of any danger,—then take a leap in the dark; or rather many leaps. A stumbling horse regains his footing by persevering in his onward course. As for moving cautiously, that I detest.'

'And yet one must think;—for instance, whether one will succeed or not.'

'Take that for granted always. Remember, I do not recommend motion at all. Repose is my idea of life;—repose and grapes.'

The Duke sat for a while silent, taking his repose as far as the outer man was concerned, looking at his top brick of the chimney, as from time to time she ate one of his grapes. Probably she did not eat above half-a-dozen of them altogether, but he thought that the grapes must have been made for the woman, she was so pretty in the eating of them. But it was necessary that he should speak at last. 'Have you been thinking of coming to Como?' he said.

'I told you that I never think.'

'But I want an answer to my proposition.'

'I thought I had answered your Grace on that question.'

Then she put down the grapes, and moved herself on her chair, so that she sat with her face turned away from him.

'But a request to a lady may be made twice.'

'Oh, yes. And I am grateful, knowing how far it is from your intention to do me any harm. And I am somewhat ashamed of my warmth on the other day. But still there can be but one answer. There are delights which a woman must deny herself, let them be ever so delightful.'

'I had thought,—' the Duke began, and then he stopped himself.

'Your Grace was saying that you thought,—'

'Marie, a man at my age does not like to be denied.'

'What man likes to be denied anything by a woman at any age? A woman who denies anything is called cruel at once,—even though it be her very soul.' She had turned round upon him now, and was leaning forward towards him from her chair, so that he could touch her if he put out his hand.

He put out his hand and touched her. 'Marie,' he said, 'will you deny me if I ask?'

'Nay, my lord; how shall I say? There is many a trifle I would deny you. There is many a great gift I would give you willingly.'

'But the greatest gift of all?'

'My lord, if you have anything to say, you must say it plainly. There never was a woman worse than I am at the reading of riddles.'

'Could you endure to live in the quietude of an Italian lake with an old man?' Now he touched her again, and had taken her hand.

'No, my lord;—nor with a young one,—for all my days. But I do not know that age would guide me.'

Then the Duke rose and made his proposition in form. 'Marie, you know that I love you. Why it is that I at my age should feel so sore a love, I cannot say.'

'So sore a love!'

'So sore, if it be not gratified. Marie, I ask you to be my wife.'

'Duke of Omnium, this from you!'

'Yes, from me. My coronet is at your feet. If you will allow me to raise it, I will place it on your brow.'

Then she went away from him, and seated herself at a distance. After a moment or two he followed her, and stood with his arm upon her shoulder. 'You will give me an answer, Marie?'

'You cannot have thought of this, my lord.'

'Nay; I have thought of it much.'

'And your friends?'

'My dear, I may venture to please myself in this,—as in everything. Will you not answer me?'

'Certainly not on the spur of the moment, my lord. Think how high is the position you offer me, and how immense is the change you propose to me. Allow me two days, and I will answer you by letter. I am so fluttered now that I must leave you.' Then he came to her, took her hand, kissed her brow, and opened the door for her.

## In Prison

'Phineas, the time has come in which you must show yourself to be a man.'

'A man! Oh, yes, I can be a man. A murderer you mean. I shall have to be—hung, I suppose.'

'May God, in His mercy, forbid.'

'No;—not in His mercy; in His justice. There can be no need for mercy here,—not even from Heaven. When they take my life may He forgive my sins through the merits of my Saviour. But for this there can be no mercy. Why do you not speak? Do you mean to say that I am guilty?'

'I am sure that you are innocent.'

'And yet, look here. What more can be done to prove it than has been done? That blundering fool will swear my life away.' Then he threw himself on his bed, and gave way to his sobs.

That evening he was alone,—as, indeed, most of his evenings had been spent, and the minutes were minutes of agony to him. The external circumstances of his position were as comfortable as circumstances would allow. He had a room to himself looking out through heavy iron bars into one of the courts of the prison. The chamber was carpeted, and was furnished with bed and chairs and two tables. Books were allowed him as he pleased, and pen and ink. It was May, and no fire was necessary. At certain periods of the day he could walk alone in the court below,—the restriction on such liberty being that at other certain hours the place was wanted for other prisoners. As far as he knew no friend who called was denied to him, though he was by no means certain that his privilege in that respect would not be curtailed now that he had been committed for trial. His food had been plentiful and well cooked, and even luxuries, such as fish and wine and fruit, had been supplied to him. That the fruit had come from the hot-houses of the Duchess of Omnium, and the wine from Mr. Low's cellar, and the fish and lamb and spring vegetables, the cream and coffee and fresh butter from the unrestricted orders of another friend, that Lord Chiltern had sent him champagne and cigars, and that Lady Chiltern had given directions about the books and stationery, he did not know. But as far as he could be consoled by such comforts, there had been the consolation. If lamb and salad could make him happy he might have enjoyed his sojourn in Newgate. Now, this evening, he was past all enjoyment. It was impossible that he should read. How could a man fix his attention on any book, with a charge of murder against himself affirmed by the deliberate decision of a judge? And he knew himself to be as innocent as the magistrate himself. Every now and then he would rise from his bed, and almost rush across the room as though he would dash his head against the wall. Murder! They really believed that he had deliberately murdered the man;—he, Phineas Finn, who had served his country with repute, who had sat in Parliament, who had prided himself on living with the best of his fellow-creatures, who had been the friend of Mr. Monk and of Lord Cantrip, the trusted intimate of such women as Lady Laura and Lady Chiltern, who had never put his hand to a mean action, or allowed his tongue to speak a mean word! He laughed in his wrath, and then almost howled in his agony.

## At Tenway Junction

It was raining hard, and when he got into the street he looked about for a cab, but there was none to be found. In Baker Street he got an omnibus which took him down to the underground railway, and by that he went to Gower Street. Through the rain he walked up to the Euston Station, and there he ordered breakfast. Could he have a mutton chop and some tea? And he was very particular that the mutton chop should be well cooked. He was a good-looking man, of fashionable appearance, and the young lady who attended him noticed him and was courteous to him. He condescended even to have a little light conversation with her, and, on the whole, he seemed to enjoy his breakfast. 'Upon my word, I should like to breakfast here every day of my life,' he said. The young lady assured him that, as far as she could see, there was no objection to such an arrangement. 'Only it's a bore, you know, coming out in the rain when there are no cabs,' he said. Then there were various little jokes between them, till the young lady was quite impressed with the gentleman's pleasant affability.

After a while he went back into the hall and took a first-class return ticket, not for Birmingham, but for the Tenway Junction. It is quite unnecessary to describe the Tenway Junction, as everybody knows it. From this spot, some six or seven miles distant from London, lines diverge east, west, and north, north-east, and north-west, round the metropolis in every direction, and with direct communication with every other line in and out of London. It is a marvellous place, quite unintelligible to the uninitiated, and yet daily used by thousands who only know that when they get there, they are to do what some one tells them. The space occupied by the convergent rails seems to be sufficient for a large farm. And these rails always run one into another with sloping points, and cross passages, and mysterious meandering sidings, till it seems to the thoughtful stranger to be impossible that the best trained engine should know its own line. Here and there and around there is ever a wilderness of wagons, some loaded, some empty, some smoking with close-packed oxen, and others furlongs in length black with coals, which look as though they had been stranded there by chance, and were never destined to get again into the right path of traffic. Not a minute passes without a train going here or there, some rushing by without noticing Tenway in the least, crashing through like flashes of substantial lightning, and others stopping, disgorging and taking up passengers by the hundreds. Men and women,— especially the men, for the women knowing their ignorance are generally willing to trust to the pundits of the place,— look doubtful, uneasy, and bewildered. But they all do get properly placed and unplaced, so that the spectator at last acknowledges that over all this apparent chaos there is presiding a great genius of order. From dusky morn to dark night, and indeed almost throughout the night, the air is loaded with a succession of shrieks. The theory goes that each separate shriek,—if there can be any separation where the sound is so nearly continuous,—is a separate notice to separate ears of the coming or going of a separate train. The stranger, as he speculates on these pandemoniac noises, is able to realize the idea that were they discontinued the excitement necessary for the minds of the pundits might be lowered, and that activity might be lessened, and evil results might follow. But he cannot bring himself to credit that theory of individual notices.

At Tenway Junction there are half-a-dozen long platforms,

on which men and women and luggage are crowded. On one of these for awhile Ferdinand Lopez walked backwards and forwards as though waiting for the coming of some especial train. The crowd is ever so great that a man might be supposed to walk there from morning to night without exciting special notice. But the pundits are very clever, and have much experience in men and women. A well-taught pundit, who has exercised authority for a year or two at such a station as that of Tenway, will know within a minute of the appearance of each stranger what is his purpose there,—whether he be going or has just come, whether he is himself on the way or waiting for others, whether he should be treated with civility or with some curt command,—so that if his purport be honest all necessary assistance may be rendered him. As Lopez was walking up and down, with smiling face and leisurely pace, now reading an advertisement and now watching the contortions of some amazed passenger, a certain pundit asked him his business. He was waiting, he said, for a train from Liverpool, intending, when his friend arrived, to go with him to Dulwich by a train which went round the west of London. It was all feasible, and the pundit told him that the stopping train from Liverpool was due there in six minutes, but that the express from the north would pass first. Lopez thanked the pundit and gave him sixpence,—which made the pundit suspicious. A pundit hopes to be paid when he handles luggage, but has no such expectation when he merely gives information.

The pundit still had his eye on our friend when the shriek and the whirr of the express from the north was heard. Lopez walked quickly up towards the edge of the platform, when the pundit followed him, telling him that this was not his train. Lopez then ran a few yards along the platform, not noticing the man, reaching a spot that was unoccupied;—and there he stood fixed. And as he stood the express flashed by. 'I am fond of seeing them pass like that,' said Lopez to the man who had followed him.

'But you shouldn't do it, sir,' said the suspicious pundit. 'No one isn't allowed to stand near like that. The very hair of it might take you off your legs when you're not used to it.'

'All right, old fellow,' said Lopez, retreating. The next train was the Liverpool train; and it seemed that our friend's friend had not come, for when the Liverpool passengers had cleared themselves off, he was still walking up and down the platform. 'He'll come by the next,' said Lopez to the pundit, who now followed him about and kept an eye on him.

'There ain't another from Liverpool stopping here till the 2.20,' said the pundit. 'You had better come again if you mean to meet him by that.'

'He has come on part of the way, and will reach this by some other train,' said Lopez.

'There ain't nothing he can come by,' said the pundit. 'Gentlemen can't wait here all day, sir. The horders is against waiting on the platform.'

'All right,' said Lopez, moving away as though to make his exit through the station.

Now Tenway Junction is so big a place, and so scattered, that it is impossible that all the pundits should by any combined activity maintain to the letter that order of which our special pundit had spoken. Lopez, departing from the platform which he had hitherto occupied, was soon to be seen on another, walking up and down, and again waiting. But the old pundit had had his eye upon him, and had followed him round. At that moment there came a shriek louder than all the other shrieks, and the morning express down from Euston to Inverness was seen coming round the curve at a thousand miles an hour. Lopez turned round and looked at it, and again walked towards the edge of the platform. But now it was not exactly the edge that he neared, but a descent to a pathway,—an inclined plane leading down to the level of the rails, and made there for certain purposes of traffic. As he did so the pundit called to him, and then made a rush at him,—for our friend's back was turned to the coming train.

But Lopez heeded not the call, and the rush was too late. With quick, but still with gentle and apparently unhurried steps, he walked down before the flying engine—and in a moment had been knocked into bloody atoms.

## The Earl and the Bull

THE BOUNDARY of the earl's property was very plainly marked, for with it commenced also the shady elms along the roadside, and the broad green margin of turf, grateful equally to those who walked and to those who rode. Eames had got himself on to the grass, but, in the fulness of his thoughts, was unconscious of the change in his path, when he was startled by a voice in the next field and the loud bellowing of a bull. Lord De Guest's choice cattle he knew were there, and there was one special bull which was esteemed by his lordship as of great value, and regarded as a high favourite. The people about the place declared that the beast was vicious, but Lord De Guest had often been heard to boast that it was never vicious with him. 'The boys tease him, and the men are almost worse than the boys,' said the earl; 'but he'll never hurt any one that has not hurt him.' Guided by faith in his own teaching the earl had taught himself to look upon his bull as a large, horned, innocent lamb of the flock.

As Eames paused on the road, he fancied that he recognized the earl's voice, and it was the voice of one in distress. Then the bull's roar sounded very plain in his ear, and almost close; upon hearing which he rushed on to the gate, and, without much thinking what he was doing, vaulted over it, and advanced a few steps into the field.

'Halloo!' shouted the earl. 'There's a man. Come on.' And then his continued shoutings hardly formed themselves into intelligible words; but Eames plainly understood that he was invoking assistance under great pressure and stress of circumstances. The bull was making short runs at his owner, as though determined in each run to have a toss at his lordship; and at each run the earl would retreat quickly for a few paces, but he retreated always facing his enemy, and as the animal got near to him, would make digs at his face with the long spud which he carried in his hand. But in thus making good his retreat he had been unable to keep in a direct line to the gate, and there seemed to be great danger lest the bull should succeed in pressing him up against the hedge. 'Come on!' shouted the earl, who was fighting his battle manfully, but was by no means anxious to carry off all the laurels of the victory himself. 'Come on, I say!' Then he stopped in his path, shouted into the bull's face, brandished his spud, and threw about his arms, thinking that he might best dismay the beast by the display of these warlike gestures.

Johnny Eames ran on gallantly to the peer's assistance, as he would have run to that of any peasant in the land. . . He rushed to the earl's assistance, brandishing his stick, and roaring in emulation of the bull.

When the animal saw with what unfairness he was treated, and that the number of his foes was doubled, while no assistance had lent itself on his side, he stood for a while, disgusted by the injustice of humanity. He stopped, and throwing his head up to the heavens, bellowed out his complaint. 'Don't come close!' said the earl, who was almost out of breath. 'Keep a little apart. Ugh! ugh! whoop, whoop!' And he threw up his arms manfully, jobbing about with his spud, ever and anon rubbing the perspiration from off his eyebrows with the back of his hand.

As the bull stood pausing, meditating whether under such circumstances flight would not be preferable to gratified passion, Eames made a rush in at him, attempting to hit him on the head. The earl, seeing this, advanced a step also, and got his spud almost up to the animal's eye. But these indignities the beast could not stand. He made a charge, bending his head first towards John Eames, and then, with that weak vacillation which is as disgraceful in a bull as in a general, he changed his purpose, and turned his horns upon his other enemy. The consequence was that his steps carried him in between the two, and that the earl and Eames found themselves for a while behind his tail.

'Now for the gate,' said the earl.

'Slowly does it; slowly does it; don't run!' said Johnny, assuming in the heat of the moment a tone of counsel which would have been very foreign to him under other circumstances.

The earl was not a whit offended. 'All right,' said he, taking with a backward motion the direction of the gate. Then as the bull again faced towards him, he jumped from the ground, labouring painfully with arms and legs, and ever keeping his spud well advanced against the foe. Eames, holding his position a little apart from his friend, stooped low and beat the ground with his stick, and as though defying the creature. The bull felt himself defied, stood still and roared, and then made another vacillating attack.

'Hold on till we reach the gate,' said Eames.

'Ugh! ugh! Whoop! whoop!' shouted the earl. And so gradually they made good their ground.

'Now get over,' said Eames, when they had both reached the corner of the field in which the gate stood.

'And what'll you do?' said the earl.

'I'll go at the hedge to the right.' And Johnny as he spoke dashed his stick about, so as to monopolize, for a moment, the attention of the brute. The earl made a spring at the gate, and got well on to the upper rung. The bull, seeing that his prey was going, made a final rush upon the earl and struck the timber furiously with his head, knocking his lordship down on the other side. Lord De Guest was already over, but not off the rail; and thus, though he fell, he fell in safety on the sward beyond the gate. He fell in safety, but utterly exhausted. Eames, as he had purposed, made a leap almost sideways at a thick hedge which divided the field from one of the Guestwick copses. There was a fairly broad ditch, and on the other side a quickset hedge, which had, however, been weakened and injured by trespassers at this corner, close to the gate. Eames was young and active and jumped well. He jumped so well that he carried his body full into the middle of the quickset, and then scrambled through to the other side, not without much injury to his clothes, and some damage also to his hands and face.

The beast, recovering from his shock against the wooden bars, looked wistfully at his last retreating enemy, as he still struggled amidst the bushes. He looked at the ditch and at the broken hedge, but he did not understand how weak were the impediments in his way. He had knocked his head against the stout timber, which was strong enough to oppose him, but was dismayed by the brambles which he might have trodden under foot without an effort. How many of us are like the bull, turning away conquered by opposition which should be as nothing to us, and breaking our feet, and worse still, our hearts, against rocks of adamant. The bull at last made up his mind that he did not dare to face the hedge; so he gave one final roar, and then turning himself round, walked placidly back amidst the herd.

### Entering the Pyramids

This entrance into the Pyramids is a terrible task, which should be undertaken by no lady. Those who perform it have to creep down, and then to be dragged up, through infinite dirt, foul smells, and bad air; and when they have done it, they see nothing. But they do earn the gratification of saying that they have been inside a Pyramid.

'Well, I've done that once,' said Mr. Damer, coming out, 'and I do not think that any one will catch me doing it again. I never was in such a filthy place in my life.'

'Oh, Fanny! I am so glad you did not go; I am sure it is not fit for ladies,' said poor Mrs. Damer, forgetful of her friend Miss Dawkins.

'I should have been ashamed of myself,' said Miss Dawkins,

bristling up, and throwing back her head as she stood, 'if I had allowed any consideration to have prevented my visiting such a spot. If it be not improper for men to go there, how can it be improper for women?'

'I did not say improper, my dear,' said Mrs. Damer, apologetically.

'And as for fatigue, what can a woman be worth who is afraid to encounter as much as I have now gone through for the sake of visiting the last resting-place of such a king as Cheops?' And Miss Dawkins, as she pronounced the last words, looked round her with disdain upon poor Fanny Damer.

'But I meant the dirt,' said Mrs. Damer.

'Dirt!' ejaculated Miss Dawkins, and then walked away. Why should she now submit her high tone of feeling to the Damers, or why care longer for their good opinion? Therefore she scattered contempt around her as she ejaculated the last word, 'dirt.'

And then the return home! 'I know I shall never get there,' said Mrs. Damer, looking piteously up into her husband's face.

'Nonsense, my dear; nonsense; you must get there.' Mrs. Damer groaned, and acknowledged in her heart that she must,—either dead or alive.

## Descent into a Mine

It was an ugly uninviting place to look at, with but few visible signs of wealth. The earth, which had been burrowed out by these human rabbits in their search after tin, lay around in huge ungainly heaps; the overground buildings of the establishment consisted of a few ill-arranged sheds, already apparently in a state of decadence; dirt and slush, and pools of water confined by muddy dams, abounded on every side; muddy men, with muddy carts and muddy horses, slowly crawled hither and thither, apparently with no object, and evidently indifferent as to whom they might overset in their course. The inferior men seemed to show no respect to those above them, and the superiors to exercise no authority over those below them. There was a sullen equality among them all. On the ground around was no vegetation; nothing green met the eye, some few stunted bushes appeared here and there, nearly smothered by heaped-up mud, but they had about them none of the attractiveness of foliage. The whole scene, though consisting of earth alone, was unearthly, and looked as though the devil had walked over the place with hot hoofs, and then raked it with a huge rake.

'I am afraid I am very late,' said Neverbend, getting out of his fly in all the haste he could muster, and looking at his watch the moment his foot touched the ground, 'very late indeed, gentlemen; I really must apologize, but it was the driver; I was punctual to the minute, I was indeed. But come, gentlemen, we won't lose another moment,' and Mr. Neverbend stepped out as though he were ready at an instant's notice to plunge head foremost down the deepest shaft in all that region of mines.

'Oh, sir, there a'n't no cause of hurry whatsomever,' said one of the mining authorities; 'the day is long enough.'

'Oh, but there is cause of hurry, Mr. Undershot,' said Neverbend, angrily, 'great cause of hurry; we must do this work very thoroughly; and I positively have not time to get through all that I have before me.'

'But a'n't the other gen'leman a-coming?' said Mr. Undershot.

'Surely Mr. Tooder isn't a-going to cry off?' said the other. 'Why, he was so hot about it yesterday.'

'Mr. Tudor is not very well this morning,' said Mr. Neverbend. 'As his going down is not necessary for the inquiry, and is merely a matter of taste on his part, he has not joined me this morning. Come, gentlemen, are we ready?'

It was then for the first time explained to Mr. Neverbend that he had to go through a rather complicated adjustment of his toilet before he would be considered fit to meet the infernal gods. He must, he was informed, envelop himself from head to foot in miner's habiliments, if he wished to save every stitch he had on him from dirt and destruction. He must also cover up his head with a linen cap, so constituted as to carry a lump of mud with a candle stuck in it, if he wished to save either his head from filth or his feet from falling. Now Mr. Neverbend, like most clerks in public offices, was somewhat particular about his wardrobe; it behoved him, as a gentleman frequenting the West End, to dress well, and it also behoved him to dress cheaply; he was, moreover, careful both as to his head and feet; he could not, therefore, reject the recommended precautions, but yet the time!—the time thus lost might destroy all.

He hurried into the shed where his toilet was to be made, and suffered himself to be prepared in the usual way. He took off his own great-coat, and put on a muddy coarse linen jacket that covered the upper portion of his body completely; he then dragged on a pair of equally muddy overalls; and, lastly, submitted to a most uninviting cap, which came down over his ears, and nearly over his eyes, and on the brow of which a lump of mud was then affixed, bearing a short tallow candle.

But though dressed thus in miner's garb, Mr. Neverbend could not be said to look the part he filled. He was a stout, reddish-faced gentleman, with round shoulders and huge whiskers, he was nearly bald, and wore spectacles, and in the costume in which he now appeared he did not seem to be at his ease. Indeed, all his air of command, all his personal dignity and dictatorial tone, left him as soon as he found himself metamorphosed into a fat pseudo-miner. He was like a cock whose feathers had been trailed through the mud, and who could no longer crow aloud, or claim the dunghill as his own. His appearance was somewhat that of a dirty dissipated cook who, having been turned out of one of the clubs for drunkenness, had been wandering about the streets all night.

He began to wish that he was once more in the well-known neighbourhood of Charing Cross.

The adventure, however, must now be carried through. There was still enough of manhood in his heart to make him feel that he could not return to his colleague at Tavistock without visiting the wonders which he had come so far to see. When he reached the head of the shaft, however, the affair did appear to him to be more terrible than he had before conceived. He was invited to get into a rough square bucket, in which there was just room for himself and another to stand; he was specially cautioned to keep his head straight, and his hands and elbows from protruding, and then the windlass began to turn, and the upper world, the sunlight, and all humanity receded from his view.

The world receded from his view, but hardly soon enough; for as the windlass turned and the bucket descended, his last terrestrial glance, looking out among the heaps of mud, descried Alaric Tudor galloping on Mr. Boteldale's pony up to the very mouth of the mine.

*'Facilis descensus Averni.'* The bucket went down easy enough, and all too quick. The manner in which it grounded itself on the first landing grated discordantly on Mr. Neverbend's finer perceptibilities. But when he learnt, after the interchange of various hoarse and to him unintelligible bellowings, that he was to wait in that narrow damp lobby for the coming of his fellow-Commissioner, the grating on his feelings was even more discordant. He had not pluck enough left to grumble: but he grunted his displeasure. He grunted, however, in vain; for in about a quarter of an hour Alaric was close to him, shoulder to shoulder. He also wore a white jacket, &c., with a nightcap of mud and candle on his head; but somehow he looked as though he had worn them all his life. The fast gallop, and the excitement of the masquerade, which for him had charms the sterner Neverbend could not feel, had dissipated his sickness; and he was once more all himself.

'So I've caught you at the first stage,' said he, good-humouredly; for though he knew how badly he had been treated, he was much too wise to show his knowledge. 'It shall go hard but I'll distance you before we have done,' he said to himself. Poor Neverbend only grunted.

And then they all went down a second stage in another bucket; and then a third in a third bucket; and then the business commenced. As far as this point passive courage alone had been required; to stand upright in a wooden tub and go down, and down, and down, was in itself easy enough, so long as the heart did not utterly faint. Mr. Neverbend's heart had grown faintish, but still he had persevered, and now stood on a third lobby, listening with dull, unintelligent ears to eager questions asked by his colleague, and to the rapid answers of their mining guides. Tudor was absolutely at work with paper and pencil, taking down notes in that wretched Pandemonium.

'There now, sir,' said the guide; 'no more of them ugly buckets, Mr. Neverbend; we can trust to our own arms and legs for the rest of it,' and so saying, he pointed out to Mr. Neverbend's horror-stricken eyes a perpendicular iron ladder fixed firmly against the upright side of a shaft, and leading—for aught Mr. Neverbend could see—direct to hell itself.

'Down here, is it?' said Alaric, peeping over.

'I'll go first,' said the guide; and down he went, down, down, down, till Neverbend looking over, could barely see the glimmer of his disappearing head light. Was it absolutely intended that he should disappear in the same way? Had he bound himself to go down that fiendish upright ladder? And were he to go down it, what then? Would it be possible that a man of his weight should ever come up again?

'Shall it be you or I next?' said Alaric, very civilly. Neverbend could only pant and grunt, and Alaric, with a courteous nod, placed himself on the ladder, and went down, down, down, till of him also nothing was left but the faintest glimmer. Mr. Neverbend remained above with one of the mining authorities; one attendant miner also remained with them.

'Now, sir,' said the authority, 'if you are ready, the ladder is quite free.'

Free! What would not Neverbend have given to be free also himself! He looked down the free ladder, and the very look made him sink. It seemed to him as though nothing but a spider could creep down that perpendicular abyss. And then a sound, slow, sharp, and continuous, as of drops falling through infinite space on to deep water, came upon his ear; and he saw that the sides of the abyss were covered with slime; and the damp air made him cough, and the cap had got over his spectacles and nearly blinded him; and he was perspiring with a cold, clammy sweat.

'Well, sir, shall we be going on?' said the authority. 'Mr. Tooder 'll be at the foot of the next set before this.'

Mr. Neverbend wished that Mr. Tudor's journey might still be down, and down, and down, till he reached the globe's centre, in which conflicting attractions might keep him for ever fixed. In his despair he essayed to put one foot upon the ladder, and then looked piteously up to the guide's face. Even in that dark, dingy atmosphere the light of the farthing candle on his head revealed the agony of his heart. His companions, though they were miners, were still men. They saw his misery, and relented.

'Maybe thee be afeared?' said the working miner, 'and if so be thee bee'st, thee'd better bide.'

'I am sure I should never come up again,' said Neverbend, with a voice pleading for mercy, but with all the submission of one prepared to suffer without resistance if mercy should not be forthcoming.

'Thee bee'st for sartan too thick and weazy like for them stairs,' said the miner.

'I am, I am,' said Neverbend, turning on the man a look of the warmest affection, and shoving the horrid, heavy, encumbered cap from off his spectacles; 'yes, I am too fat.' How would he have answered, with what aspect would he have annihilated the sinner, had such a man dared to call him

[ 102 ]

weazy up above, on *terra firma,* under the canopy of heaven?

His troubles, however, or at any rate his dangers, were brought to an end. As soon as it became plainly manifest that his zeal in the public service would carry him no lower, and would hardly suffice to keep life throbbing in his bosom much longer, even in his present level, preparations were made for his ascent. A bell was rung; hoarse voices were again heard speaking and answering in sounds quite unintelligible to a Cockney's ears; chains rattled, the windlass whirled, and the huge bucket came tumbling down, nearly on their heads. Poor Neverbend was all but lifted into it. Where now was all the pride of the morn that had seen him go forth the great dictator of the mines? Where was that towering spirit with which he had ordered his tea and toast, and rebuked the slowness of his charioteer? Where the ambition that had soared so high over the pet of the Weights and Measures? Alas, alas! how few of us there are who have within us the courage to be great in adversity. *'Aequam memento'*—&c., &c.!—if thou couldst but have thought of it, O Neverbend, who need'st must some day die.

But Neverbend did not think of it. How few of us do remember such lessons at those moments in which they ought to be of use to us! He was all but lifted into the tub, and then out of it, and then again into another, till he reached the upper world, a sight piteous to behold. His spectacles had gone from him, his cap covered his eyes, his lamp had reversed itself, and soft globules of grease had fallen on his nose, he was bathed in perspiration, and was nevertheless chilled through to his very bones, his whiskers were fringed with mud, and his black cravat had been pulled from his neck and lost in some infernal struggle. Nevertheless, the moment in which he seated himself on a hard stool in that rough shed was perhaps the happiest in his life; some Christian brought him beer; had it been nectar from the brewery of the gods, he could not have drunk it with greater avidity.

## The Archdeacon Reads Rabelais

AFTER BREAKFAST, on the morning of which we are writing, the archdeacon, as usual, retired to his study, intimating that he was going to be very busy, but that he would see Mr. Chadwick if he called. On entering this sacred room he carefully opened the paper case on which he was wont to compose his favourite sermons, and spread on it a fair sheet of paper and one partly written on; he then placed his inkstand, looked at his pen, and folded his blotting paper; having done so, he got up again from his seat, stood with his back to the fireplace, and yawned comfortably, stretching out vastly his huge arms and opening his burly chest. He then walked across the room and locked the door; and having so prepared himself, he threw himself into his easy chair, took from a secret drawer beneath his table a volume of Rabelais, and began to amuse himself with the witty mischief of Panurge; and so passed the archdeacon's morning on that day.

He was left undisturbed at his studies for an hour or two, when a knock came to the door, and Mr. Chadwick was announced. Rabelais retired into the secret drawer, the easy chair seemed knowingly to betake itself off, and when the archdeacon quickly undid his bolt, he was discovered by the steward working, as usual, for that church of which he was so useful a pillar.

# Daily Life

### Food

'I HATE MUTTON-BONES,' she said to her aunt one morning soon after her return.

'No doubt we would all like meat joints the best,' said her aunt, frowning.

'I hate joints too.'

'You have, I dare say, been cockered up at the Marchesa's with made dishes.'

'I hate dishes,' said Ayala, petulantly.

'You don't hate eating?'

'Yes, I do. It is ignoble. Nature should have managed it differently. We ought to have sucked it in from the atmosphere through our fingers and hairs, as the trees do by their leaves. There should have been no butchers, and no grease, and no nasty smells from the kitchen,—and no gin.'

### Presents from the Archdeacon

BUT THE MOST REMARKABLE feature in the whole occasion was the excessive liberality of the archdeacon. He literally made presents to everybody... He sent down a magnificent piano by Erard, gave Mr. Arabin a cob which any dean in the land might have been proud to bestride, and made a special present to Eleanor of a new pony chair that had gained a prize in the Exhibition. Nor did he even stay his hand here; he bought a set of cameos for his wife, and a sapphire bracelet for Miss Bold; showered pearls and workboxes on his daughters, and to each of his sons he presented a cheque for 20*l*. On Mr.

Harding he bestowed a magnificent violoncello with all the new-fashioned arrangements and expensive additions, which, on account of these novelties, that gentleman could never use with satisfaction to his audience or pleasure to himself.

## Life at Aylmer Park

Aylmer Park and the great house of the Aylmers together formed an important and, as regarded in some minds, an imposing country residence. The park was large, including some three or four hundred acres, and was peopled, rather thinly, by aristocratic deer. It was surrounded by an aristocratic paling, and was entered, at three different points, by aristocratic lodges. The sheep were more numerous than the deer, because Sir Anthony, though he had a large income, was not in very easy circumstances. The ground was quite flat; and though there were thin belts of trees, and some ornamental timber here and there, it was not well wooded. It had no special beauty of its own, and depended for its imposing qualities chiefly on its size, on its three sets of double lodges, and on its old established character as an important family place in the country. The house was of stone, with a portico of Ionic columns which looked as though it hardly belonged of right to the edifice, and stretched itself out grandly, with two pretentious wings, which certainly gave it a just claim to be called a mansion. It required a great many servants to keep it in order, and the numerous servants required an experienced duenna, almost as grand in appearance as Lady Aylmer herself, to keep them in order. There was an open carriage and a close carriage, and a butler, and two footmen, and three gamekeepers, and four gardeners, and there was a coachman, and there were grooms, and sundry inferior men and boys about the place to do the work which the gardeners and gamekeepers and grooms did not choose to do themselves. And they all became fat, and lazy, and stupid, and respectable together; so that, as the reader will at once perceive, Aylmer

Park was kept up in the proper English style. Sir Anthony very often discussed with his steward the propriety of lessening the expenditure of his residence, and Lady Aylmer always attended and probably directed these discussions; but it was found that nothing could be done. Any attempt to remove a gamekeeper or a gardener would evidently throw the whole machinery of Aylmer Park out of gear. If retrenchment was necessary Aylmer Park must be abandoned, and the glory of the Aylmers must be allowed to pale. But things were not so bad as that with Sir Anthony. The gardeners, grooms, and gamekeepers were maintained; ten domestic servants sat down to four heavy meals in the servants' hall every day, and Lady Aylmer contented herself with receiving little or no company, and with stingy breakfasts and bad dinners for herself and her husband and daughter. By all this it must be seen that she did her duty as the wife of an English country gentleman, and properly maintained his rank as a baronet.

He was a heavy man, over seventy years of age, much afflicted with gout, and given to no pursuit on earth which was available for his comfort. He had been a hunting man, and he had shot also; but not with that energy which induces a sportsman to carry on those amusements in opposition to the impediments of age. He had been, and still was, a county magistrate; but he had never been very successful in the justice-room, and now seldom troubled the county with his judicial incompetence. He had been fond of good dinners and good wine, and still, on occasions, would make attempts at enjoyment in that line; but the gout and Lady Aylmer together were too many for him, and he had but small opportunity for filling up the blanks of his existence out of the kitchen or cellar. He was a big man, with a broad chest, and a red face, and a quantity of white hair,—and was much given to abusing his servants. He took some pleasure in standing, with two sticks, on the top of the steps before his own front door, and railing at any one who came in his way. But he could not do this when Lady Aylmer was by; and his dependents, knowing his habits, had fallen into an ill-natured way of deserting the side of the house which he frequented. With his eldest son, Anthony Aylmer, he was not on very good terms; and though there was no positive quarrel, the heir did not often come to Aylmer Park. Of his son Frederic he was proud,—and the best days of his life were probably those which Captain Aylmer spent at the house. The table was then somewhat more generously spread, and this was an excuse for having up the special port in which he delighted. Altogether his life was not very attractive; and though he had been born to a baronetcy, and eight thousand a-year, and the possession of Aylmer Park, I do not think that he was, or had been, a happy man.

Lady Aylmer was more fortunate. She had occupations of which her husband knew nothing, and for which he was altogether unfit. Though she could not succeed in making retrenchments, she could and did succeed in keeping the household books. Sir Anthony could only blow up the servants when they were thoughtless enough to come in his way, and in doing that was restricted by his wife's presence. But Lady Aylmer could get at them day and night. She had no gout to impede her progress about the house and grounds, and could make her way to places which the master never saw; and then she wrote many letters daily, whereas Sir Anthony hardly ever took a pen in his hand. And she knew the cottages of all the poor about the place, and knew also all their sins of omission and commission. She was driven out, too, every day, summer and winter, wet and dry, and consumed enormous packets of wool and worsted, which were sent to her monthly from York. And she had a companion in her daughter, whereas Sir Anthony had no companion. Wherever Lady Aylmer went, Miss Aylmer went with her, and relieved what might otherwise have been the tedium of her life. She had been a beauty on a large scale, and was still aware that she had much in her personal appearance which justified pride. She carried herself uprightly, with a commanding nose and broad forehead; and though the graces of her own hair had given way to a front, there was something even in the front which added to her dignity, if it did not make her a handsome woman.

Miss Aylmer, who was the eldest of the younger generation, and who was now gently descending from her fortieth year, lacked the strength of her mother's character, but admired her mother's ways, and followed Lady Aylmer in all things,—at a distance. She was very good,—as indeed was Lady Aylmer,—entertaining a high idea of duty, and aware that her own life admitted of but little self-indulgence. She had no pleasures, she incurred no expenses; and was quite alive to the fact that as Aylmer Park required a regiment of lazy, gormandizing servants to maintain its position in the county, the Aylmers themselves should not be lazy, and should not gormandize. No one was more careful with her few shillings than Miss Aylmer. She had, indeed, abandoned a life's correspondence with an old friend because she would not pay the postage on letters to Italy. She knew that it was for the honour of the family that one of her brothers should sit in Parliament, and was quite willing to deny herself a new dress because sacrifices must be made to lessen electioneering expenses. She knew that it was her lot to be driven about slowly in a carriage with a livery servant before her and another behind her, and then eat a dinner which the cook-maid would despise. She was aware that it was her duty to be snubbed by her mother, and to encounter her father's ill-temper, and to submit to her brother's indifference, and to have, so to say, the slightest possible modicum of personal individuality. She knew that she had never attracted a man's love, and might hardly hope to make friends for the comfort of her coming age. But still she was contented, and felt that she had consolation for it all in the fact that she was an Aylmer. She read many novels, and it cannot but be supposed that something of regret would steal over her as she remembered that nothing of the romance of life had ever, or could ever, come in her way. She wept over the loves of many women, though she had never been happy or unhappy in her own. She read of gaiety, though she never encountered it, and must have known that the world elsewhere was less dull than it was at Aylmer Park. But she took her life as it came, without a complaint, and prayed that God would make her humble in the high position to which it had pleased Him to call her. She hated Radicals, and thought that Essays and Reviews, and Bishop Colenso, came direct from the Evil One. She taught the little children in the parish, being specially urgent to them always to courtesy when they saw any of the family; —and was as ignorant, meek, and stupid a poor woman as you shall find anywhere in Europe.

It may be imagined that Captain Aylmer, who knew the comforts of his club and was accustomed to life in London, would feel the dullness of the paternal roof to be almost unendurable. In truth, he was not very fond of Aylmer Park, but he was more gifted with patience than most men of his age and position, and was aware that it behoved him to keep the Fifth Commandment if he expected to have his own days prolonged in the land. He therefore made his visits periodically, and contented himself with clipping a few days at both ends from the length prescribed by family tradition, which his mother was desirous of exacting. September was always to be passed at Aylmer Park, because of the shooting. In September, indeed, the eldest son himself was wont to be there,—probably with a friend or two,—and the fat old servants bestirred themselves, and there was something of life about the place. At Christmas, Captain Aylmer was there as the only visitor, and Christmas was supposed to extend from the middle of December to the opening of Parliament.

## Letters at Breakfast

THAT HABIT of bringing in letters at the breakfast-table has its good points, certainly. It is well that one should have one's

## DAILY LIFE

letters before the work or pleasure of the day commences; it is well to be able to discuss the different little subjects of mutual interest as they are mentioned. 'Eliza's baby has got her first tooth; it's all right. There's nothing like Daffy's Elixir, after all.' 'My dear, the guano will be here to-day; so the horses will be wanted all the week—remember that.' 'What a bore, papa; for here's a letter to say that Kate Carnabie's coming, and we must go over to the Poldoodles. Frank Poldoodle is quite smitten with Kate.' This is all very convenient; but the plan has its drawbacks. Some letters will be in their nature black and brow-compelling. Tidings will come from time to time at which men can not smile. There will be news that ruffles the sweetest temper, and a receipt of which clouds will darken the most kindly face. One would fain receive such letters in private.

### The Family Horse

IN SUCH ESTABLISHMENTS as that at Vavasor Hall the family horse is generally used for double duties. Though he draws the lady of the house one day, he is not too proud to draw manure on the next. And it will always be found that the master of the house gives a great preference to the manure over the lady. The squire at Vavasor had come to do so to such an extent that he regarded any application for the animal's services as an encroachment.

### Food for a House Guest

LADY SCATCHERD besought her, almost with tears, to say what she liked best to eat and drink; and was in despair when Mary declared she didn't care, that she liked anything, and that she was in nowise particular in such matters.

'A roast fowl, Miss Thorne?'

'Very nice, Lady Scatcherd.'

'And bread sauce?'

'Bread sauce—yes; oh, yes—I like bread sauce,'—and poor Mary tried hard to show a little interest.

'And just a few sausages. We make them all in the house, Miss Thorne; we know what they are. And mashed potatoes —do you like them best mashed or baked?'

Mary, finding herself obliged to vote, voted for mashed potatoes.

'Very well. But, Miss Thorne, if you would like boiled fowl better, with a little bit of ham, you know, I do hope you'll say so. And there's lamb in the house, quite beautiful; now do 'ee say something; do 'ee, Miss Thorne.'

So invoked, Mary felt herself obliged to say something, and declared for the roast fowl and sausages.

## The Doctor and His Port

The doctor loved his port wine, and thawed a little in his manner. He loved it not as a toper, but as a collector loves his pet pictures. He liked to talk about it, and think about it; to praise it, and hear it praised; to look at it turned towards the light, and to count over the years it had lain in his cellar.

'Yes,' said he, 'it's pretty fair wine. It was, at least, when I got it, twenty years ago, and I don't suppose time has hurt it'; and he held the glass up to the window, and looked at the evening light through the ruby tint of the liquid. 'Ah, dear, there's not much of it left; more's the pity.'

## Summer-Drinks

'What a broiling day!' he said, and he threw himself into a chair. 'For mercy's sake give me something to drink.' Now the doctor was a great man for summer-drinks. In his house, lemonade, currant-juice, orange-mixtures, and raspberry-vinegar were used by the quart. He frequently disapproved of these things for his patients, as being apt to disarrange the digestion; but he consumed enough himself to throw a large family into such difficulties.

## Doing the Flowers

She held her peace, and went on arranging her flowers—now with a more satisfied air, and without destruction to the geraniums. And when she had grouped her bunches properly she carried the jar from one part of the room to another, backwards and forwards, trying the effect of the colours, as though her mind was quite intent upon her flowers, and was for the moment wholly unoccupied with any other subject. But Miss Dunstable was not the woman to put up with this. She sat silent in her place, while her friend made one or two turns about the room; and then she got up from her seat also. 'Mary,' she said, 'give over about those wretched bits of green branches, and leave the jars where they are. You're trying to fidget me into a passion.'

'Am I?' said Mrs. Gresham, standing opposite to a big bowl, and putting her head a little on one side, as though she could better look at her handiwork in that position.

## Feminine Gear

Inwardly she trembled, and was intensely anxious as to the first appearance of her niece. Of course there would be a little morsel of a bonnet. She hated those vile patches,—dirty flat daubs of millinery as she called them; but they had become too general for her to refuse admittance for such a thing within her doors. But a chignon,—a bandbox behind the noddle,—she would not endure. And then there were other details of feminine gear, which shall not be specified, as to which she was painfully anxious,—almost forgetting in her anxiety that the dress of this young woman whom she was about to see must have ever been regulated by the closest possible economy.

The first thing she saw on entering the room was a dark straw hat, a straw hat with a strong penthouse flat to it, and her heart was immediately softened.

'My dear,' she said, 'I am glad to see you.'

## On Smoking

'But what rakes you are here! It's past eleven o'clock, and I must go and have a smoke.'

'Have a what?' said Miss Stanbury, with a startled air.

'A smoke. You needn't be frightened, I don't mean in the house.'

'No;—I hope you don't mean that.'

'But I may take a turn round the Close with a pipe;—mayn't I?'

'I suppose all young men do smoke now,' said Miss Stanbury, sorrowfully.

'Every one of them; and they tell me that the young women mean to take to it before long.'

'If I saw a young woman smoking, I should blush for my sex; and though she were the nearest and dearest that I had, I would never speak to her;—never. Dorothy, I don't think Mr. Gibson smokes.'

'I'm sure I don't know, aunt.'

'I hope he doesn't. I do hope that he does not. I cannot understand what pleasure it is that men take in making chimneys of themselves, and going about smelling so that no one can bear to come near them.'

## Shopping for a Lady

'Go to Blackie's in Regent Street, and bring me down all the colours in wool that I ordered. I said you would call. And tell them at Dolland's the last spectacles don't suit at all, and I won't keep them, they had better send me down, by you, one or two more pairs to try. And you had better see Smithers and Smith, in Lincoln's Inn Fields, No. 57—but you have been there before,—and beg them to let me know how my poor dear brother's matters are to be settled at last. As far as I can see I shall be dead before I shall know what income I have got to spend.'

## Christmas Greens

It was Christmas-time down at Allington, and at three o'clock on Christmas Eve, just as the darkness of the early winter evening was coming on, Lily Dale and Grace Crawley were seated together, one above the other, on the steps leading up to the pulpit in Allington Church. They had been working all day at the decorations of the church, and they were now looking round them at the result of their handiwork. To an eye unused to the gloom the place would have been nearly dark; but they could see every corner turned by the ivy sprigs, and every line on which the holly-leaves were shining. And the greeneries of the winter had not been stuck up in the old-fashioned, idle way, a bough just fastened up here and a twig inserted there; but everything had been done with some meaning, with some thought towards the original architecture of the building. The Gothic lines had been followed, and all the lower arches which it had been possible to reach with an ordinary ladder had been turned as truly with the laurel cuttings as they had been turned originally with the stone.

'I wouldn't tie another twig,' said the elder girl, 'for all the Christmas pudding that was ever boiled.'

'It's lucky then that there isn't another twig to tie.'

'I don't know about that. I see a score of places where the work has been scamped. This is the sixth time I have done the church, and I don't think I'll ever do it again. When we first began it, Bell and I, you know,—before Bell was married, —Mrs. Boyce, and the Boycian establishment generally, used to come and help. Or rather we used to help her. Now she hardly ever looks after it at all... You don't mean to say that you did all those capitals yourself?'

'Every twig, with Hopkins to hold the ladder and cut the sticks; and as Hopkins is just a hundred and one years old, we could have done it pretty nearly as well alone.'

'I do not think that,' said Grace.

'He has been grumbling all the time,' said Lily, 'and swears he never will have the laurels so robbed again.'

## A Material Festival

'But blindman's buff at three, with snap-dragon at a quarter to four—charades at five, with wine and sweet cake at half-past six, is ponderous. And that's our mistake. The big turkey would be very good;—capital fun to see a turkey twice as big as it ought to be! But the big turkey, and the mountain of beef, and the pudding weighing a hundredweight, oppress one's spirits by their combined gravity. And then they impart a memory of indigestion, a halo as it were of apoplexy, even to the church services.'

'I do not agree with you the least in the world.'

'I ask you to answer me fairly. Is not additional eating an ordinary Englishman's ordinary idea of Christmas-day?'

'I am only an ordinary Englishwoman and therefore cannot say. It is not my idea.'

'I believe that the ceremony, as kept by us, is perpetuated by the butchers and beersellers, with a helping hand from the grocers. It is essentially a material festival; and I would not object to it even on that account if it were not so grievously overdone.'

## Breakfast in the Sitting-Room

The countess and her youngest daughter had been breakfasting together in the elder lady's sitting-room, and were now seated in a very graceful and well-arranged deshabille.

The tea-cups out of which they had been drinking were made of some elegant porcelain, the teapot and cream-jug were of chased silver and as delicate in their way. The remnant of food consisted of morsels of French roll which had not even been allowed to crumble themselves in a disorderly fashion, and of infinitesimal pats of butter. If the morning meal of the two ladies had been as unsubstantial as the appearance of the fragments indicated, it must be presumed that they intended to lunch early. The countess herself was arrayed in an elaborate morning wrapper of figured silk, but the simple Alexandrina wore a plain white muslin peignoir, fastened with pink ribbon. Her hair, which she usually carried in long rolls, now hung loose over her shoulders, and certainly added something to her stock of female charms.

### The Flues of the Grape-House

It was now very nearly the end of the year, but the weather was still soft and open. The air was damp rather than cold, and the lawns and fields still retained the green tints of new vegetation. As the squire was walking on the terrace Hopkins came up to him, and touching his hat, remarked that they should have frost in a day or two.

'I suppose we shall,' said the squire.

'We must have the mason to the flues of that little grape-house, sir, before I can do any good with a fire there.'

'Which grape-house?' said the squire, crossly.

'Why, the grape-house in the other garden, sir. It ought to have been done last year by rights.' This Hopkins said to punish his master for being cross to him. On that matter of the flues of Mrs. Dale's grape-house he had, with much consideration, spared his master during the last winter, and he felt that this ought to be remembered now. 'I can't put any fire in it, not to do any real good, till something's done. That's sure.'

'Then don't put any fire in it,' said the squire.

Now the grapes in question were supposed to be peculiarly fine, and were the glory of the garden of the Small House. They were always forced, though not forced so early as those at the Great House, and Hopkins was in a state of great confusion.

'They'll never ripen, sir; not the whole year through.'

'Then let them be unripe,' said the squire, walking about.

Hopkins did not at all understand it. The squire in his natural course was very unwilling to neglect any such matter as this, but would be specially unwilling to neglect anything touching the Small House. So Hopkins stood on the terrace, raising his hat and scratching his head. 'There's something wrong amongst them,' said he to himself, sorrowfully.

But when the squire had walked to the end of the terrace and had turned upon the path which led round the side of the house, he stopped and called to Hopkins.

'Have what is needful done to the flue,' he said.

'Yes, sir; very well, sir. It'll only be re-setting the bricks. Nothing more ain't needful, just this winter.'

'Have the place put in perfect order while you're about it,' said the squire, and then he walked away.

## Moving

WHO DOES NOT KNOW how terrible are those preparations for house-moving;—how infinite in number are the articles which must be packed, how inexpressibly uncomfortable is the period of packing, and how poor and tawdry is the aspect of one's belongings while they are thus in a state of dislocation? Now adays people who understand the world, and have money commensurate with their understanding, have learned the way of shunning all these disasters, and of leaving the work to the hands of persons paid for doing it. The crockery is left in the cupboards, the books on the shelves, the wine in the bins, the curtains on their poles, and the family that is understanding goes for a fortnight to Brighton. At the end of that time the crockery is comfortably settled in other cupboards, the books on other shelves, the wine in other bins, the curtains are hung on other poles, and all is arranged. But Mrs. Dale and her daughters understood nothing of such a method of moving as this. The assistance of the village carpenter in filling certain cases that he had made was all that they knew how to obtain beyond that of their own two servants. Every article had to pass through the hands of some one of the family; and as they felt almost overwhelmed by the extent of the work to be done, they began it much sooner than was necessary, so that it became evident as they advanced in their work, that they would have to pass a dreadfully dull, stupid, uncomfortable week at last, among their boxes and cases, in all the confusion of dismantled furniture.

## In the Kitchen

When Mr. Fenwick entered the kitchen, Mrs. Brattle was sitting there alone. Her daughter was away, disposing of the remnants and utensils of the dinner-table. The old lady, with her spectacles on her nose, was sitting as usual with a stocking over her left arm. On the round table was a great open Bible, and, lying on the Bible, were sundry large worsted hose, which always seemed to Mr. Fenwick as though they must have undarned themselves as quickly as they were darned. Her Bible and her stockings furnished the whole of Mrs. Brattle's occupation from her dinner to her bed. In the morning, she would still occupy herself in matters of cookery, would peel potatoes, and prepare apples for puddings, and would look into the pot in which the cabbage was being boiled. But her stockings and her Bible shared together the afternoons of her week-days. On the Sundays there would only be the Bible, and then she would pass many hours of the day asleep.

## Breakfast at the Archdeacon's

WHATEVER OF SUBMISSIVE HUMILITY may have appeared in the gait and visage of the archdeacon during his colloquy with his wife in the sanctum of their dressing-rooms was dispelled as he entered his breakfast-parlour with erect head and powerful step. In the presence of a third person he assumed the lord and master; and that wise and talented lady too well knew the man to whom her lot for life was bound, to stretch her authority beyond the point at which it would be borne. Strangers at Plumstead Episcopi, when they saw the imperious brow with which he commanded silence from the large circle of visitors, children, and servants who came together in the morning to hear him read the word of God, and watched how meekly that wife seated herself behind her basket of keys with a little girl on each side, as she caught that commanding glance; strangers, I say, seeing this, could little guess that some fifteen minutes since she had stoutly held her ground against him, hardly allowing him to open his mouth in his own defence. But such is the tact and talent of women!

And now let us observe the well-furnished breakfast-parlour at Plumstead Episcopi, and the comfortable air of all the belongings of the rectory. Comfortable they certainly were, but neither gorgeous nor even grand; indeed, considering the money that had been spent there, the eye and taste might have been better served; there was an air of heaviness about the rooms which might have been avoided without any sacrifice of propriety; colours might have been better chosen and lights more perfectly diffused; but perhaps in doing so the thorough clerical aspect of the whole might have been somewhat marred; at any rate, it was not without ample consideration that those thick, dark, costly carpets were put down; those embossed, but sombre papers hung up; those heavy curtains draped so as to half exclude the light of the sun: nor were these old-fashioned chairs bought at a price far exceeding that now given for more modern goods, without a purpose. The breakfast-service on the table was equally costly and equally plain; the apparent object had been to spend money without obtaining brilliancy or splendour. The urn was of thick and solid silver, as were also the tea-pot, coffee-pot, cream-ewer, and sugar-bowl; the cups were old, dim dragon china, worth about a pound apiece, but very despicable in the eyes of the uninitiated. The silver forks were so heavy as to be disagreeable to the hand, and the bread-basket was of a weight really formidable to any but robust persons. The tea consumed was the very best, the coffee the very blackest, the cream the very thickest; there was dry toast and buttered toast, muffins and crumpets; hot bread and cold bread, white bread and brown bread, home-made bread and bakers' bread, wheaten bread and oaten bread; and if there be other breads than these, they were there; there were eggs in napkins, and crispy bits of bacon under silver covers; and there were little fishes in a little box, and devilled kidneys frizzling on a hot-water dish; which, by-the-by, were placed closely contiguous to the plate of the worthy archdeacon himself. Over and above this, on a snow-white napkin, spread upon the sideboard, was a huge ham and a huge sirloin; the latter having laden the dinner table on the previous evening. Such was the ordinary fare at Plumstead Episcopi.

## Mutton Chop and Pint of Port

HE THEN JOURNEYED back sadly to the Chapter Coffee House, digesting his great thoughts, as best he might, in a clattering omnibus, wedged in between a wet old lady and a journeyman glazier returning from his work with his tools in his lap. In melancholy solitude he discussed his mutton chop and pint of port. What is there in this world more melancholy than such a dinner? A dinner, though eaten alone, in a country hotel may be worthy of some energy; the waiter, if you are known, will make much of you; the landlord will make you a bow and perhaps put the fish on the table; if you ring you are attended to, and there is some life about it. A dinner at a London eating-house is also lively enough, if it have no other attraction. There is plenty of noise and stir about it, and the rapid whirl of voices and rattle of dishes disperses sadness. But a solitary dinner in an old, respectable, sombre, solid London inn, where nothing makes any noise but the old waiter's creaking shoes; where one plate slowly goes and another slowly comes without a sound; where the two or three guests would as soon think of knocking each other down as of speaking; where the servants whisper, and the whole household is disturbed if an order be given above the voice—what can be more melancholy than a mutton chop and a pint of port in such a place?

## The Privileges of a Daughter

BUT NOW A DAUGHTER'S PRIVILEGES were accorded to her. When the old squiress was driven out about the county, Bessy was expected, but was asked rather than ordered to accompany her. She always went; but went because she decided on going, not because she was told. And she had a horse to ride; and she was allowed to arrange flowers for the drawing-room; and the gardener did what she told him. What daughter could have more extensive privileges?

# Servants

### STEWARD OF ULLATHORNE

BUT PERHAPS THE MOST OVERTASKED, the most anxious, and the most effective of all the Ullathorne household was Mr. Plomacy, the steward. This last personage had, in the time of Mr. Thorne's father, when the Directory held dominion in France, gone over to Paris with letters in his boot heel for some of the royal party; and such had been his good luck that he had returned safe. He had then been very young and was now very old, but the exploit gave him a character for political enterprise and secret discretion which still availed him as thoroughly as it had done in its freshest gloss. Mr. Plomacy had been steward of Ullathorne for more than fifty years, and a very easy life he had had of it. Who could require much absolute work from a man who had carried safely at his heel that which if discovered would have cost him his head? Consequently Mr. Plomacy had never worked hard, and of latter years had never worked at all. He had a taste for timber, and therefore he marked the trees that were to be cut down; he had a taste for gardening, and would therefore allow no shrub to be planted or bed to be made without his express sanction.

### MISS THORNE'S FAVOURITE

THIS WAS FARMER GREENACRE'S ELDEST SON; who, to tell the truth, had from his earliest years taken the exact measure of Miss Thorne's foot. In his boyhood he had never failed to obtain from her, apples, pocket money, and forgiveness for his numerous trespasses; and now in his early manhood he got privileges and immunities which were equally valuable. He was allowed a day or two's shooting in September; he schooled the squire's horses; got slips of trees out of the orchard, and roots of flowers out of the garden; and had the fishing of the little river altogether in his own hands.

## Gardeners

MRS. WINTERFIELD WAS ALWAYS UNHAPPY about her gardener Serious footmen are very plentiful, and even coachmen are to be found who, at a certain rate of extra payment, will be punctual at prayer time, and will promise to read good little books; but gardeners, as a class, are a profane people, who think themselves entitled to claim liberty of conscience, and who will not submit to the domestic despotism of a serious Sunday. They live in cottages by themselves, and choose to have an opinion of their own on church matters. Mrs. Winterfield was aware that she ought to bid high for such a gardener as she wanted. A man must be paid well who will submit to daily inquiries as to the spiritual welfare of himself, his wife, and family. But even though she did bid high, and though she paid generously, no gardener would stop with her. One conscientious man attempted to bargain for freedom from religion during the six unimportant days of the week, being strong, and willing therefore to give up his day of rest; but such liberty could not be allowed to him, and he also went. 'He couldn't stop,' he said, 'in justice to the greenhouses, when missus was so constant down upon him about his sprittual backsliding. And after all, where did he backslide? It was only a pipe of tobacco with the babby in his arms, instead of that darned evening lecture.'

## The Loyalty of Servants

THERE ARE PEOPLE, in that respect very fortunately circumstanced, whose servants, as a matter of course, know all their affairs, have an interest in their concerns, sympathise with their demands, feel their wants, and are absolutely at one with them. But in such cases the servants are really known, and are almost as completely a part of the family as the sons and daughters. There may be disruptions and quarrels; causes may arise for ending the existing condition of things; but while this condition lasts, the servants in such households are, for the most part, only too well inclined to fight the battles of their employers. Mr. Binns, the butler, would almost foam at the mouth if it were suggested to him that the plate at Silvercup Hall was not the undoubted property of the old squire; and Mrs. Pouncebox could not be made to believe, by any amount of human evidence, that the jewels which her lady has worn for the last fifteen years are not her ladyship's very own. Binns would fight for the plate, and so would Pouncebox for the jewels, almost till they were cut to pieces. The preservation of these treasures on behalf of those who paid them their wages, and fed them, who occasionally scolded them but always succoured them, would be their point of honour. No torture would get the key of the cellar from Binns; no threats extract from Pouncebox a secret of the toilet.

## The Lady's Maid

Lizzie, when she was in her own room of course found her maid waiting for her. It was necessarily part of the religion of such a woman as Lizzie Eustace that she could not go to bed, or change her clothes, or get up in the morning, without the assistance of her own young woman. She would not like to have it thought that she could stick a pin into her own belongings without such assistance. Nevertheless it was often the case with her, that she was anxious to get rid of her girl's attendance. It had been so on this morning, and before dinner, and was so now again. She was secret in her movements, and always had some recess in her boxes and bags and dressing apparatuses to which she did not choose that Miss Patience

Crabstick should have access. She was careful about her letters, and very careful about her money. And then as to that iron box in which the diamonds were kept! Patience Crabstick had never yet seen the inside of it. Moreover, it may be said, —either on Lizzie's behalf or to her discredit, as the reader may be pleased to take it,—that she was quite able to dress herself, to brush her own hair, to take off her own clothes; and that she was not, either by nature or education, an incapable young woman. But that honour and glory demanded it, she would almost as lief have had no Patience Crabstick to pry into her most private matters. All which Crabstick knew, and would often declare her missus to be 'of all missusses the most slyest and least come-at-able.'

## Waiters at Parties

And indeed this handing round has become a vulgar and an intolerable nuisance among us second-class gentry with our eight hundred a year—there or thereabouts;—doubly intolerable as being destructive of our natural comforts, and a wretchedly vulgar aping of men with large incomes. The Duke of Omnium and Lady Hartletop are undoubtedly wise to have everything handed round. Friends of mine who occasionally dine at such houses tell me that they get their wine quite as quickly as they can drink it, that their mutton is brought to them without delay, and that the potato bearer follows quick upon the heels of carnifer. Nothing can be more comfortable, and we may no doubt acknowledge that these first-class grandees do understand their material comforts. But we of the eight hundred can no more come up to them in this than we can in their opera-boxes and equipages. . . And may I not further say that the lamentable consequence to us eight hundreders dining out among each other is this, that we too often get no dinner at all. Phyllis, with the potatoes, cannot reach us till our mutton is devoured, or in a lukewarm state past our power of managing; and Ganymede, the greengrocer, though we admire the skill of his necktie and the whiteness of his unexceptionable gloves, fails to keep us going in sherry.

## SALLY

MRS. KELLY kept two ordinary in-door servants to assist in the work of the house; one, an antiquated female named Sally, who was more devoted to her tea-pot than ever was any bacchanalian to his glass. Were there four different teas in the inn in one evening, she would have drained the pot after each, though she burst in the effort. Sally was, in all, an honest woman, and certainly a religious one—she never neglected her devotional duties, confessed with most scrupulous accuracy the various peccadillos of which she might consider herself guilty; and it was thought, with reason, by those who knew her best, that all the extra prayers she said—and they were very many—were in atonement for commissions of continual petty larceny with regard to sugar. On this subject did her old mistress quarrel with her, her young mistress ridicule her; of this sin did her fellow-servant accuse her; and, doubtless, for this sin did her Priest continually reprove her; but in vain. Though she would not own it, there was always sugar in her pocket, and though she declared that she usually drank her tea unsweetened, those who had come upon her unawares had seen her extracting the pinches of moist brown saccharine from the huge slit in her petticoat, and could not believe her.

## A RISE IN WAGES

'Guestwick Cottage,—December, 186—.

'MY DEAR JOHN,

'I AM much obliged to you for going to Jones's. I send stamps for two shillings and fourpence, which is what I owe to you. It used only to be two shillings and twopence, but they say everything has got to be dearer now, and I suppose pills as well as other things. Only think of Pritchard coming to me, and saying she wanted her wages raised, after living with me for twenty years! I was *very* angry, and scolded her roundly; but as she acknowledged she had been wrong, and cried and begged my pardon, I did give her two guineas a year more.'

## Waiter at the 'Dragon'

Mr. Toogood reached the 'Dragon' about eleven o'clock, and allowed the boots to give him a pair of slippers and a candlestick. But he would not go to bed just at that moment. He would go into the coffee-room first, and have a glass of hot brandy-and-water. So the hot brandy-and-water was brought to him, and a cigar, and as he smoked and drank he conversed with the waiter. The man was a waiter of the ancient class, a gray-haired waiter, with seedy clothes, and a dirty towel under his arm; not a dapper waiter, with black shiny hair, and dressed like a guest for a dinner-party. There are two distinct classes of waiters, and as far as I have been able to perceive, the special status of the waiter in question cannot be decided by observation of the class of waiter to which he belongs. In such a town as Barchester you may find the old waiter with the dirty towel in the head inn, or in the second-class inn, and so you may the dapper waiter. Or you may find both in each, and not know which is senior waiter and which junior waiter. But for service I always prefer the old waiter with the dirty towel, and I find it more easy to satisfy him in the matter of sixpences when my relations to the inn come to an end.

'Have you been here long, John?' said Mr. Toogood.

'A goodish many years, sir.'

'So I thought, by the look of you. One can see that you belong in a way to the place. You do a good deal of business here, I suppose, at this time of the year?'

'Well, sir, pretty fair. The house ain't what it used to be, sir.'

'Times are bad at Barchester,—are they?'

'I don't know much about the times. It's the people is worse than the times, I think. They used to like to have a little bit of dinner now and again at a hotel;—and a drop of something to drink after it.'

'And don't they like it now?'

'I think they like it well enough, but they don't do it. I suppose it's their wives as don't let 'em come out and enjoy themselves. There used to be the Goose and Glee club;—that was once a month. They've gone and clean done away with themselves,—that club has. There's old Bumpter in the High Street,—he's the last of the old Geese. They died off, you see, and when Mr. Biddle died they wouldn't choose another president. A club for having dinner, sir, ain't nothing without a president.'

'I suppose not.'

'And there's the Freemasons. They must meet, you know, sir, in course, because of the dooties. But if you'll believe me, sir, they don't so much as wet their whistles. They don't indeed. It always used to be a supper, and that was once a month. Now they pays a rent for the use of the room! Who is to get a living out of that, sir?—not in the way of a waiter, that is.'

'If that's the way things are going on I suppose the servants leave their places pretty often?'

'I don't know about that, sir. A man may do a deal worse than "The Dragon of Wantly." Them as goes away to better themselves, often worses themselves, as I call it. I've seen a good deal of that.'

'And you stick to the old shop?'

'Yes, sir; I've been here fifteen year, I think it is. There's a many goes away, as doesn't go out of their own heads, you know, sir.'

'They get the sack, you mean?'

'There's words between them and master,—or more likely, missus. That's where it is. Servants is so foolish. I often tell

## JAM

'You oughtn't to be angry with me, because I've done nothing,' said Jane the housemaid, sobbing.

'That's just about it,' said Mrs. Baggett. 'And why haven't you done nothing? Do you suppose you come here to do nothing? Was it doing nothing when Eliza tied down them strawberries without putting in e'er a drop of brandy? It drives me mortial mad to think what you young folks are coming to.'

'I ain't a-going anywhere, Mrs. Baggett, because of them strawberries being tied down which, if you untie them, as I always intended, will have the sperrits put on them as well now as ever. And as for your going mad, Mrs. Baggett, I hope it won't be along of me.'

'Drat your imperence.'

'I ain't imperence at all. Here's Miss Lawrie, and she shall say whether I'm imperence.'

'Mrs. Baggett, I want to speak to you, if you'll come into the other room,' said Mary.

'You are imperent, both of you. I can't say a word but I'm taken up that short that—. They've been and tied all the jam down, so that it'll all go that mouldy that nobody can touch it. And then, when I says a word, they turns upon me.' Then Mrs. Baggett walked out of the kitchen into her own small parlour, which opened upon the passage just opposite the kitchen door. 'They was a-going to be opened this very afternoon,' said Eliza, firing a parting shot after the departing enemy.

## SERVANTS

### Housekeeper's Sunday Morning

IT WAS QUITE PLEASANT to see Mrs. Baggett start for her slow Sabbath morning walk, and to observe how her appearance altogether belied that idea of rags and tatters which she had given as to her own wardrobe. A nicer dressed old lady, or a more becoming black silk gown, you shall not see on a Sunday morning making her way to any country church in England. While she was looking so pleasant and demure,— one may say almost so handsome, in her old-fashioned and apparently new bonnet,—what could have been her thoughts respecting the red-nosed, one-legged warrior, and her intended life, to be passed in fetching two-penn'orths of gin for him, and her endeavours to get for him a morsel of wholesome food? She had had her breakfast out of her own china tea-cup, which she used to boast was her own property, as it had been given to her by Mr. Whittlestaff's mother, and had had her little drop of cream, and, to tell the truth, her boiled egg, which she always had on a Sunday morning, to enable her to listen to the long sermon of the Rev. Mr. Lowlad. She would talk of her hopes and her burdens, and undoubtedly she was in earnest. But she certainly did seem to make her hay very comfortably while the sun shone.

### Caterer from Wigmore Street

LOPEZ RELIEVED HIS WIFE from all care as to provision for his guests. 'I've been to a shop in Wigmore Street,' he said, 'and everything will be done. They'll send in a cook to make the things hot, and your father won't have to pay even for a crust of bread. . . Stewam and Sugarscraps will send in everything, if you'll only tell the old fogies downstairs not to interfere.' . . .

She did speak to the 'old fogies' downstairs,—the house-keeper, who had lived with her father since she was a child, and the butler, who had been there still longer, and the cook, who, having been in her place only three years, resigned impetuously within half an hour after the advent of Mr. Sugarscraps' head man. The 'fogies' were indignant. The butler expressed his intention of locking himself up in his own peculiar pantry, and the housekeeper took upon herself to tell her young mistress that 'Master wouldn't like it.' Since she had known Mr. Wharton such a thing as cooked food being sent into the house from a shop had never been so much as heard of.

## The Butler

RALPH SAT DOWN to dinner all alone. Let what will happen to break hearts and ruin fortunes, dinner comes as long as the means last for providing it. The old butler waited upon him in absolute silence, fearing to speak a word, lest the word at such a time should be ill-spoken. No doubt the old man was thinking of the probable expedience of his retiring upon his savings; feeling, however, that it became him to show, till the last, every respect to all who bore the honoured name of Newton. When the meat had been eaten, the old servant did say a word. 'Won't you come round to the fire, Mr. Ralph?' and he placed comfortably before the hearth one of the heavy arm-chairs with which the corners of the broad fire-place were flanked. But Ralph only shook his head, and muttered some refusal. There he sat, square to the table, with the customary bottle of wine before him, leaning back with his hands in his pockets, thinking of his condition in life. The loneliness of the room, the loneliness of the house, were horrible to him. And yet he would not that his solitude should be interrupted. He had been so sitting, motionless, almost overcome by the gloom of the big dark room, for so long a period that he hardly knew whether it was night or not, when a note was brought to him from Gregory. 'Dear Ralph,—Shall I not come down to you for an hour?—G. N.' He read the note, and sent back a verbal message. 'Tell Mr. Gregory that I had rather not.' And so he sat motionless till the night had really come, till the old butler brought him his candlestick and absolutely bade him betake himself to bed. He had watched during the whole of the previous night, and now had slumbered in his chair from time to time. But his sleeping had been of that painful, wakeful nature which brings with it no refreshment... 'Mr. Ralph, you must go to bed;—you must indeed, sir,' said the old butler, standing over him with a candle during one of these fitful dreamings.

'Yes, Grey;—yes, I will; directly. Put it down. Thank you. Don't mind sitting up,' said Ralph, rousing himself in his chair.

'It's past twelve, Mr. Ralph.'

'You can go to bed, you know, Grey.'

'No, sir;—no. I'll see you to bed first. It'll be better so. Why, Mr. Ralph, the fire's all out, and you're sitting here perished. You wasn't in bed last night, and you ought to be there now. Come, Mr. Ralph.'

Then Ralph rose from his chair and took the candlestick. It was true enough that he had better be in bed. As he shook himself, he felt that he had never been so cold in his life. And then as he moved there came upon him that terrible feeling that everything was amiss with him, that there was no consolation on any side. 'That'll do, Grey; good night,' he said, as the old man prepared to follow him upstairs. But Grey was not to be shaken off. 'I'll just see you to your room, Mr. Ralph.' He wanted to accompany his young master past the door of that chamber in which was lying all that remained of the old master. But Ralph would open the door. 'Not tonight, Mr. Ralph,' said Grey. But Ralph persisted, and stood again by the bedside. 'He would have given me his flesh and blood;—his very life,' said Ralph to the butler. 'I think no father ever so loved a son. And yet, what has it come to?' Then he stooped down, and put his lips to the cold clay-blue forehead.

'It ain't come to much surely,' said old Grey to himself, as he crept away to his own room.

## Gardener vs. Squire

There was in those days, and had been for years, a vexed question between Hopkins and Jolliffe the bailiff on the matter of—stable manure. Hopkins had pretended to the right of taking what he required from the farmyard, without asking leave of any one. Jolliffe in return had hinted, that if this were so, Hopkins would take it all. 'But I can't eat it,' Hopkins had said. Jolliffe merely grunted, signifying by the grunt, as Hopkins thought, that though a gardener couldn't eat a mountain of manure fifty feet long and fifteen high—couldn't eat in the body,—he might convert it into things edible for his own personal use. And so there had been a great feud. The unfortunate squire had of course been called on to arbitrate, and having postponed his decision by every contrivance possible to him, had at last been driven by Jolliffe to declare that Hopkins should take nothing that was not assigned to him. Hopkins, when the decision was made known to him by his master, bit his old lips, and turned round upon his old heel, speechless. 'You'll find it's so at all other places,' said the squire, apologetically. 'Other places!' sneered Hopkins. Where would he find other gardeners like himself? It is hardly necessary to declare that from that moment he resolved that he would abide by no such order. Jolliffe on the next morning informed the squire that the order had been broken, and the squire fretted and fumed, wishing that Jolliffe were well buried under the mountain in question. 'If they all is to do as they like,' said Jolliffe, 'then nobody won't care for nobody.' The squire understood that an order if given must be obeyed, and therefore, with many inner groanings of the spirit, resolved that war must be waged against Hopkins.

On the following morning he found the old man himself

wheeling a huge barrow of manure round from the yard into the kitchen-garden. Now, on ordinary occasions, Hopkins was not required to do with his own hands work of that description. He had a man under him who hewed wood, and carried water, and wheeled barrows,—one man always, and often two. The squire knew when he saw him that he was sinning, and bade him stop upon his road.

'Hopkins,' he said, 'why didn't you ask for what you wanted, before you took it?' The old man put down the barrow on the ground, looked up in his master's face, spat into his hands, and then again resumed his barrow. 'Hopkins, that won't do,' said the squire. 'Stop where you are.'

'What won't do?' said Hopkins, still holding the barrow from the ground, but not as yet progressing.

'Put it down, Hopkins,' and Hopkins did put it down. 'Don't you know that you are flatly disobeying my orders?'

'Squire, I've been here about this place going on nigh seventy years.'

'If you've been going on a hundred and seventy it wouldn't do that there should be more than one master. I'm the master here, and I intend to be so to the end. Take that manure back into the yard.'

'Back into the yard?' said Hopkins, very slowly.

'Yes; back into the yard.'

'What,—afore all their faces?'

'Yes; you've disobeyed me before all their faces?'

Hopkins paused a moment, looking away from the squire, and shaking his head as though he had need of deep thought, but by the aid of deep thought had come at last to a right conclusion. Then he resumed the barrow, and putting himself almost into a trot, carried away his prize into the kitchen-garden. At the pace which he went it would have been beyond the squire's power to stop him, nor would Mr. Dale have wished to come to a personal encounter with his servant. But he called after the man in dire wrath that if he were not obeyed the disobedient servant should rue the consequences for ever. Hopkins, equal to the occasion, shook his head as he trotted on, deposited his load at the foot of the cucumber-frames, and then at once returning to his master, tendered to him the key of the greenhouse.

'Master,' said Hopkins, speaking as best he could with his scanty breath, 'there it is;—there's the key; of course I don't want no warning, and doesn't care about my week's wages. I'll be out of the cottage afore night, and as for the work'us, I suppose they'll let me in at once, if your honour'll give 'em a line.'

Now as Hopkins was well known by the squire to be the owner of three or four hundred pounds, the hint about the workhouse must be allowed to have been melodramatic.

'Don't be a fool,' said the squire, almost gnashing his teeth.

'I know I've been a fool,' said Hopkins, 'about that 'ere doong; my feelings has been too much for me. When a man's feelings has been too much for him, he'd better just take hisself off, and lie in the work'us till he dies.' And then he again tendered the key. But the squire did not take the key, and so Hopkins went on. 'I s'pose I'd better just see to the lights and the like of that, till you've suited yourself, Mr. Dale. It 'ud be a pity all them grapes should go off, and they, as you may say, all one as fit for the table. It's a long way the best crop I ever see on 'em. I've been that careful with 'em that I haven't had a natural night's rest, not since February. There ain't nobody about this place as understands grapes, nor yet anywhere nigh that could be got at. My lord's head man is wery ignorant; but even if he knew ever so, of course he couldn't come here. I suppose I'd better keep the key till you're suited, Mr. Dale.'

Then for a fortnight there was an interregnum in the gardens, terrible in the annals of Allington. Hopkins lived in his cottage indeed, and looked most sedulously after the grapes. In looking after the grapes, too, he took the greenhouses under his care; but he would have nothing to do with the outer gardens, took no wages, returning the amount sent to him back to the squire, and insisted with everybody that he had been dismissed. He went about with some terrible horticultural implement always in his hand, with which it was said that he intended to attack Jolliffe; but Jolliffe prudently kept out of his way... Hopkins, when his feelings had become altogether too much for him 'about the doong,' came at last to Lily, and laying down at her feet all the weight and all the glory of his sixty odd years of life, implored her to make matters straight for him. 'It's been a killing me, miss, so it has; to see the way they've been a cutting that 'sparagus. It ain't cutting at all. It's just hocking it up;—what is fit, and what isn't, all together. And they've been a-putting the plants in where I didn't mean 'em, though they know'd I didn't mean 'em. I've stood by, miss, and said never a word. I'd a died sooner. But, Miss Lily, what my sufferings have been, 'cause of my feelings getting the better of me about that— you know, miss—nobody will ever tell;—nobody—nobody— nobody.' Then Hopkins turned away and wept.

'Uncle,' said Lily, creeping close up against his chair, 'I want to ask you a great favour.' ...

'Uncle, you must forgive poor Hopkins.'

'Forgive a fiddlestick!' said the squire.

'No, but you must. You can't think how unhappy he is.'

'How can I forgive a man who won't forgive me. He goes prowling about the place doing nothing; and he sends me back his wages, and he looks as though he were going to murder some one; and all because he wouldn't do as he was told. How am I to forgive such a man as that?'

'But, uncle, why not?'

'It would be his forgiving me. He knows very well that he may come back whenever he pleases; and, indeed, for the matter of that he has never gone away.'

'But he is so very unhappy.'

'What can I do to make him happier?'

'Just go down to his cottage and tell him that you forgive him.'

'Then he'll argue with me.'

'No; I don't think he will. He is too much down in the world for arguing now.'

'Ah! you don't know him as I do. All the misfortunes in the world wouldn't stop that man's conceit. Of course I'll go if you ask me, but it seems to me that I'm made to knock under to everybody. I hear a great deal about other people's feelings, but I don't know that mine are very much thought of.' He was not altogether in a happy mood, and Lily almost regretted that she had persevered; but she did succeed in carrying him off across the garden to the cottage, and as they went together she promised him that she would think of him always,—always. The scene with Hopkins cannot be described now, as it would take too many of our few remaining pages. It resulted, I am afraid I must confess, in nothing more triumphant to the squire than a treaty of mutual forgiveness. Hopkins acknowledged, with much self-reproach, that his feelings had been too many for him; but then, look at his provocation! He could not keep his tongue from that matter, and certainly said as much in his own defence as he did in confession of his sins. The substantial triumph was altogether his, for nobody again ever dared to interfere with his operations in the farmyard. He showed his submission to his master mainly by consenting to receive his wages for the two weeks which he had passed in idleness.

*HE CONSIDERS ITS PATTERNS*

# 'Society'

## Country House Prospects

'My own One,

'Your governor is a brick. Of course, Glenbogie will be better than the Tyrol, as you are to be there. Not but what the Tyrol is a very jolly place, and we'll go and see it together some day. Ask Tom to let me know whether one can wear heavy boots in the Glenbogie mountains. They are much the best for the heather; but I have shot generally in Yorkshire, and there they are too hot. What number does he shoot with generally? I fancy the birds are wilder with you than with us.

'As for riding, I don't dare to sit upon a horse this weather. Nobody but a woman can stand it. Indeed, now I think of it, I sold my horse last week to pay the fellow I buy paints from. I've got the saddle and bridle, and if I stick them up upon a rail, under the trees, it would be better than any horse while the thermometer is near 80. All the ladies could come round and talk to one so nicely.

'I hate lunch, because it makes me red in the face, and nobody will give me my breakfast before eleven at the earliest. But I'll come in about three as often as you like to have me. I think I perhaps shall run over to the Tyrol after Glenbogie. A man must go somewhere when he has been turned out in that fashion...

'Can I do anything for you except riding or eating lunch,—which are simply feminine exercises? Always your own,

'Frank.'

## Country House Sunday

The next morning was Sunday, and they all went to church. It was a law at Stalham that every one should go to church on Sunday morning. Sir Harry himself, who was not supposed to be a peculiarly religious man, was always angry when any male guest did not show himself in the enormous family pew. 'I call it d—— indecent,' he has been heard to say. But nobody was expected to go twice,—and consequently nobody ever did go twice. Lunch was protracted later than usual. The men would roam about the grounds with cigars in their mouths, and ladies would take to reading in their own rooms, in following which occupation they would spend a considerable part of the afternoon asleep.

## Mrs. Proudie's Party

Mrs. Proudie's heart beat high as she inspected her suite of rooms. They were really very magnificent, or at least would be so by candlelight; and they had nevertheless been got up with commendable economy. Large rooms when full of people and full of light look well, because they are large, and are full, and are light. Small rooms are those which require costly fittings and rich furniture. Mrs. Proudie knew this, and made the most of it; she had therefore a huge gas lamp with a dozen burners hanging from each of the ceilings.

People were to arrive at ten, supper was to last from twelve till one, and at half-past one everybody was to be gone. Carriages were to come in at the gate in the town and depart at the gate outside. They were desired to take up at a quarter before one. It was managed excellently, and Mr. Slope was invaluable.

At half-past nine the bishop and his wife and their three daughters entered the great reception-room, and very grand and very solemn they were. Mr. Slope was down-stairs giving the last orders about the wine. He well understood that curates and country vicars with their belongings did not require so generous an article as the dignitaries of the close. There is a useful gradation in such things, and Marsala at 20s. a dozen did very well for the exterior supplementary tables in the corner.

## Morning Parties

MORNING PARTIES, as a rule, are failures. People never know how to get away from them gracefully. A picnic on an island or a mountain or in a wood may perhaps be permitted. There is no master of the mountain bound by courtesy to bid you stay while in his heart he is longing for your departure. But in a private house or in private grounds a morning party is a bore. One is called on to eat and drink at unnatural hours. One is obliged to give up the day which is useful, and is then left without resource for the evening which is useless. One gets home fagged and *désœuvré,* and yet at an hour too early for bed. There is no comfortable resource left. Cards in these genteel days are among the things tabooed, and a rubber of whist is impracticable.

## At the Seaside

THERE ARE THREE SETS of persons who resort to Littlebath: there is the heavy fast, and the lighter fast set; there is also the pious set. Of the two fast sets neither is scandalously fast. The pace is never very awful. Of the heavies, it may be said that the gentlemen generally wear their coats padded, are frequently seen standing idle about the parades and terraces, that they always keep a horse, and trot about the roads a good deal when the hounds go out. The ladies are addicted to whist and false hair, but pursue their pleasures with a discreet economy. Of the lighter fast set, assembly balls are the ruling passion; but even in these there is no wild extravagance. The gentlemen of this division keep usually two horses, on the sale of one of which their mind is much bent. They drink plentifully of cherry brandy on hunting days, but, as a rule, they do not often misbehave themselves. They are very careful not to be caught in marriage, and talk about women much as a crafty, knowing salmon might be presumed to talk about anglers. The ladies are given to dancing, of course, and are none of them nearly so old as you might, perhaps, be led to imagine. They greatly eschew card-playing; but, nevertheless, now and again one of them may be seen to lapse from her sphere and fall into that below, if we may justly say that the votaries of whist are below the worshipers of Terpsichore. Of the pious set much needs not be said, as their light has never been hid under a bushel. In spite of hunt-clubs and assembly-rooms, they are the predominant power. They live on the fat of the land. They are a strong, unctuous, moral, uncharitable people. The men never cease making money for themselves, nor the women making slippers for their clergymen.

## Coming of Age

In the year 1854, the eldest son came of age. He had been educated at Harrow, and was now still at Cambridge; but, of course, on such a day as this he was at home. That coming of age must be a delightful time to a young man born to inherit broad acres and wide wealth. Those full-mouthed congratulations; those warm prayers with which his manhood is welcomed by the grey-haired seniors of the county; the affectionate, all but motherly caresses of neighbouring mothers who have seen him grow up from his cradle, of mothers who have daughters, perhaps, fair enough, and good enough, and sweet enough even for him; the soft-spoken, half-bashful, but tender greetings of the girls, who now, perhaps for the first time, call him by his stern family name, instructed by instinct rather than precept that the time has come when the familiar Charles or familiar John must by them be laid aside; the 'lucky dogs,' and hints of silver spoons

'SOCIETY'

which are poured into his ears as each young compeer slaps his back and bids him live a thousand years and then never die; the shouting of the tenantry, the good wishes of the old farmers who come up to wring his hand, the kisses which he gets from the farmers' wives, and the kisses which he gives to the farmers' daughters; all these things must make the twenty-first birthday pleasant enough to a young heir. To a youth, however, who feels that he is now liable to arrest, and that he inherits no other privilege, the pleasure may very possibly not be quite so keen.

The case with young Frank Gresham may be supposed to be much nearer the former than the latter; but yet the ceremony of his coming of age was by no means like that which fate had accorded to his father. Mr. Gresham was now an embarrassed man, and though the world did not know it, or, at any rate, did not know that he was deeply embarrassed, he had not the heart to throw open his mansion and park and receive the county with a free hand as though all things were going well with him.

Nothing was going well with him. Lady Arabella would allow nothing near him or around him to be well. Everything with him now turned to vexation; he was no longer a joyous, happy man, and the people of East Barsetshire did not look for gala doings on a grand scale when young Gresham came of age.

Gala doings, to a certain extent, there were there. It was in July, and tables were spread under the oaks for the tenants. Tables were spread, and meat, and beer, and wine were there, and Frank, as he walked round and shook his guests by the hand, expressed a hope that their relations with each other might be long, close, and mutually advantageous. . .

But we have kept the Greshamsbury tenantry waiting under the oak-trees by far too long. Yes; when young Frank came of age there was still enough left of Greshamsbury, still means enough at the squire's disposal, to light one bonfire, to roast, whole in its skin, one bullock. Frank's virility came on him not quite unmarked, as that of the parson's son might do, or the son of the neighbouring attorney. It could still be reported in the Barsetshire Conservative *Standard* that 'The beards wagged all' at Greshamsbury, now as they had done for many centuries on similar festivals. Yes; it was so reported. But this, like so many other such reports, had but a shadow of truth in it. 'They poured the liquor in,' certainly, those who were there; but the beards did not wag as they had been wont to wag in former years. Beards won't wag for the telling. The squire was at his wits' end for money, and the tenants one and all had so heard. Rents had been raised on them; timber had fallen fast; the lawyer on the estate was growing rich; tradesmen in Barchester, nay, in Greshamsbury itself, were beginning to mutter; and the squire himself would not be merry. Under such circumstances the throats of a tenantry will still swallow, but their beards will not wag.

'I minds well,' said Farmer Oaklerath to his neighbour, 'when the squoire hisself comed of age. Lord love 'ee! there was fun going that day. There was more yale drank then than's been brewed at the big house these two years. T'old squoire was a one'er.'

'And I minds when squoire was borned; minds it well,' said an old farmer sitting opposite. 'Them was the days! it an't that long ago neither. Squoire a'nt come o' fifty yet; no, nor an't nigh it, though he looks it. Things be altered at Greemsbury'—such was the rural pronunciation—'altered sadly, neebor Oaklerath. Well, well; I'll soon be gone, I will, and so it an't no use talking; but arter paying one pound fifteen for them acres for more nor fifty year, I didn't think I'd ever been axed for forty shilling.'

Such was the style of conversation which went on at the various tables. It had certainly been of a very different tone when the squire was born, when he came of age, and when, just two years subsequently, his son had been born. On each of these events similar rural fêtes had been given, and the squire himself had on these occasions been frequent among his guests. On the first, he had been carried round by his father, a whole train of ladies and nurses following. On the second, he had himself mixed in all the sports, the gayest of the gay, and each tenant had squeezed his way up to the lawn to get a sight of the Lady Arabella, who, as was already known, was to come from Courcy Castle to Greshamsbury to be their mistress. It was little they any of them cared now for the Lady Arabella. On the third, he himself had borne his child in his arms as his father had before borne him; he was then in the zenith of his pride, and though the tenantry whispered that he was somewhat less familiar with them than of yore, that he had put on somewhat too much of the De Courcy airs, still he was their squire, their master, the rich man in whose hand they lay. The old squire was then gone, and they were proud of the young member and his lady bride in spite of a little hauteur. None of them were proud of him now.

He walked once round among the guests, and spoke a few words of welcome at each table; and as he did so the tenants got up and bowed and wished health to the old squire, happiness to the young one, and prosperity to Greshamsbury; but, nevertheless, it was but a tame affair.

## An Evening Party

To ACCOMMODATE WITH CHAIRS AND SOFAS as many as the furniture of her noble suite of rooms would allow, especially with the two chairs and padded bench against the wall in the back closet—the small inner drawing-room, as she would call it to the clergymen's wives from Barsetshire—and to let the others stand about upright, or 'group themselves,' as she described it. Then four times during the two hours' period of her conversazione tea and cake were to be handed round on salvers. It is astonishing how far a very little cake will go in this way, particularly if administered tolerably early after dinner. The men can't eat it, and the women, having no plates and no table, are obliged to abstain. Mrs. Jones knows that she cannot hold a piece of crumbly cake in her hand till it be consumed without doing serious injury to her best dress. When Mrs. Proudie, with her weekly books before her, looked into the financial upshot of her conversazione, her conscience told her that she had done the right thing. Going out to tea is not a bad thing, if one can contrive to dine early, and then be allowed to sit round a big table with a tea urn in the middle.

## County and Town Society

Miss Jemima Stanbury, the aunt of our friend Hugh, was a maiden lady, very much respected, indeed, in the city of Exeter. It is to be hoped that no readers of these pages will be so un-English as to be unable to appreciate the difference between county society and town society,—the society, that is, of a provincial town,—or so ignorant as not to know also that there may be persons so privileged, that although they live distinctly within a provincial town, there is accorded to them, as though by brevet rank, all the merit of living in the county. In reference to persons so privileged, it is considered that they have been made free from the contamination of contiguous bricks and mortar by certain inner gifts, probably of birth, occasionally of profession, possibly of merit. It is very rarely, indeed, that money alone will bestow this acknowledged rank; and in Exeter, which by the stringency and excellence of its well-defined rules on such matters, may perhaps be said to take the lead of all English provincial towns, money alone has never availed. Good blood, especially if it be blood good in Devonshire, is rarely rejected. Clergymen are allowed within the pale,—though by no means as certainly as used to be the case; and, indeed, in these days of literates, clergymen have to pass harder examinations than those ever imposed upon them by bishops' chaplains, before they are admitted *ad eundem* among the chosen ones of the city of Exeter. The

'SOCIETY'

wives and daughters of the old prebendaries see well to that. And, as has been said, special merit may prevail. Sir Peter Mancrudy, the great Exeter physician, has won his way in,—not at all by being Sir Peter, which has stood in his way rather than otherwise,—but by the acknowledged excellence of his book about saltzes. Sir Peter Mancrudy is supposed to have quite a metropolitan, almost a European reputation,—and therefore is acknowledged to belong to the county set, although he never dines out at any house beyond the limits of the city. Now, let it be known that no inhabitant of Exeter ever achieved a clearer right to be regarded as 'county,' in opposition to 'town,' than had Miss Jemima Stanbury. There was not a tradesman in Exeter who was not aware of it, and who did not touch his hat to her accordingly. The men who drove the flies, when summoned to take her out at night, would bring oats with them, knowing how probable it was that they might have to travel far. A distinct apology was made if she was asked to drink tea with people who were simply 'town.' The Noels of Doddescombe Leigh, the Cliffords of Budleigh Salterton, the Powels of Haldon, the Cheritons of Alphington,—all county persons, but very frequently in the city,—were greeted by her, and greeted her, on terms of equality. Her most intimate friend was old Mrs. MacHugh, the widow of the last dean but two, who could not have stood higher had she been the widow of the last bishop. And then, although Miss Stanbury was intimate with the Frenches of Heavitree, with the Wrights of Northernhay, with the Apjohns of Helion Villa,—a really magnificent house, two miles out of the city on the Crediton Road,—and with the Crumbies of Cronstadt House, Saint Ide's,—who would have been county people, if living in the country made the difference; —although she was intimate with all these families, her manner to them was not the same, nor was it expected to be the same, as with those of her own acknowledged set. These things are understood in Exeter so well!

Miss Stanbury belonged to the county set, but she lived in

[ 149 ]

a large brick house, standing in the Close, almost behind the Cathedral. Indeed it was so close to the eastern end of the edifice that a carriage could not be brought quite up to her door. It was a large brick house, very old, with a door in the middle, and five steps ascending to it between high iron rails. On each side of the door there were two windows on the ground floor, and above that there were three tiers of five windows each, and the house was double throughout, having as many windows looking out behind into a gloomy courtyard. But the glory of the house consisted in this, that there was a garden attached to it, a garden with very high walls, over which the boughs of trees might be seen, giving to the otherwise gloomy abode a touch of freshness in the summer, and a look of space in the winter, which no doubt added something to the reputation even of Miss Stanbury. The fact, —for it was a fact,—that there was no gloomier or less attractive spot in the whole city than Miss Stanbury's garden, when seen inside, did not militate against this advantage. There were but half-a-dozen trees, and a few square yards of grass that was never green, and a damp ungravelled path on which no one ever walked. Seen from the inside the garden was not much; but, from the outside, it gave a distinct character to the house, and produced an unexpressed acknowledgment that the owner of it ought to belong to the county set.

The house and all that was in it belonged to Miss Stanbury herself, as did also many other houses in the neighbourhood. She was the owner of the 'Cock and Bottle,' a very decent second-class inn on the other side of the Close, an inn supposed to have clerical tendencies, which made it quite suitable for a close. The choristers took their beer there, and the landlord was a retired verger. Nearly the whole of one side of a dark passage leading out of the Close towards the High Street belonged to her; and though the passage be narrow and the houses dark, the locality is known to be good for trade. And she owned two large houses in the High Street, and a great warehouse at St. Thomas's, and had been bought out of land

'SOCIETY'

by the Railway at St. David's,—much to her own dissatisfaction, as she was wont to express herself, but, undoubtedly, at a very high price. It will be understood therefore, that Miss Stanbury was wealthy, and that she was bound to the city in which she lived by peculiar ties.

### New Marchioness

THERE WAS AN INFINITY of clothes which someone had ordered for her, and on all the things which would bear a mark, there was a coronet. The coronets on the pocket-handkerchiefs seemed to be without end. And there was funereal note-paper, on which the black edges were not more visible than the black coronets. And there came invoices to her from the tradesmen, addressed to the Marchioness of Brotherton. And then there came the first letter from her father with her rank and title on the envelope. At first she was almost afraid to open it.

### Black Sheep

IN THE FIRST PLACE, whose eyes are good enough to know whether in truth a sheep be black or not? And then is it not the fact that some little amount of shade in the fleece of male sheep is considered, if not absolutely desirable, at any rate quite pardonable? A male sheep with a fleece as white as that of a ewe-lamb, is he not considered to be, among muttons, somewhat insipid? It was this taste of which Pope was conscious when he declared that every woman was at heart a rake. And so it comes to pass that very black sheep indeed are admitted into society.

### Slang

'I DON'T LIKE those slang words, Lily.'
'What slang words?'
'You know what you called Bernard's friend.'

'Oh; a swell. I fancy I do like slang. I think it's awfully jolly to talk about things being jolly. Only that I was afraid of your nerves I should have called him stunning. It's so slow, you know, to use nothing but words out of a dictionary.'

'I don't think it's nice in talking of gentlemen.'

'Isn't it? Well, I'd like to be nice—if I knew how.'

If she knew how! There is no knowing how, for a girl, in that matter. If nature and her mother have not done it for her, there is no hope for her on that head. I think I may say that nature and her mother had been sufficiently efficacious for Lilian Dale in this respect.

'Mr. Crosbie is, at any rate, a gentleman, and knows how to make himself pleasant. That was all that I meant. Mamma said a great deal more about him than I did.'

'Mr. Crosbie is an Apollo; and I always look upon Apollo as the greatest—you know what—that ever lived. I mustn't say the word, because Apollo was a gentleman.'

## Buying Carpets

It was pleasant to see the Ladies Amelia and Alexandrina, as they sat within a vast emporium of carpets in Bond Street, asking questions of the four men who were waiting upon them, putting their heads together and whispering, calculating accurately as to extra twopences a yard, and occasioning as much trouble as it was possible for them to give. It was pleasant because they managed their large hoops cleverly among the huge rolls of carpets, because they were enjoying themselves thoroughly, and taking to themselves the homage of the men as clearly their due. But it was not so pleasant to look at Crosbie, who was fidgeting to get away to his office, to whom no power of choosing in the matter was really given, and whom the men regarded as being altogether supernumerary. The ladies had promised to be at the shop by half-past ten, so that Crosbie should reach his office at eleven—or a little after. But it was nearly eleven before they left the

'SOCIETY'

Gazebee residence, and it was very evident that half-an-hour among the carpets would be by no means sufficient. It seemed as though miles upon miles of gorgeous colouring were unrolled before them; and then when any pattern was regarded as at all practicable, it was unrolled backwards and forwards till a room was nearly covered by it. Crosbie felt for the men who were hauling about the huge heaps of material; but Lady Amelia sat as composed as though it were her duty to inspect every yard of stuff in the warehouse. 'I think we'll look at that one at the bottom again.' Then the men went to work and removed a mountain. 'No, my dear, that green in the scroll-work won't do. It would fly directly, if any hot water were spilt.' The man smiling ineffably, declared that that particular green never flew anywhere. But Lady Amelia paid no attention to him, and the carpet for which the mountain had been removed became part of another mountain.

'That might do,' said Alexandrina, gazing upon a magnificent crimson ground through which rivers of yellow meandered, carrying with them in their streams an infinity of blue flowers. And as she spoke she held her head gracefully on one side, and looked down upon the carpet doubtingly. Lady Amelia poked it with her parasol as though to test its durability, and whispered something about yellows showing the dirt. Crosbie took out his watch and groaned.

'It's a superb carpet, my lady, and about the newest thing we have. We put down four hundred and fifty yards of it for the Duchess of South Wales, at Cwddglwlch Castle, only last month. Nobody has had it since, for it has not been in stock.' Whereupon Lady Amelia again poked it, and then got up and walked upon it. Lady Alexandrina held her head a little more on one side.

'Five and three?' said Lady Amelia.

'Oh, no, my lady; five and seven; and the cheapest carpet we have in the house. There is twopence a yard more in the colour; there is, indeed.'

'And the discount?' asked Lady Amelia.

[ 153 ]

## HE CONSIDERS ITS PATTERNS

'Two and a half, my lady.'

'Oh, dear, no,' said Lady Amelia. 'I always have five per cent. for immediate payment—quite immediate, you know.' Upon which the man declared the question must be referred to his master. Two and a half was the rule of the house. Crosbie, who had been looking out of the window, said that upon his honour he couldn't wait any longer.

'And what do you think of it, Adolphus?' asked Alexandrina.

'Think of what?'

'Of the carpet—this one, you know!'

'Oh—what do I think of the carpet? I don't think I quite like all these yellow bands; and isn't it too red? I should have thought something brown with a small pattern would have been better. But, upon my word, I don't much care.'

'Of course he doesn't,' said Lady Amelia. Then the two ladies put their heads together for another five minutes, and the carpet was chosen—subject to that question of the discount. 'And now about the rug,' said Lady Amelia. But here Crosbie rebelled, and insisted that he must leave them and go to his office. 'You can't want me about the rug,' he said. 'Well, perhaps not,' said Lady Amelia. But it was manifest that Alexandrina did not approve of being thus left by her male attendant.

### DINNER-PARTIES

WHO DOES NOT KNOW the way in which a lately married couple's little dinner-party stretches itself out from the pure simplicity of a fried sole and a leg of mutton to the attempt at clear soup, the unfortunately cold dish of round balls which is handed about after the sole, and the brightly red jelly, and beautifully pink cream, which are ordered, in the last agony of ambition, from the next pastrycook's shop?

'We cannot give a dinner, my dear, with only cook and Sarah.'

It has thus begun, and the husband has declared that he

has no such idea. 'If Phipps and Dowdney can come here and eat a bit of mutton, they are very welcome; if not, let them stay away. And you might as well ask Phipps's sister; just to have some one to go with you into the drawing-room.'

'I'd much rather go alone, because then I can read,'—or sleep, we may say.

But her husband has explained that she would look friendless in this solitary state, and therefore Phipps's sister has been asked. Then the dinner has progressed down to those costly jellies which have been ordered in a last agony. There has been a conviction on the minds of both of them that the simple leg of mutton would have been more jolly for them all. Had those round balls not been carried about by a hired man; had simple mutton with hot potatoes been handed to Miss Phipps by Sarah, Miss Phipps would not have simpered with such unmeaning stiffness when young Dowdney spoke to her. They would have been much more jolly. 'Have a bit more mutton, Phipps; and where do you like it?' How pleasant it sounds! But we all know that it is impossible. My young friend had intended this, but his dinner had run itself away to cold round balls and sugared forms from the pastrycook.

## Lord Dumbello Buys a Necklace

AND WHITHER DID LORD DUMBELLO betake himself when he left his wife's room in so great a hurry at twelve o'clock? Not to the Park, nor to Tattersall's, nor to a committee-room of the House of Commons, nor yet to the bow-window of his club. But he went straight to a great jeweller's in Ludgate-hill, and there purchased a wonderful green necklace, very rare and curious, heavy with green sparkling drops, with three rows of shining green stones embedded in chaste gold,—a necklace amounting almost to a jewelled cuirass in weight and extent. It had been in all the exhibitions, and was very costly and magnificent. While Lady Dumbello was still dressing in the evening this was brought to her with her lord's love, as his token of renewed confidence, and Lady Dumbello, as she counted the sparkles, triumphed inwardly, telling herself that she had played her cards well.

## The Flower-Show

'I am not going to stay a moment, my dear,' said Mrs. Val, seating herself on Gertrude's sofa, having rushed up almost unannounced into the drawing-room, followed by Clementina; 'indeed, Lady Howlaway is waiting for me this moment; but I must settle with you about the June flower-show.'

'Oh! thank you, Mrs. Scott, don't trouble yourself about me,' said Gertrude; 'I don't think I shall go.'

'Oh! nonsense, my dear; of course you'll go; it's the show of the year, and the Grand duke is to be there—baby is all right now, you know; I must not hear of your not going.'

'All the same—I fear I must decline,' said Gertrude; 'I think I shall be at Hampton.'

'Oh! nonsense, my dear; of course you must show yourself. People will say all manner of things else. Clementina has promised to meet Victoire Jaquêtanápes there and a party of French people, people of the very highest ton. You'll be delighted, my dear.'

'M. Jaquêtanápes is the most delicious polkist you ever met,' said Clementina. 'He has got a new back step that will quite amaze you.' As Gertrude in her present condition was not much given to polkas, this temptation did not have great effect.

'Oh, you must come, of course, my dear—and pray let me recommend you to go to Madame Bosconi for your bonnet; she has such darling little ducks, and as cheap as dirt. But I want you to arrange about the carriage; you can do that with Mr. Tudor, and I can settle with you afterwards. Captain Scott won't go, of course; but I have no doubt Undecimus and Mr. Tudor will come later and bring us home; we can manage very well with the one carriage.'

'SOCIETY'

In spite of her thousand a year the Honourable Mrs. Val was not ashamed to look after the pounds, shillings, and pence. And so, having made her arrangements, Mrs. Val took herself off, hurrying to appease the anger of Lady Howlaway, and followed by Clementina, who since her little outburst as to the new back step of M. Jaquêtanápes had not taken much part in the conversation.

Flower-shows are a great resource for the Mrs. Scotts of London life. They are open to ladies who cannot quite penetrate the inner sancta of fashionable life, and yet they are frequented by those to whom those sancta are everyday household walks. There at least the Mrs. Scotts of the outer world can show themselves in close contiguity, and on equal terms, with the Mrs. Scotts of the inner world.

## The Warden's Tea Party

THE PARTY WENT OFF as such parties do. There were fat old ladies in fine silk dresses, and slim young ladies, in gauzy muslin frocks; old gentlemen stood up with their backs to the empty fire-place, looking by no means so comfortable as they would have done in their own armchairs at home; and young gentlemen, rather stiff about the neck, clustered near the door, not as yet sufficiently in courage to attack the muslin frocks, who awaited the battle, drawn up in a semicircular array. The warden endeavoured to induce a charge, but failed signally, not having the tact of a general; his daughter did what she could to comfort the forces under her command, who took in refreshing rations of cake and tea, and patiently looked for the coming engagement. . .

Soon, however, sweeter sounds began timidly to make themselves audible. Little movements were made in a quarter notable for round stools and music stands. Wax candles were arranged in sconces, big books were brought from hidden recesses, and the work of the evening commenced.

How often were those pegs twisted and retwisted before our friend found that he had twisted them enough; how many discordant scrapes gave promise of the coming harmony. How much the muslin fluttered and crumpled before Eleanor and another nymph were duly seated at the piano; how closely did that tall Apollo pack himself against the wall, with his flute, long as himself, extending high over the heads of his pretty neighbours; into how small a corner crept that round and florid little minor canon, and there with skill amazing found room to tune his accustomed fiddle!

And now the crash begins: away they go in full flow of harmony together—up hill and down dale—now louder and louder, then lower and lower; now loud, as though stirring the battle; then low, as though mourning the slain. In all, through all, and above all, is heard the violoncello. Ah, not for nothing were those pegs so twisted and retwisted—listen, listen! Now alone that saddest of instruments tells its touching tale. Silent, and in awe, stand fiddle, flute, and piano, to hear the sorrows of their wailing brother. 'Tis but for a moment: before the melancholy of those low notes had been fully realised, again comes the full force of all the band—down go the pedals, away rush twenty fingers scouring over the bass notes with all the impetus of passion. Apollo blows till his stiff neckcloth is no better than a rope, and the minor canon works with both arms till he falls in a syncope of exhaustion against the wall.

How comes it that now, when all should be silent, when courtesy, if not taste, should make men listen—how is it at this moment the black-coated corps leave their retreat and begin skirmishing? One by one they creep forth, and fire off little guns timidly, and without precision. Ah, my men, efforts such as these will take no cities, even though the enemy should be never so open to assault. . .

The archdeacon is engaged against two prebendaries, a pursy full-blown rector assisting him, in all the perils and all the enjoyments of short whist. With solemn energy do they watch the shuffled pack, and, all-expectant, eye the coming trump. With what anxious nicety do they arrange their cards, jealous of each other's eyes! Why is that lean doctor so slow —cadaverous man with hollow jaw and sunken eye, ill beseeming the richness of his mother church! Ah, why so slow, thou meagre doctor? See how the archdeacon, speechless in his agony, deposits on the board his cards, and looks to heaven or to the ceiling for support. Hark, how he sighs, as with thumbs in his waistcoat pocket he seems to signify that the end of such torment is not yet even nigh at hand! Vain is the hope, if hope there be, to disturb that meagre doctor. With care precise he places every card, weighs well the value of each mighty ace, each guarded king, and comfort-giving queen; speculates on knave and ten, counts all his suits, and sets his price upon the whole. At length a card is led, and quick three others fall upon the board. The little doctor leads again, while with lustrous eye his partner absorbs the trick. Now thrice has this been done—thrice has constant fortune favoured the brace of prebendaries, ere the archdeacon rouses himself to the battle; but at the fourth assault he pins to the earth a prostrate king, laying low his crown and sceptre, bushy beard, and lowering brow, with a poor deuce.

'As David did Goliath,' says the archdeacon, pushing over the four cards to his partner. And then a trump is led, then another trump; then a king—and then an ace—and then a long ten, which brings down from the meagre doctor his only remaining tower of strength—his cherished queen of trumps.

'What, no second club?' says the archdeacon to his partner.

'Only one club,' mutters from his inmost stomach the pursy rector, who sits there red-faced, silent, impervious, careful, a safe but not a brilliant ally.

But the archdeacon cares not for many clubs, or for none. He dashes out his remaining cards with a speed most annoying to his antagonists, pushes over to them some four cards as their allotted portion, shoves the remainder across the table to the red-faced rector; calls out 'two by cards and two by honours, and the odd trick last time,' marks a treble under the candle-stick, and has dealt round the second pack before the meagre doctor has calculated his losses.

And so went off the warden's party, and men and women arranging shawls and shoes declared how pleasant it had been; and Mrs. Goodenough, the red-faced rector's wife, pressing the warden's hand, declared she had never enjoyed herself better; which showed how little pleasure she allowed herself in this world, as she had sat the whole evening through in the same chair without occupation, not speaking, and unspoken to. And Matilda Johnson, when she allowed young Dickson of the bank to fasten her cloak round her neck, thought that two hundred pounds a year and a little cottage would really do for happiness; besides, he was sure to be manager some day. And Apollo, folding his flute into his pocket, felt that he had acquitted himself with honour; and the archdeacon pleasantly jingled his gains; but the meagre doctor went off without much audible speech, muttering ever and anon as he went, 'three and thirty points!' 'three and thirty points!'

## The Beargarden Club

CLUBS ARE PLEASANT RESORTS in all respects but one. They require ready money or even worse than that in respect to annual payments,—money in advance; and the young baronet had been absolutely forced to restrict himself. He, as a matter of course, out of those to which he had possessed the right of entrance, chose the worst. It was called the Beargarden, and had been lately opened with the express view of combining parsimony with profligacy. Clubs were ruined, so said certain young parsimonious profligates, by providing comforts for old fogies who paid little or nothing but their subscriptions, and took out by their mere presence three times as much as they gave. This club was not to be opened till three o'clock in the afternoon, before which hour the promoters of the

Beargarden thought it improbable that they and their fellows would want a club. There were to be no morning papers taken, no library, no morning-room. Dining-rooms, billiard-rooms, and card-rooms would suffice for the Beargarden. Everything was to be provided by a purveyor, so that the club should be cheated only by one man. Everything was to be luxurious, but the luxuries were to be achieved at first cost. It had been a happy thought, and the club was said to prosper. Herr Vossner, the purveyor, was a jewel, and so carried on affairs that there was no trouble about anything. He would assist even in smoothing little difficulties as to the settling of card accounts, and had behaved with the greatest tenderness to the drawers of cheques whose bankers had harshly declared them to have 'no effects.' Herr Vossner was a jewel, and the Beargarden was a success. Perhaps no young man about town enjoyed the Beargarden more thoroughly than did Sir Felix Carbury. The club was in the close vicinity of other clubs, in a small street turning out of St. James's Street, and piqued itself on its outward quietness and sobriety. Why pay for stone-work for other people to look at;—why lay out money in marble pillars and cornices, seeing that you can neither eat such things, nor drink them, nor gamble with them? But the Beargarden had the best wines,—or thought that it had,—and the easiest chairs, and two billiard-tables than which nothing more perfect had ever been made to stand upon legs.

## Nouveau Riche

Sir Damask was a man of great wealth, whose father had been a contractor. But Sir Damask himself was a sportsman, keeping many horses on which other men often rode, a yacht in which other men sunned themselves, a deer forest, a moor, a large machinery for making pheasants. He shot pigeons at Hurlingham, drove four-in-hand in the park, had a box at every race-course, and was the most good-natured fellow known. He had really conquered the world, had got over the difficulty of being the grandson of a butcher, and was now as good as though the Monograms had gone to the crusades. Julia Triplex was equal to her position, and made the very most of it. She dispensed champagne and smiles, and made everybody, including herself, believe that she was in love with her husband. Lady Monogram had climbed to the top of the tree.

# Marriage

### WEDDING PRESENTS

BEFORE THE DAY came round Arabella was quite astonished to find how popular and fashionable her wedding was likely to be, and how the world at large approved of what she was doing. The newspapers had paragraphs about alliances and noble families, and all the relatives sent tribute. There was a gold candlestick from the duke, a gilt dish from the duchess, —which came, however, without a word of personal congratulation,—and a gorgeous set of scent-bottles from cousin Mistletoe. The Connop Greens were lavish with sapphires, the De Brownes with pearls, and the Smijths with opal. Mrs. Gore sent a huge carbuncle which Arabella strongly suspected to be glass. From her paternal parent there came a pair of silver nut-crackers, and from the maternal a second-hand dressing-case newly done up. Old Mrs. Green gave her a couple of ornamental butter-boats, and salt-cellars innumerable came from distant Greens. But there was a diamond ring —with a single stone—from a friend, without a name, which she believed to be worth all the rest in money value.

### A YOUNG MAN'S PROSPECTS

WHEN FRANK HOUSTON, after the manner of would-be sons-in-law, had applied to Sir Thomas, Sir Thomas, who already knew all about it, asked after his income, his prospects, and his occupation. Fifty years ago young men used to encounter the misery of such questions, and to live afterwards often in the enjoyment of the stern questioner's money and daughters. But there used in those days to be a bad quarter of an hour while the questions were being asked, and not unfrequently a bad six months afterwards, while the stern questioner was gradually undergoing a softening process under the hands of the females of the family. But the young man of to-day has no bad quarter of an hour. 'You are a mercantile old brick, with money and a daughter. I am a jeunesse dorée,—gilded by blood and fashion, though so utterly impecunious! Let us know your terms. How much is it to be, and then I can say whether we can afford to live upon it.' The old brick surrenders himself more readily and speedily to the latter than to the former manner;—but he hardly surrenders himself quite at once.

## An Elopement

'Dear Mamma,

'You will be surprised on your return from London to find that we have gone. After much thinking about it we determined it would be best, because we had quite made up our mind *not to be kept separated*. Ben was so eager about it that I was obliged to yield. We were afraid that if we asked papa at once he would not have given his consent. Pray give him my most dutiful love, and tell him that I am sure he will never have occasion to be ashamed of his son-in-law. I don't suppose he knows, but it is the fact that Captain Batsby has about three thousand a year of his own. It is very different from having nothing, like that wretch Frank Houston, or, for that matter, Mr. Traffick. Ben was quite in a position to ask papa, but things had happened which made us both feel that papa would not like it just at present. We mean to be married at Ostend, and then will come back as soon as you and papa say that you will receive us. In the meantime I wish you would send some of my clothes after me. Of course I had to come away with very little luggage, because I was obliged to have my things mixed up with Ben's. I did not dare to have my boxes brought down by the servants. Could you send me the green silk in which I went to church the last two Sundays, and my pink gauze, and the grey poplin? Please send two or three flannel petticoats, as I could not put them among his things, and as many cuffs and collars as you can cram in. I suppose I can get boots at Ostend, but I should like to have the hat with the little brown feather. There is my silk jacket with the fur trimming; I should like to have that. I suppose I shall have to be married without any regular dress, but I am sure papa will make up my trousseau to me afterwards. I lent a little lace fichu to Augusta; tell her I shall so like to have it.

'Give papa my best love, and Augusta, and poor Tom, and accept the same from your affectionate daughter,

'GERTRUDE.

'I suppose I must not add the other name yet.'

### BACHELOR MEMORIES

'BUT WHY ON EARTH you should go and marry, seeing that you're not the eldest son, and that you've got everything on earth that you want as a bachelor, I can't understand. I can't indeed, Fred. By heaven, I can't!' Then Sir Anthony gave a long sigh, and sat musing awhile, thinking of the club in London to which he belonged, but which he never entered;— of the old days in which he had been master of a bedroom near St. James's Street,—of his old friends whom he never saw now, and of whom he never heard, except as one and another, year after year, shuffled away from their wives to that world in which there is no marrying or giving in marriage.

### 'A WIFE—LIKE A HORSE'

'BUT MEN have very different ideas about women. I could do, and have done, and am doing with a small income myself, but a wife is in some respects like a horse. If a gentleman does keep a horse, it should be well groomed.'

'You could not endure a woman who was not always got up in satin and velvet?'

'Not satin and velvet exactly. I do not require a curiously-mounted saddle for my horse. But I don't think I should have much enjoyment with a cheap wife. I like cold mutton and candle-ends myself very well, but I do not love feminine economies. Family washing-bills kept at the lowest, a maid-of-all-work with an allowance in lieu of beer, and a dark morning-gown for household work, would not, if I know myself, add fuel to the ardor of my conjugal affection. I love women dearly; I like them to be near me; but then I like them to be nice. When a woman is nasty she is very nasty.'

### Specifications for a Wife

'But it would be so great a thing if he could be settled. Sophia Mellerby has promised to come here for a couple of months in the winter. He could not possibly do better than that.'

'The Mellerbys are very good people,' said the Earl. 'Her grandmother, the duchess, is one of the very best women in England. Her mother, Lady Sophia, is an excellent creature,—religious, and with the soundest principles. Mr. Mellerby, as a commoner, stands as high as any man in England.'

'They have held the same property since the Wars of the Roses. And then I suppose the money should count for something,' added the lady.

Lord Scroope would not admit the importance of the money, but was quite willing to acknowledge that were his heir to make Sophia Mellerby the future Lady Scroope he would be content.

### Designing Mammas

But to tell the truth openly and at once—a virtue for which a novelist does not receive very much commendation—

Griselda Grantly was, to a certain extent, already given away. Not that she, Griselda, knew anything about it, or that the thrice happy gentleman had been made aware of his good fortune; nor even had the archdeacon been told. But Mrs. Grantly and Lady Lufton had been closeted together more than once, and terms had been signed and sealed between them. Not signed on parchment, and sealed with wax, as is the case with treaties made by kings and diplomats—to be broken by the same; but signed with little words, and sealed with certain pressings of the hand—a treaty which between two such contracting parties would be binding enough. And by the terms of this treaty Griselda Grantly was to become Lady Lufton. Lady Lufton had hitherto been fortunate in her matrimonial speculations. She had selected Sir George for her daughter, and Sir George, with the utmost good-nature, had fallen in with her views. She had selected Fanny Monsell for Mr. Robarts, and Fanny Monsell had not rebelled against her for a moment. There was a prestige of success about her doings, and she felt almost confident that her dear son Ludovic must fall in love with Griselda. As to the lady herself, nothing, Lady Lufton thought, could be much better than such a match for her son. Lady Lufton, I have said, was a good Churchwoman, and the archdeacon was the very type of that branch of the Church which she venerated. The Grantlys, too, were of a good family—not noble, indeed; but in such matters Lady Lufton did not want everything. She was one of those persons who, in placing their hopes at a moderate pitch, may fairly trust to see them realized. She would fain that her son's wife should be handsome; this she wished for his sake, that he might be proud of his wife, and because men love to look on beauty. But she was afraid of vivacious beauty, of those soft, sparkling feminine charms which are spread out as lures for all the world, soft dimples, laughing eyes, luscious lips, conscious smiles, and easy whispers. What if her son should bring her home a rattling, rapid-spoken, painted piece of Eve's flesh such as this? Would not the glory and joy of her life be over, even though such child of their first mother should have come forth to the present day ennobled by the blood of two dozen successive British peers?

And then, too, Griselda's money would not be useless. Lady Lufton, with all her high-flown ideas, was not an imprudent woman. She knew that her son had been extravagant, though she did not believe that he had been reckless; and she was well content to think that some balsam from the old bishop's coffers should be made to cure the slight wounds which his early imprudence might have inflicted on the carcass of the family property. And thus, in this way, and for these reasons, Griselda Grantly had been chosen out from all the world to be the future Lady Lufton.

## A Daily Hour of Gibbon

It did not perhaps surprise her so much as the serious view of life which her husband from day to day impressed upon her... But Lord George made out a course of reading for her,—so much for the two hours after breakfast, so much for the hour before dressing,—so much for the evening; and also a table of results to be acquired in three months,—in six months,—and so much by the close of the first year; and even laid down the sum total of achievements to be produced by a dozen years of such work! Of course she determined to do as he would have her do. The great object of her life was to love him; and, of course, if she really loved him, she would comply with his wishes. She began her daily hour of Gibbon after breakfast with great zeal. But there was present to her an idea that if the Gibbon had come from her father, and the instigations to amuse herself from her husband, it would have been better.

# MARRIAGE

## The Choice of a Wife

'There are many things which go to the choice of a wife, and the worst of it is that they are not compatible one with another. A woman should be handsome; but then she is proud. A woman should have a certain air of dignity; but when she has got it she knows that herself, and shows it off in the wrong place. She should be young; but if she is too young she is silly: wait a little and she becomes strong-minded and headstrong. If she don't read anything she becomes an ass and a bore; but if she do she despises a man because he is not always doing the same thing. If she is a nobody the world thinks nothing of her. If she come of high birth she thinks a deal too much of herself. It is difficult.'

## The Wedding-Breakfast

Then came the breakfast, that dullest, saddest, hour of all. To feed heavily about twelve in the morning is always a nuisance,—a nuisance so abominable that it should be avoided under any other circumstances than a wedding in your own family. But that wedding-breakfast, when it does come, is the worst of all feeding. The smart dresses and bare shoulders seen there by daylight, the handing people in and out among the seats, the very nature of the food, made up of chicken and sweets and flummery, the profusion of champagne, not sometimes of the very best on such an occasion;—and then the speeches! They fall generally to the lot of some middle-aged gentlemen, who seem always to have been selected for their incapacity! But there is a worse trouble yet remaining,—in the unnatural repletion which the sight even of so much food produces, and the fact that your dinner for that day is destroyed utterly and for ever.

### Send-off for Bride and Groom

'A good husband is the greatest blessing that God can send a girl, and I do think that he is good and sterling.'

'He is, mamma, he is. I know he is.'

'And when that woman talks about brewery chimneys, I know what a comfort it is that there should be chimneys, and that they should be near. Brewery chimneys are better than a do-nothing scamp that can't earn a meal for himself or his children. And when I see Joe with his pink coat on going to the meet, I thank God that my Molly has got a lad that can work hard, and ride his own horses, and go out hunting with the best of them.'

'Oh! mamma, I do like to see him then. He is handsome.' . . .

Then Molly went down with her travelling hat on, looking twice prettier than she had done during the whole of the morning ceremonies. It is, I suppose, on the bridegroom's behalf that the bride is put forth in all her best looks just as she is about to become, for the first time, exclusively his own. Molly on the present occasion was very pretty, and Joe was very proud. . .

And then, as they went, came the normal shower of rice, to be picked up in the course of the next hour by the vicarage fowls, and not by the London beggars, and the air was darkened by a storm of old shoes. In London, white satin slippers are the fashion. But Buston and Buntingford combined could not afford enough of such missiles; and, from the hands of the boys, black shoes, and boots too, were thrown freely. 'There go my best pair,' said one of the boys, as the chariot was driven off, 'and I don't mean to let them lie there.' Then the boots were recovered and taken up to the bedroom.

## On Moulding a Wife

The idea of a wife thus moulded to fit a man's own grooves, and educated to suit matrimonial purposes according to the exact views of the future husband was by no means original with him. Other men have moulded their wives, but I do not know that as a rule the practice has been found to answer. It is open, in the first place, to this objection,—that the moulder does not generally conceive such idea very early in life, and the idea when conceived must necessarily be carried out on a young subject. Such a plan is the result of much deliberate thought, and has generally arisen from long observation, on the part of the thinker, of the unhappiness arising from marriages in which there has been no moulding. Such a frame of mind comes upon a bachelor, perhaps about his thirty-fifth year, and then he goes to work with a girl of fourteen. The operation takes some ten years, at the end of which the moulded bride regards her lord as an old man. On the whole I think that the ordinary plan is the better, and even the safer. Dance with a girl three times, and if you like the light of her eye and the tone of voice with which she, breathless, answers your little questions about horseflesh and music—about affairs masculine and feminine,—then take the leap in the dark. There is danger, no doubt; but the moulded wife is, I think, more dangerous.

## Stiff-necked as an Ox

Mr. Kennedy, though he was a most scrupulously attentive member of Parliament, was a man very punctual to hours and rules in his own house,—and liked that his wife should be as punctual as himself. Lady Laura, who in marrying him had firmly resolved that she would do her duty to him in all ways, even though the ways might sometimes be painful,— and had been perhaps more punctilious in this respect than

## HE CONSIDERS ITS PATTERNS

she might have been had she loved him heartily,—was not perhaps quite so fond of accurate regularity as her husband; and thus, by this time, certain habits of his had become rather bonds than habits to her. He always had prayers at nine, and breakfasted at a quarter past nine, let the hours on the night before have been as late as they might before the time for rest had come. After breakfast he would open his letters in his study, but he liked her to be with him, and desired to discuss with her every application he got from a constituent. He had his private secretary in a room apart, but he thought that everything should be filtered to his private secretary through his wife. He was very anxious that she herself should superintend the accounts of their own private expenditure, and had taken some trouble to teach her an excellent mode of bookkeeping. He had recommended to her a certain course of reading,—which was pleasant enough; ladies like to receive such recommendations; but Mr. Kennedy, having drawn out the course, seemed to expect that his wife should read the books he had named, and, worse still, that she should read them in the time he had allocated for the work. This, I think, was tyranny. Then the Sundays became very wearisome to Lady Laura. Going to church twice, she had learnt, would be a part of her duty; and though in her father's household attendance at church had never been very strict, she had made up her mind to this cheerfully. But Mr. Kennedy expected also that he and she should always dine together on Sundays, that there should be no guests, and that there should be no evening company. After all, the demand was not very severe, but yet she found that it operated injuriously upon her comfort. The Sundays were very wearisome to her, and made her feel that her lord and master was—her lord and master. She made an effort or two to escape, but the efforts were all in vain. He never spoke a cross word to her. He never gave a stern command. But yet he had his way. 'I won't say that reading a novel on a Sunday is a sin,' he said; 'but we must at any rate

## MARRIAGE

admit that it is a matter on which men disagree, that many of the best of men are against such occupation on Sunday, and that to abstain is to be on the safe side.' So the novels were put away, and Sunday afternoon with the long evening became rather a stumbling-block to Lady Laura.

Those two hours, moreover, with her husband in the morning became very wearisome to her. At first she had declared that it would be her greatest ambition to help her husband in his work, and she had read all the letters from the Mac-Nabs and MacFies, asking to be made gaugers and landing-waiters, with an assumed interest. But the work palled upon her very quickly. Her quick intellect discovered soon that there was nothing in it which she really did. It was all form and verbiage, and pretence at business. Her husband went through it all with the utmost patience, reading every word, giving orders as to every detail, and conscientiously doing that which he conceived he had undertaken to do. But Lady Laura wanted to meddle with high politics, to discuss reform bills, to assist in putting up Mr. This and in putting down my Lord That. Why should she waste her time in doing that which the lad in the next room, who was called a private secretary, could do as well?

Still she would obey. Let the task be as hard as it might, she would obey. If he counselled her to do this or that, she would follow his counsel,—because she owed him so much. If she had accepted the half of all his wealth without loving him, she owed him the more on that account. But she knew,— she could not but know,—that her intellect was brighter than his; and might it not be possible for her to lead him? Then she made efforts to lead her husband, and found that he was as stiff-necked as an ox. Mr. Kennedy was not, perhaps, a clever man; but he was a man who knew his own way, and who intended to keep it.

## The Wedding Journey

By the proper administration of a slight bribe Crosbie secured for himself and his wife a compartment in the railway carriage to themselves. And as he seated himself opposite to Alexandrina, having properly tucked her up with all her bright-coloured trappings, he remembered that he had never in truth been alone with her before. He had danced with her frequently, and been left with her for a few minutes between the figures. He had flirted with her in crowded drawing-rooms, and had once found a moment at Courcy Castle to tell her that he was willing to marry her, in spite of his engagement with Lilian Dale. But he had never walked with her for hours together as he had walked with Lily. He had never talked to her about government, and politics, and books, nor had she talked to him of poetry, of religion, and of the little duties and comforts of life. He had known the Lady Alexandrina for the last six or seven years; but he had never known her,—perhaps never would know her,—as he had learned to know Lily Dale within the space of two months.

And now that she was his wife, what was he to say to her? . . .

'Are you quite comfortable?' he said, at last.

'Oh, yes, quite, thank you. By-the-by, what did you do with my dressing-case?'

And that question she did ask with some energy.

'It is under you. You can have it as foot-stool if you like it.'

'Oh, no; I should scratch it. I was afraid that if Hannah had it, it might be lost.' Then again there was silence, and Crosbie again considered as to what he would next say to his wife.

We all know the advice given us of old as to what we should do under such circumstances; and who can be so thoroughly justified in following that advice as a newly-married husband? So he put out his hand for hers and drew her closer to him.

'Take care of my bonnet,' she said, as she felt the motion of the railway carriage when he kissed her. I don't think he kissed her again till he had landed her and her bonnet safely at Folkestone...

So he sat without speaking, till the train came to the tunnel.

'I do so hate tunnels,' said Alexandrina.

He had half intended to put out his hand again, under some mistaken idea that the tunnel afforded him an opportunity. The whole journey was one long opportunity, had he desired it; but his wife hated tunnels, so he drew his hand back again...

He had *The Times* newspaper in his dressing-bag. She also had a novel with her. Would she be offended if he took out the paper and read it? The miles seemed to pass by very slowly, and there was still another hour down to Folkestone. He longed for his *Times,* but resolved at last that he would not read unless she read first. She also had remembered her novel; but by nature she was more patient than he, and she thought that on such a journey any reading might perhaps be almost improper. So she sat tranquilly, with her eyes fixed on the netting over her husband's head.

# Hunting and Racing

## On Fox Hunting

'The truth is, I have had a letter this morning from a benevolent philosopher which has almost settled the question for me. He wants me to join a society for the suppression of British sports as being barbarous and anti-pathetic to the intellectual pursuits of an educated man. I would immediately shoot, fish, hunt, and go out ratting, if I could hope for the least success. I know I should never shoot anything but the dog and the gamekeepers, and that I should catch every weed in the river; but I think that in the process of seasons I might jump over a hedge.'

'Kate will show you the way to do that.'

'With Kate and Mr. Twentyman to help me, and a judicious system of liberal tips to Tony Tuppett, I could make my way about on a quiet old nag, and live respected by my neighbours. The fact is, I hate with my whole heart the trash of the phil-animalists.'

'What is a—a—I didn't quite catch the thing you hate?'

'The thing is a small knot of self-anxious people who think that they possess among them all the bowels of the world.'

'Possess all the what, Reginald?'

'I said bowels,—using an ordinary but very ill-expressed metaphor. The ladies and gentlemen to whom I allude, not looking very clearly into the system of pains and pleasures in accordance with which we have to live, put their splay feet down now upon this ordinary operation and now upon that, and call upon the world to curse the cruelty of those who will not agree with them. A lady whose tippet is made from the skins of twenty animals who have been wired in the snow and then left to die of starvation—'

'Oh, Reginald!'

'That is the way of it. I am not now saying whether it is right or wrong. The lady with the tippet will justify the wires and the starvation because, as she will say, she uses the fur. An honest blanket would keep her just as warm. But the fox, who suffers perhaps ten minutes of agony, should he not succeed as he usually does in getting away,—is hunted only for amusement! It is true that the one fox gives amusement for hours to perhaps some hundred;—but it is only for amusement. What riles me most is that these would-be philosophers do not or will not see that recreation is as necessary to the world as clothes or food, and the providing of the one is as legitimate a business as the purveying of the other.'

## The Roebury Club and the Brown Horse

There were men who lived together at Roebury in a kind of club,—four or five of them, who came thither from London, running backwards and forwards as hunting arrangements enabled them to do so,—a brewer or two and a banker, with a would-be fast attorney, a sporting literary gentleman, and a young unmarried Member of Parliament who had no particular home of his own in the country. These men formed the Roebury Club, and a jolly life they had of it. They had their own wine closet at the King's Head,—or Roebury Inn as the house had come to be popularly called,—and supplied their own game. The landlord found everything else; and as they were not very particular about their bills, they were allowed to do pretty much as they liked in the house. They were rather imperious, very late in their hours, sometimes, though not often, noisy, and once there had been a hasty quarrel which had made the landlord in his anger say that the club should be turned out of his house. But they paid well, chaffed the servants much oftener than they bullied them, and on the whole were very popular.

To this club Vavasor did not belong, alleging that he could not afford to live at their pace, and alleging, also, that his stays at Roebury were not long enough to make him a desirable member. The invitation to him was not repeated and he lodged elsewhere in the little town. But he occasionally went in of an evening, and would make up with the members a table at whist.

He had come down to Roebury by mail train, ready for hunting the next morning, and walked into the club-room just at midnight. There he found Maxwell the banker, Grindley the would-be fast attorney, and Calder Jones the Member of Parliament, playing dummy. Neither of the brewers were there, nor was the sporting literary gentleman.

'Here's Vavasor,' said Maxwell, 'and now we won't play this blackguard game any longer. Somebody told me, Vavasor, that you were gone away.'

'Gone away;—what, like a fox?'

'I don't know what it was; that something had happened to you since last season; that you were married, or dead, or gone abroad. By George, I've lost the trick after all! I hate dummy like the devil. I never hold a card in dummy's hand. Yes, I know; that's seven points on each side. Vavasor, come and cut. . .'

The club breakfasted the next morning at nine o'clock, in order that they might start at half-past for the meet at Edgehill. Edgehill is twelve miles from Roebury, and the hacks would do it in an hour and a half,—or perhaps a little less. 'Does anybody know anything about that brown horse of Vavasor's?' said Maxwell. 'I saw him coming into the yard yesterday with that old groom of his.'

'He had a brown horse last season,' said Grindley;—'a little thing that went very fast, but wasn't quite sound on the road.'

'That was a mare,' said Maxwell, 'and he sold her to Cinquebars.'*

'For a hundred and fifty,' said Calder Jones, 'and she wasn't worth the odd fifty.'

'He won seventy with her at Leamington,' said Maxwell, 'and I doubt whether he'd take his money now.'

'Is Cinquebars coming down here this year?'

'I don't know,' said Maxwell. 'I hope not. He's the best fellow in the world, but he can't ride, and he don't care for hunting, and he makes more row than any fellow I ever met. I wish some fellow could tell me something about that fellow's brown horse.'

'I'd never buy a horse of Vavasor's if I were you,' said Grindley. 'He never has anything that's all right all round.'

'And who has?' said Maxwell, as he took into his plate a second mutton chop, which had just been brought up hot into the room especially for him. 'That's the mistake men make about horses, and that's why there's so much cheating. I never ask for a warranty with a horse, and don't very often have a horse examined. Yet I do as well as others. You can't have perfect horses any more than you can perfect men, or perfect women. You put up with red hair, or bad teeth, or big feet,—or sometimes with the devil of a voice. But a man when he wants a horse won't put up with anything! Therefore those who've got horses to sell must lie. When I go into the market with three hundred pounds I expect a perfect animal. As I never do that now I never expect a perfect animal. I like 'em to see; I like 'em to have four legs; and I like 'em to have a little wind. I don't much mind anything else.'

'By Jove, you're about right,' said Calder Jones. The reader will therefore readily see that Mr. Maxwell the banker reigned as king in that club.

* Ah, my friend [Thackeray], from whom I have borrowed this scion of the nobility! Had he been left with us he would have forgiven me my little theft, and now that he has gone I will not change the name.

## The Derby

Now had come the night before the Derby, and it must be acknowledged that the young Lord was much fluttered by the greatness of the coming struggle. Tifto, having seen his horse conveyed to Epsom, had come up to London in order that he might dine with his partner and hear what was being said about the race at the Beargarden. The party dining there consisted of Silverbridge, Dolly Longstaff, Popplecourt, and Tifto. Nidderdale was to have joined them, but he told them on the day before, with a sigh, that domestic duties were too strong for him. Lady Nidderdale,—or if not Lady Nidderdale herself, then Lady Nidderdale's mother,—was so far potent over the young nobleman as to induce him to confine his Derby practices to the Derby-day. Another guest had also been expected, the reason for whose non-appearance must be explained somewhat at length. Lord Gerald Palliser, the Duke's second son, was at this time at Cambridge,—being almost as popular at Trinity as his brother had been at Christ Church. It was to him quite a matter of course that he should see his brother's horse run for the Derby. But, unfortunately, in this very year a stand was being made by the University pundits against a practice which they thought had become too general. For the last year or two it had been considered almost as much a matter of course that a Cambridge undergraduate should go to the Derby as that a Member of Parliament should do so. Against this three or four rigid disciplinarians had raised their voices,—and as a result, no young man up at Trinity could get leave to be away on the Derby pretext.

Lord Gerald raged against the restriction very loudly. He at first proclaimed his intention of ignoring the college authorities altogether. Of course he would be expelled. But the order itself was to his thinking so absurd,—the idea that he should not see his brother's horse run was so extravagant,—that he argued that his father could not be angry with him for incurring dismissal in so excellent a cause. But his brother saw things in a different light. He knew how his father had looked at him when he had been sent away from Oxford, and he counselled moderation. Gerald should see the Derby, but should not encounter that heaviest wrath of all which comes from a man's not sleeping beneath his college roof. There was a train which left Cambridge at an early hour, and would bring him into London in time to accompany his friends to the racecourse;—and another train, a special, which would take him down after dinner, so that he and others should reach Cambridge before the college gates were shut.

The dinner at the Beargarden was very joyous. Of course the state of betting in regard to Prime Minister was the subject generally popular for the night. Mr. Lupton came in, a gentleman well known in all fashionable circles, parliamentary, social, and racing, who was rather older than his company on this occasion, but still not so much so as to be found to be an incumbrance. Lord Glasslough too, and others joined them, and a good deal was said about the horse. 'I never keep these things dark,' said Tifto. 'Of course he's an uncertain horse.'

'Most horses are,' said Lupton.

'Just so, Mr. Lupton. What I mean is, the Minister has got a bit of temper. But if he likes to do his best I don't think any three-year-old in England can get his nose past him.'

'For half a mile he'd be nowhere with the Provence filly,' said Glasslough.

'I'm speaking of a Derby distance, my Lord.'

'That's a kind of thing nobody really knows,' said Lupton.

'I've seen him 'ave his gallops,' said the little man, who in his moments of excitement would sometimes fall away from that exact pronunciation which had been one of the studies of his life, 'and have measured his stride. I think I know what pace means. Of course I'm not going to answer for the 'orse. He's a temper, but if things go favourably, no animal that ever showed on the Downs was more likely to do the trick. Is there any gentleman here who would like to bet me fifteen to one in hundreds against the two events,—the Derby and the Leger?' The desired odds were at once offered by Mr. Lupton, and the bet was booked.

This gave rise to other betting and before the evening was over Lord Silverbridge had taken three-and-a-half to one against his horse to such an extent that he stood to lose twelve hundred pounds. The champagne which he had drunk, and the news that Quousque, the first favourite, had so gone to pieces that now there was a question which was the first favourite, had so inflated him that, had he been left alone, he would almost have wagered even money on his horse. In the midst of his excitement there came to him a feeling that he was allowing himself to do just that which he had intended to avoid. But then the occasion was so peculiar! How often can it happen to a man in his life that he shall own a favourite for the Derby? The affair was one in which it was almost necessary that he should risk a little money.

Tifto, when he got into his bed, was altogether happy. He had added whisky-and-water to his champagne, and feared nothing. If Prime Minister should win the Derby he would be able to pay all that he owed, and to make a start with money in his pocket. And then there would be attached to him all the infinite glory of being the owner of a winner of the Derby. The horse was run in his name. Thoughts as to great successes crowded themselves upon his heated brain. What might not be open to him? Parliament! The Jockey Club! The mastership of one of the crack shire packs! Might it not come to pass that he should some day become the great authority in England upon races, racehorses, and hunters? If he could be the winner of a Derby and Leger he thought that Glasslough and Lupton would snub him no longer, that even Tregear would speak to him, and that his pal the Duke's son would never throw him aside again.

Lord Silverbridge had bought a drag with all its appendages. There was a coach, the four bay horses, the harness, and the two regulation grooms. When making this purchase he had condescended to say a word to his father on the subject. 'Everybody belongs to the four-in-hand club now,' said the son.

'I never did,' said the Duke.

'Ah,—if I could be like you!'

The Duke had said that he would think about it, and then had told Mr. Morton that he was to pay the bill for this new toy. He had thought about it, and had assured himself that driving a coach and four was at present regarded as a fitting amusement for young men of rank and wealth. He did not understand it himself. It seemed to him to be as unnatural as though a gentleman should turn blacksmith and make horseshoes for his amusement. Driving four horses was hard work. But the same might be said of rowing. There were men, he knew, who would spend their days standing at a lathe, making little boxes for their recreation. He did not sympathise with it. But the fact was so, and this driving of coaches was regarded with favour. He had been a little touched by that word his son had spoken, 'Ah,—if I could be like you!' So he had given the permission; the drag, horses, harness, and grooms had come into the possession of Lord Silverbridge; and now they were put into requisition to take their triumphant owner and his party down to Epsom. Dolly Longstaff's team was sent down to meet them half-way. Gerald Palliser, who had come up from Cambridge that morning, was allowed to drive the first stage out of town to compensate him for the cruelty done to him by the University pundits. Tifto, with a cigar in his mouth, with a white hat and a blue veil, and a new light-coloured coat, was by no means the least happy of the party.

How that race was run, and how both Prime Minister and Quousque were beaten by an outsider named Fishknife, Prime Minister, however, coming in a good second, the present writer

## HE CONSIDERS ITS PATTERNS

having no aptitude in that way, cannot describe. Such, however, were the facts, and then Dolly Longstaff and Lord Silverbridge drove the coach back to London. The coming back was not so triumphant, though the young fellows bore their failure well. Dolly Longstaff had lost a 'pot of money,' Silverbridge would have to draw upon that inexhaustible Mr. Morton for something over two thousand pounds,—in regard to which he had no doubt as to the certainty with which the money would be forthcoming, but he feared that it would give rise to special notice from his father. Even the poor younger brother had lost a couple of hundred pounds, for which he would have to make his own special application to Mr. Morton.

But Tifto felt it more than anyone. The horse ought to have won. Fishknife had been favoured by such a series of accidents that the whole affair had been a miracle. Tifto had these circumstances at his fingers' ends, and in the course of the afternoon and evening explained them accurately to all who would listen to him. He had this to say on his own behalf,—that before the party had left the course their horse stood first favourite for the Leger. But Tifto was unhappy as he came back to town, and in spite of the lunch, which had been very glorious, sat moody and sometimes even silent within his gay apparel.

'It was the unfairest start I ever saw,' said Tifto, almost getting up from his seat on the coach so as to address Dolly and Silverbridge on the box.

'What the —— is the good of that?' said Dolly from the coach-box. 'Take your licking and don't squeal.'

'That's all very well. I can take my licking as well as another man. But one has to look to the causes of these things. I never saw Pepperment ride so badly. Before he got round the corner I wished I'd been on the horse myself.'

'I don't believe it was Pepperment's fault a bit,' said Silverbridge.

'Well;—perhaps not. Only I did think that I was a pretty

[ 184 ]

good judge of riding.' Then Tifto again settled down into silence.

## Lizzie's First Hunt

Among the crowd of Ayrshire hunting men,—a lord or two, a dozen lairds, two dozen farmers, and as many men of business out of Ayr, Kilmarnock, and away from Glasgow,—it was soon told that Lady Eustace and her party were among them. A good deal had been already heard of Lizzie, and it was at least known of her that she had, for her life, the Portray estate in her hands. So there was an undercurrent of whispering, and that sort of commotion which the appearance of new-comers does produce at a hunt-meet. Lord George knew one or two men, who were surprised to find him in Ayrshire, and Mrs. Carbuncle was soon quite at home with a young nobleman whom she had met in the vale with the baron. Sir Griffin did not leave Lucinda's side, and for a while poor Lizzie felt herself alone in a crowd.

Who does not know that terrible feeling, and the all but necessity that exists for the sufferer to pretend that he is not suffering,—which again is aggravated by the conviction that the pretence is utterly vain? This may be bad with a man, but with a woman, who never looks to be alone in a crowd, it is terrible. For five minutes, during which everybody else was speaking to everybody,—for five minutes, which seemed to her to be an hour, Lizzie spoke to no one, and no one spoke to her. Was it for such misery as this that she was spending hundreds upon hundreds, and running herself into debt? For she was sure that there would be debt before she had parted with Mrs. Carbuncle. There are people, very many people, to whom an act of hospitality is in itself a good thing; but there are others who are always making calculations, and endeavouring to count up the thing purchased against the cost. Lizzie had been told that she was a rich woman,—as women go, very rich. Surely she was entitled to entertain a few friends; and if Mrs. Carbuncle and Miss Roanoke could hunt, it could not be that hunting was beyond her own means. And yet she was spending a great deal of money. She had seen a large waggon loaded with sacks of corn coming up the hill to the Portray stables, and she knew that there would be a long bill at the corn-chandler's. There had been found a supply of wine in the cellars at Portray,—which at her request had been inspected by her cousin Frank;—but it had been necessary, so he had told her, to have much more sent down from London,—champagne, and liqueurs, and other nice things that cost money. 'You won't like not to have them if these people are coming?' 'Oh, no; certainly not,' said Lizzie with enthusiasm. What other rich people did, she would do. But now, in her five minutes of misery, she counted it all up, and was at a loss to find what was to be her return for her expenditure. And then, if on this her first day she should have a fall, with no tender hand to help her, and then find that she had knocked out her front teeth!

But the cavalcade began to move, and then Lord George was by her side. 'You mustn't be angry if I seem to stick too close to you,' he said. She gave him her sweetest smile as she told him that that would be impossible. 'Because, you know, though it's the easiest thing in the world to get along out hunting, and women never come to grief, a person is a little astray at first.'

'I shall be so much astray,' said Lizzie. 'I don't at all know how we are going to begin. Are we hunting a fox now?' At this moment they were trotting across a field or two, through a run of gates up to the first covert.

'Not quite yet. The hounds haven't been put in yet. You see that wood there? I suppose they'll draw that.'

'What is drawing, Lord George? I want to know all about it, and I am so ignorant. Nobody else will tell me.' Then Lord George gave his lesson, and explained the theory and system of fox-hunting. 'We're to wait here, then, till the fox runs away? But it's ever so large, and if he runs away, and nobody sees him? I hope he will, because it will be nice to go on easily.'

'A great many people hope that, and a great many think it nice to go on easily. Only you must not confess to it.' Then he went on with his lecture, and explained the meaning of scent, was great on the difficulty of getting away, described the iniquity of heading the fox, spoke of up wind and down wind, got as far as the trouble of 'carrying,' and told her that a good ear was everything in a big wood,—when there came upon them the thrice-repeated note of an old hound's voice, and the quick scampering, and low, timid, anxious, trustful whinnying of a dozen comrade younger hounds, who recognised the sagacity of their well-known and highly-appreciated elder,—'That's a fox,' said Lord George.

'What shall I do now?' said Lizzie, all in a twitter.

'Sit just where you are and light a cigar, if you're given to smoking.'

'Pray don't joke with me. You know I want to do it properly.'

'And therefore you must sit just where you are, and not gallop about. There's a matter of a hundred and twenty acres here I should say, and a fox doesn't always choose to be evicted at the first notice. It's a chance whether he goes at all from a wood like this. I like woods myself, because, as you say, we can take it easy; but if you want to ride, you should— By George, they've killed him!'

'Killed the fox?'

'Yes; he's dead. Didn't you hear?'

'And is that a hunt?'

'Well;—as far as it goes, it is.'

'Why didn't he run away? What a stupid beast! I don't see so very much in that. Who killed him? That man that was blowing the horn?'

'The hounds chopped him.'

'Chopped him!' Lord George was very patient, and explained to Lizzie, who was now indignant and disappointed, the misfortune of chopping. 'And are we to go home now? Is it all over?'

'They say the country is full of foxes,' said Lord George. 'Perhaps we shall chop half-a-dozen.'

'Dear me! Chop half-a-dozen foxes! Do they like to be chopped? I thought they always ran away.'

Lord George was constant and patient, and rode at Lizzie's side from covert to covert. A second fox they did kill in the same fashion as the first; a third they couldn't hunt a yard; a fourth got to ground after five minutes, and was dug out ingloriously;—during which process a drizzling rain commenced. 'Where is the man with my waterproof?' demanded Mrs. Carbuncle. Lord George had sent the man to see whether there was shelter to be had in a neighbouring yard. And Mrs. Carbuncle was angry. 'It's my own fault,' she said, 'for not having my own man. Lucinda, you'll be wet.'

'I don't mind the wet,' said Lucinda. Lucinda never did mind anything.

'If you'll come with me, we'll get into a barn,' said Sir Griffin.

'I like the wet,' said Lucinda. All the while seven men were at work with picks and shovels, and the master and four or five of the more ardent sportsmen were deeply engaged in what seemed to be a mining operation on a small scale. The huntsman stood over giving his orders. One enthusiastic man, who had been lying on his belly, grovelling in the mud for five minutes, with a long stick in his hand, was now applying the point of it scientifically to his nose. An ordinary observer with a magnifying-glass might have seen a hair at the end of the stick. 'He's there,' said the enthusiastic man, covered with mud, after a long-drawn, eager sniff at the stick. The huntsman deigned to give one glance. 'That's rabbit,' said the huntsman. A conclave was immediately formed over the one visible hair that stuck to the stick, and three experienced farmers decided that it was rabbit. The muddy enthusiastic man, silenced but not convinced, retired from the crowd, leaving his stick behind him, and comforted himself with his brandy-flask.

'He's here, my lord,' said the huntsman to his noble master, 'only we ain't got nigh him yet.' He spoke almost in a whisper, so that the ignorant crowd should not hear the words of wisdom, which they wouldn't understand or perhaps believe. 'It's that full of rabbits that the holes is all hairs. They ain't got no terrier here, I suppose. They never has aught that is wanted in these parts. Work round to the right, there;—that's his line.' The men did work round to the right, and in something under an hour the fox was dragged out by his brush and hind legs, while the experienced whip who dragged him held the poor brute tight by the back of his neck. 'An old dog, my lord. There's such a many of 'em here, that they'll be a deal better for a little killing.' Then the hounds ate their third fox for that day.

Lady Eustace, in the meantime, and Mrs. Carbuncle, with Lord George, had found their way to the shelter of a cattle-shed. Lucinda had slowly followed, and Sir Griffin had followed her. The gentlemen smoked cigars, and the ladies, when they had eaten their luncheons and drank their sherry, were cold and cross. 'If this is hunting,' said Lizzie, 'I really don't think so much about it.'

## The Reluctant Hunter

BUT THE MAN WHO HUNTS and doesn't like it, has his moments of gratification, and finds a source of pride in his penance. In the summer, hunting does much for him. He does not usually take much personal care of his horses, as he is probably a town man and his horses are summered by a keeper of hunting stables; but he talks of them. He talks of them freely, and the keeper of the hunting stables is occasionally forced to write to him. And he can run down to look at his nags, and spend a few hours eating bad mutton chops, walking about the yards and paddocks, and, bleeding halfcrowns through the nose. In all this there is a delight which offers some compensation for his winter misery to our friend who hunts and doesn't like it.

## Irish M.F.H.

He not only knew every hound in his pack, but he knew their ages, their sires and their dams; and the sires and the dams of most of their sires and dams. He knew the constitution of each, and to what extent their noses were to be trusted. 'It's a very heavy scent to-day,' he would say, 'because Gaylap carries it over the plough. It's only a catching scent because the drops don't hang on the bushes.' His lore on all such matters was incredible, but he would never listen to any argument. A man had a right to his own opinion; but then the man who differed from him knew nothing. He gave out his little laws to favoured individuals; not by way of conversation, for which he cared nothing, but because it might be well that the favoured individual should know the truth on that occasion.

As a man to ride he was a complete master of his art. There was nothing which a horse could do with a man on his back, which Daly could not make him do; and when he had ridden a horse he would know exactly what was within his power. But there was no desire with him for the showing off of a horse. He often rode to sell a horse, but he never seemed to do so. He never rode at difficult places unless driven to do so by the exigencies of the moment. He was always quiet in the field, unless when driven to express himself as to the faults of some young man. Then he could blaze forth in his anger with great power. He was constantly to be seen trotting along a road when hounds were running, because he had no desire to achieve for himself a character for hard riding. But he was always with his hounds when he was wanted, and it was boasted of him that he had ridden four days a week through the season on three horses, and had never lamed one of them.

He was rarely known to have a second horse out, and when he did so, it was for some purpose peculiar to the day's work. On such days he had generally a horse to sell.

It is hardly necessary to say that Black Daly was an unmarried man. No one who knew him could conceive that he should have had a wife. His hounds were his children, and he could have taught no wife to assist him in looking after them, with the constant attention and tender care which was given to them by Barney Smith, his huntsman. A wife, had she seen to the feeding of the numerous babies, would have given them too much to eat, and had she not undertaken this care, she would have been useless at Daly's Bridge. But Barney Smith was invaluable; double the amount of work got usually from a huntsman was done by him. There was no kennel man, no second horseman, no stud-groom at the Ahaseragh kennels. It may be said that Black Daly filled all these positions himself, and that in each Barney Smith was his first lieutenant. Circumstances had given him the use of the Ahaseragh kennels, which had been the property of his cousin, and circumstances had not enabled him to build others at Daly's Bridge. Gradually he had found it easier to move himself than the hounds. And so it had come to pass that two rooms had been prepared for him close to the kennels, and that Mr. Barney Smith gave him such attendance as was necessary. Of strictly personal attendance Black Daly wanted very little; but the discomforts of that home, while one pair of breeches were supposed to be at Daly's Bridge, and the others at Ahaseragh, were presumed by the world at large to be very grievous.

But the personal appearance of Mr. Daly on hunting mornings, was not a matter of indifference. It was not that he wore beautiful pink tops, or came out guarded from the dust by little aprons, or had his cravat just out of the bandbox, or his scarlet coat always new, and in the latest fashion, nor had his hat just come from the shop in Piccadilly with the newest twist to its rim. But there was something manly, and even powerful about his whole apparel. He was always the same, so that by men even in his own county, he would hardly have been known in other garments. The strong, broad-brimmed high hat, with the cord passing down his back beneath his coat, that had known the weather of various winters; the dark, red coat, with long swallow tails, which had grown nearly black under many storms; the dark, buff striped waistcoat, with the stripes running downwards, long, so as to come well down over his breeches; the breeches themselves, which were always of leather, but which had become nearly brown under the hands of Barney Smith or his wife, and the mahogany top-boots, of which the tops seemed to be a foot in length, could none of them have been worn by any but Black Daly. His very spurs must have surely been made for him, they were in length and weight, and general strength of leather, so peculiarly his own. He was unlike other masters of hounds in this, that he never carried a horn; but he spoke to his hounds in a loud, indistinct chirruping voice, which all County Galway believed to be understood to every hound in the pack.

## English M.F.H.

When Harry descended from the gig he found himself close to old Mr. Harkaway, the master of the hounds. Mr. Harkaway was a gentleman who had been master of these hounds for more than forty years, and had given as much satisfaction as the county could produce. His hounds, which were his hobby, were perfect. His horses were good enough for the Hertfordshire lanes and Hertfordshire hedges. His object was not so much to run a fox as to kill him in obedience to certain rules of the game. Ever so many hindrances have been created to bar the killing a fox,—as for instance that you shouldn't knock him on the head with a brickbat,—all of which had to Mr. Harkaway the force of a religion. The laws of hunting are so many, that most men who hunt cannot know them all. But no law had ever been written, or had become a law by the strength of tradition, which he did not know. To break them was to him treason. When a young man broke them he pitied the young man's ignorance, and endeavoured to instruct him after some rough fashion. When an old man broke them, he regarded him as a fool who should stay at home, or as a traitor, who should be dealt with as such. And with such men he could deal very hardly. Forty years of reigning had taught him to believe himself to be omnipotent, and he was so in his own hunt. He was a man who had never much affected social habits. The company of one or two brother sportsmen to drink a glass of port wine with him and then to go early to bed, was the most of it. He had a small library, but not a book ever came off the shelf unless it referred to farriers or the 'Res Venatica.' He was unmarried. The time which other men gave to their wives and families he bestowed upon his hounds. To his stables he never went, looking on a horse as a necessary adjunct to hunting, expensive, disagreeable, and prone to get you into danger. When anyone flattered him about his horse he would only grunt, and turn his head on one side. No one in these latter years had seen him jump any fence. But yet he was always with his hounds, and when anyone said a kind word as to their doings, that he would take as a compliment. It was they who were there to do the work of the day, which horses and men could only look at. He was a sincere, honest, taciturn, and withal, affectionate man, who could on an occasion be very angry with those who offended him. He knew well what he could do, and never attempted that which was beyond his power. 'How are you, Mr. Harkaway?' said Harry.

'How are you, Mr. Annesley; how are you?' said the master, with all the grace of which he was capable.

### Leicestershire Hunt

'You shall ride Bonebreaker to-morrow at Somerby, and you'll find that better fun.'

## HE CONSIDERS ITS PATTERNS

'Bonebreaker? Haven't I heard you say he rushes like mischief?'

'Well, he does rush. But, by George! you want a horse to rush in that country. When you have to go right through four or five feet of stiff green wood, like a bullet through a target, you want a little force, or you're apt to be left up a tree.'

'And what do you ride?'

'A brute I never put my leg on yet. He was sent down to Wilcox here, out of Lincolnshire, because they couldn't get anybody to ride him there. They say he goes with his head up in the air, and won't look at a fence that isn't as high as his breast. But I think he'll do here. I never saw a better made beast, or one with more power. Do you look at his shoulders. He's to be had for seventy pounds, and these are the sort of horses I like to buy.' . . .

The next day's meet was in Leicestershire, not far from Melton, and they started early. Phineas, to tell the truth of him, was rather afraid of Bonebreaker, and looked forward to the probability of an accident. He had neither wife nor child, and nobody had a better right to risk his neck. 'We'll put a gag on 'im,' said the groom, 'and you'll ride 'im in a ring,—so that you may well-nigh break his jaw; but he is a rum un, sir.' 'I'll do my best,' said Phineas. 'He'll take all that,' said the groom. 'Just let him have his own way at everything,' said Lord Chiltern, as they moved away from the meet to Pickwell Gorse; 'and if you'll only sit on his back, he'll carry you through as safe as a church.' Phineas could not help thinking that the counsels of the master and of the groom were very different. 'My idea is,' continued Lord Chiltern, 'that in hunting you should always avoid a crowd. I don't think a horse is worth riding that will go in a crowd. It's just like yachting,—you should have plenty of sea-room. If you're to pull your horse up at every fence till somebody else is over, I think you'd better come out on a donkey.' And so they went away to Pickwell Gorse.

There were over two hundred men out, and Phineas began to think that it might not be so easy to get out of the crowd. A crowd in a fast run no doubt quickly becomes small by degrees and beautifully less; but it is very difficult, especially for a stranger, to free himself from the rush at the first start. Lord Chiltern's horse plunged about so violently, as they stood on a little hill-side looking down upon the cover, that he was obliged to take him to a distance, and Phineas followed him. 'If he breaks down wind,' said Lord Chiltern, 'we can't be better than we are here. If he goes up wind, he must turn before long, and we shall be all right.' As he spoke an old hound opened true and sharp,—an old hound whom all the pack believed,—and in a moment there was no doubt that the fox had been found. 'There are not above eight or nine acres in it,' said Lord Chiltern, 'and he can't hang long. Did you ever see such an uneasy brute as this in your life? But I feel certain he'll go well when he gets away.'

Phineas was too much occupied with his own horse to think much of that on which Lord Chiltern was mounted. Bonebreaker, the very moment that he heard the old hound's note, stretched out his head, and put his mouth upon the bit, and began to tremble in every muscle. 'He's a great deal more anxious for it than you and I are,' said Lord Chiltern. 'I see they've given you that gag. But don't you ride him on it till he wants it. Give him lots of room, and he'll go in the snaffle.' All which caution made Phineas think that any insurance office would charge very dear on his life at the present moment.

The fox took two rings of the gorse, and then he went,— up wind. 'It's not a vixen, I'll swear,' said Lord Chiltern. 'A vixen in cub never went away like that yet. Now then, Finn, my boy, keep to the right.' And Lord Chiltern, with the horse out of Lincolnshire, went away across the brow of the hill, leaving the hounds to the left, and selected, as his point of exit into the next field, a stiff rail, which, had there been an accident, must have put a very wide margin of ground between the rider and his horse. 'Go hard at your fences, and then you'll fall clear,' he had said to Phineas. I don't think, however, that he would have ridden at the rail as he did, but that there was no help for him. 'The brute began in his own way, and carried on after in the same fashion all through,' he said afterwards. Phineas took the fence a little lower down, and what it was at which he rode he never knew. Bonebreaker sailed over it, whatever it was, and he soon found himself by his friend's side.

The ruck of the men were lower down than our two heroes, and there were others far away to the left, and others, again, who had been at the end of the gorse, and were now behind. Our friends were not near the hounds, not within two fields of them, but the hounds were below them, and therefore could be seen. 'Don't be in a hurry, and they'll be round upon us,' Lord Chiltern said. 'How the deuce is one to help being in a hurry?' said Phineas, who was doing his very best to ride Bonebreaker with the snaffle, but had already begun to feel that Bonebreaker cared nothing for that weak instrument. 'By George, I should like to change with you,' said Lord Chiltern. The Lincolnshire horse was going along with his head very low, boring as he galloped, but throwing his neck up at his fences, just when he ought to have kept himself steady. After this, though Phineas kept near Lord Chiltern throughout the run, they were not again near enough to exchange words; and, indeed, they had but little breath for such purpose.

Lord Chiltern rode still a little in advance, and Phineas, knowing his friend's partiality for solitude when taking his fences, kept a little to his left. He began to find that Bonebreaker knew pretty well what he was about. As for not using the gag rein, that was impossible. When a horse puts out what strength he has against a man's arm, a man must put out what strength he has against the horse's mouth. But Bonebreaker was cunning, and had had a gag rein on before. He contracted his lip here, and bent out his jaw there, till he had settled it to his mind, and then went away after his own fashion. He seemed to have a passion for smashing through big, high-grown ox-fences, and by degrees his rider came to feel that if there was nothing worse coming, the fun was not bad.

The fox ran up wind for a couple of miles or so, as Lord Chiltern had prophesied, and then turned,—not to the right, as would best have served him and Phineas, but to the left,— so that they were forced to make their way through the ruck of horses before they could place themselves again. Phineas found himself crossing a road, in and out of it, before he knew where he was, and for a while he lost sight of Lord Chiltern. But in truth he was leading now, whereas Lord Chiltern had led before. The two horses having been together all the morning, and on the previous day, were willing enough to remain in company, if they were allowed to do so. They both crossed the road, not very far from each other, going in and out amidst a crowd of horses, and before long were again placed well, now having the hunt on their right, whereas hitherto it had been on their left. They went over large pasture fields, and Phineas began to think that as long as Bonebreaker would be able to go through the thick grown-up hedges, all would be right. Now and again he came to a cut fence, a fence that had been cut and laid, and these were not so pleasant. Force was not sufficient for them, and they admitted of a mistake. But the horse, though he would rush at them unpleasantly, took them when they came without touching them. It might be all right yet,—unless the beast should tire with him; and then, Phineas thought, a misfortune might probably occur. He remembered, as he flew over one such impediment, that he rode a stone heavier than his friend. At the end of forty-five minutes Bonebreaker also might become aware of the fact.

The hounds were running well in sight to their right, and Phineas began to feel some of that pride which a man indulges when he becomes aware that he has taken his place comfortably, has left the squad behind, and is going well. There were men nearer the hounds than he was, but he was near enough even for ambition. There had already been enough of the run to make him sure that it would be a 'good thing,' and enough to make him aware also that probably it might be too good. When a run is over, men are very apt to regret the termination, who a minute or two before were anxiously longing that the hounds might pull down their game. To finish well is everything in hunting. To have led for over an hour is nothing, let the pace and country have been what they might, if you fall away during the last half mile. Therefore it is that those behind hope that the fox may make this or that cover, while the forward men long to see him turned over in every field. To ride to hounds is very glorious; but to have ridden to hounds is more glorious still. They had now crossed another road, and a larger one, and had got into a somewhat closer country. The fields were not so big, and the fences were not so high. Phineas got a moment to look about him, and saw Lord Chiltern riding without his cap. He was very red in the face, and his eyes seemed to glare, and he was tugging at his horse with all his might. But the animal seemed still to go with perfect command of strength, and Phineas had too much work on his own hands to think of offering Quixotic assistance to any one else. He saw some one, a farmer, as he thought, speak to Lord Chiltern as they rode close together; but Chiltern only shook his head and pulled at his horse.

There were brooks in those parts. The river Eye forms itself thereabouts, or some of its tributaries do so; and these tributaries, though small as rivers, are considerable to men on one side who are called by the exigencies of the occasion to place themselves quickly on the other. Phineas knew nothing of these brooks; but Bonebreaker had gone gallantly over two, and now that there came a third in the way, it was to be hoped that he might go gallantly over that also. Phineas, at any rate, had no power to decide otherwise. As long as the brute would go straight with him he could sit him; but he had long given up the idea of having a will of his own. Indeed, till he was within twenty yards of the brook, he did not see that it was larger than the others. He looked round, and there was Chiltern close to him, still fighting with his horse;—but the farmer had turned away. He thought that Chiltern nodded to him, as much as to tell him to go on. On he went at any rate. The brook, when he came to it, seemed to be a huge black hole, yawning beneath him. The banks were quite steep, and just where he was to take off there was an ugly stump. It was too late to think of anything. He stuck his knees against his saddle,—and in a moment was on the other side. The brute, who had taken off a yard before the stump, knowing well the danger of striking it with his foot, came down with a grunt, and did, I think, begin to feel the weight of that extra stone. Phineas, as soon as he was safe, looked back, and there was Lord Chiltern's horse in the very act of his spring,—higher up the rivulet, where it was even broader. At that distance Phineas could see that Lord Chiltern was wild with rage against the beast. But whether he wished to take the leap or wished to avoid it, there was no choice left to him. The animal rushed at the brook, and in a moment the horse and horseman were lost to sight. It was well then that that extra stone should tell, as it enabled Phineas to arrest his horse and to come back to his friend.

The Lincolnshire horse had chested the further bank, and of course had fallen back into the stream. When Phineas got down he found that Lord Chiltern was wedged in between the horse and the bank, which was better, at any rate, than being under the horse in the water. 'All right, old fellow,' he said, with a smile, when he saw Phineas. 'You go on; it's too good to lose.' But he was very pale, and seemed to be quite helpless where he lay. The horse did not move,—and never did move again. He had smashed his shoulder to pieces against a stump on the bank, and was afterwards shot on that very spot.

When Phineas got down he found that there was but little water where the horse lay. The depth of the stream had been on the side from which they had taken off, and the thick black mud lay within a foot of the surface, close to the bank against which Lord Chiltern was propped. 'That's the worst one I ever was on,' said Lord Chiltern; 'but I think he's gruelled now.'

'Are you hurt?'

'Well;—I fancy there is something amiss. I can't move my arms; and I catch my breath. My legs are all right if I could get away from this accursed brute.'

'I told you so,' said the farmer, coming and looking down upon them from the bank. 'I told you so, but you wouldn't be said.' Then he too got down, and between them both they extricated Lord Chiltern from his position, and got him on to the bank.

'That un's a dead un,' said the farmer, pointing to the horse.

'So much the better,' said his lordship. 'Give us a drop of sherry, Finn.'

He had broken his collar-bone and three of his ribs. They got a farmer's trap from Wissindine and took him into Oakham. When there, he insisted on being taken on through Stamford to the Willingford Bull before he would have his bones set,—picking up, however, a surgeon at Stamford. Phineas remained with him for a couple of days, losing his run with the Fitzwilliams and a day at the potted peas, and became very fond of his patient as he sat by his bedside.

'That was a good run, though, wasn't it?' said Lord Chiltern as Phineas took his leave. 'And, by George, Phineas, you rode Bonebreaker so well, that you shall have him as often as you'll come down. I don't know how it is, but you Irish fellows always ride.'

# HUNTING AND RACING

## Death in the Hunting-Field

Every sportsman knows, and the wives and daughters of all sportsmen know, how important a month in the calendar is the month of October. The real campaign begins in November; and even for those who do not personally attend to the earlier work of the kennel,—or look after cub-hunting, which during the last ten days of October is apt to take the shape of genuine hunting,—October has charms of its own and peculiar duties. It is the busiest month in the year in regard to horses. Is physic needed? In the Squire's stables physic was much eschewed, and the Squire's horses were usually in good condition. But it is needful to know, down to a single line on the form, whether this or that animal wants more exercise, —and if so, of what nature. We hold that for hunters which are worked regularly throughout the season, and which live in loose boxes summer and winter, but little exercise is required except in the months of September and October. Let them have been fed on oats throughout the year, and a good groom will bring them into form in two months. Such at least was the order at the Newton stables; and during this autumn,—especially during these last days of October,—this order was obeyed with infinite alacrity, and with many preparations for coming joys. And there are other cares, less onerous indeed, but still needful. What good sportsman is too proud, or even too much engaged to inspect his horse's gear,—and his own? Only let his horse's gear stand first in his mind! Let him be sure that the fit of a saddle is of more moment than the fit of a pair of breeches;—that in riding the length, strength, and nature of the bit will avail more,— should at least avail more,—than the depth, form, and general arrangement of the flask; that the question of boots, great as it certainly is, should be postponed to the question of shoes; that a man's seat should be guarded by his girths rather than by his spurs; that no run has ever been secured by the bril-

[ 201 ]

liancy of the cravat, though many a run has been lost by the insufficiency of the stirrup-leather. In the saddles and saddle-room, and throughout the whole establishment of the house at Newton, all these matters were ever sedulously regarded; but they had never been regarded with more joyful zeal than was given to them during this happy month. There was not a stable-boy about the place who did not know and feel that their Mr. Ralph was now to take his place in the hunting-field as the heir to Newton Priory.

And there were other duties at Newton of which the crowd of riding-men know little or nothing. Were there foxes in the coverts? The Squire had all his life been a staunch preserver, thinking more of a vixen with her young cubs than he would of any lady in the land with her first-born son. During the last spring and summer, however, things had made him uncomfortable; and he had not personally inquired after the well-being of each nursery in the woods as had been his wont. Ralph, indeed, had been on the alert, and the keepers had not become slack; but there had been a whisper about the place that the master didn't care so much about the foxes as he used to do. They soon found out that he cared enough now. The head-keeper opened his eyes very wide when he was told that the Squire would take it as a personal offence if the coverts were ever drawn blank. It was to be understood through the county that at Newton Priory everything was happy and prosperous. 'We'll get up a breakfast and meet on the lawn before the end of the month,' said the Squire to his son. 'I hate hunt-breakfasts myself, but the farmers like them.' From all which the reader will perceive that the Squire was in earnest.

Ralph hunted all through the latter days of October, but the Squire himself would not go out till the first regular day of the season. 'I like a law, and I like to stick to it,' he said. 'Five months is enough for the horses in all conscience.' At last the happy day arrived,—Wednesday, the 2nd of November,—and the father and son started together for the meet in the dog-cart on four wheels with two horses. On such occasions the Squire always drove himself, and professed to go no more than eight miles an hour. The meet was over in the Berkshire county in the neighbourhood of Swallowfield, about twelve miles distant, and the Squire was in his seat precisely at half-past nine. Four horses had gone on in the charge of two grooms, for the Squire had insisted on Ralph riding with a second horse. 'If you don't, I won't,' he had said, and Ralph of course had yielded. Just at this time there had grown up in the young man's mind a feeling that his father was almost excessive in the exuberance of his joy,—that he was displaying too ostensibly to the world at large the triumph which he had effected. But the checking of this elation was almost impossible to the son on whose behalf it was exhibited. Therefore, to Ralph's own regret, the two horses had on this morning been sent on to Barford Heath. The Squire was not kept waiting a moment. Ralph lit his cigar and jumped in, and the Squire started in all comfort and joy. . .

They reached Barford Heath a few minutes before eleven, and there was a little scene upon the occasion. It was the first recognised meet of the season, and the Squire had not been out before. . . In his ordinary way he was a quiet man, not often heard at much distance, and contented to be noted as Newton of Newton rather than as a man commanding attention by his conduct before other men. There certainly was a difference to-day, and it was of that kind which wine produces on some who are not habitual drinkers. The gases of his life were in exuberance, and he was as a balloon insufficiently freighted with ballast. His buoyancy, unless checked, might carry him too high among the clouds. All this Ralph saw, and kept himself a little aloof. If there were aught amiss, there was no help for it on his part; and, after all, what was amiss was so very little amiss.

'We'll draw the small gorses first,' said the old master, addressing himself specially to Mr. Newton, 'and then we'll go into Barford Wood.'

## HE CONSIDERS ITS PATTERNS

'Just so,' said the Squire; 'the gorses first by all means. I remember when there was always a fox at Barford Gorse. Come along. I hate to see time wasted. You'll be glad to hear we're full of foxes at Newton. There were two litters bred in Bostock Spring;—two, by Jove! in that little place. Dan,'—Dan was his second horseman,—'I'll ride the young one this morning. You have Paddywhack fresh for me about one.' Paddywhack was the old Irish horse which had carried him so long, and has been mentioned before. There was nothing remarkable in all this. There was no word spoken that might not have been said with a good grace by any old sportsman, who knew the men around him, and who had long preserved foxes for their use; but still it was felt that the Squire was a little loud. Ralph the son, on whose behalf all this triumph was felt, was silenter than usual, and trotted along at the rear of the long line of horsemen. . .

'My father's spirits are so high, that he can hardly control them.'

'By George, I don't wonder at it,' said George Morris.

There were three little bits of gorse about half-a-mile from Barford Wood, as to which it seemed that expectation did not run high, but from the last of which an old fox broke before the hounds were in it. It was so sudden a thing that the pack was on the scent and away before half-a-dozen men had seen what had happened. Our Squire had been riding with Cox, the huntsman, who had ventured to say how happy he was that the young squire was to be the Squire some day. 'So am I, Cox; so am I,' said the Squire. 'And I hope he'll be a friend to you for many a year.'

'By the holy, there's Dick a-hallooing,' said Cox, forgetting at once the comparatively unimportant affairs of Newton Priory in the breaking of this unexpected fox. 'Golly;—if he ain't away, Squire.' The hounds had gone at once to the whip's voice, and were in full cry in less time than it has taken to tell the story of 'the find.' Cox was with them, and so was the Squire. There were two or three others, and one of the whips. The start, indeed, was not much, but the burst was so sharp, and the old fox ran so straight, that it sufficed to enable those who had got the lead to keep it. 'Tally-ho!' shouted the Squire, as he saw the animal making across a stubble-field before the hounds, with only one fence between him and the quarry. 'Tally-ho!' It was remarked afterwards that the Squire had never been known to halloo to a fox in that way before. 'Just like one of the young 'uns, or a fellow out of the town,' said Cox, when expressing his astonishment.

But the Squire never rode a run better in his life. He gave a lead to the field, and he kept it. 'I wouldn't 'a spoilt him by putting my nose afore 'is, were it ever so,' said Cox afterwards. He went as straight as a schoolboy at Christmas, and the young horse he rode never made a mistake. Let men say what they will, a young horse will carry a man a brush like that better than an old one. It was very short. They had run their fox, pulled him down, broken him up, and eaten him within half an hour. Jack Graham, who is particular about those things, and who was, at any rate, near enough to see it all, said that it was exactly twenty-two minutes and a half. He might be right enough in that, but when he swore that they had gone over four miles of ground, he was certainly wrong. They killed within a field of Heckfield church, and Heckfield church can't be four miles from Barford Gorse. That they went as straight as a line everybody knew. Besides, they couldn't have covered the ground in the time. The pace was good, no doubt; but Jacky Graham is always given to exaggeration.

The Squire was very proud of his performance, and, when Ralph came up, was loud in praise of the young horse. 'Never was carried so well in my life,—never,' said he. 'I knew he was good, but I didn't know he would jump like that. I wouldn't take a couple of hundred for him.' This was still a little loud; but the Squire at this moment had the sense of double triumph within, and was to be forgiven. It was admitted on all sides that he had ridden the run uncommonly well.

'Just like a young man, by Jove!' said Jack Graham.

'Like what sort of a young man?' asked George Harris, who had come up at the heel of the hunt with Ralph.

'And where were you, Master Ralph?' said the Squire to his son.

'I fancy I just began to know they were running by the time you were killing your fox,' said Ralph.

'You should have your eyes better about you, my boy; shouldn't he, Cox?'

'The young squire ain't often in the wrong box,' said the huntsman.

'He wasn't in the right one to-day,' said the Squire. This was still a little loud. There was too much of that buoyancy which might have come from drink; but which, with the Squire, was the effect of that success for which he had been longing rather than hoping all his life.

From Heckfield they trotted back to Barford Wood, the master resolving that he would draw his country in the manner he had proposed to himself in the morning. There was some little repining at this, partly because the distance was long, and partly because Barford Wood was too large to be popular. 'Hunting is over for the day,' said Jack Graham. To this view of the case the Squire, who had now changed his horse, objected greatly. 'We shall find in Barford big wood, as sure as the sun rises,' said he...

They were soon on a fox in Barford Wood;—but being on a fox in Barford Wood was very different from finding a fox in Barford Gorse. Out of the gorse a fox must go; but in the big woods he might choose to remain half the day. And then the chances were that he would either beat the hounds at last, or else be eaten in covert. 'It's a very pretty place to ride about and smoke and drink one's friend's sherry.' That was Jack Graham's idea of hunting in Barford Wood, and a great deal of that kind of thing was going on to-day. Now and then there was a little excitement, and cries of 'away' were heard. Men would burst out of the wood here and there, ride about for a few minutes, and then go in again. Cox swore that they had thrice changed their fox, and was beginning to be a little short in his temper; the whips' horses were becoming jaded, and the master had once or twice answered very crossly when questioned. 'How the devil do you suppose I'm to know,' he had said to a young gentleman who had inquired, 'where they were?' But still the Squire kept on zealously, and reminded Ralph that some of the best things of the season were often lost by men becoming slack towards evening. At that time it was nearly four o'clock, and Cox was clearly of opinion that he couldn't kill a fox in Barford Wood that day.

But still the hounds were hunting. 'Darned if they ain't back to the little wood again,' said Cox to the Squire. They were at that moment in an extreme corner of an outlying copse, and between them and Barford Little Wood was a narrow strip of meadow, over which they had passed half-a-dozen times that day. Between the copse and the meadow there ran a broad ditch with a hedge,—a rotten made-up fence of sticks and bushes, which at the corner had been broken down by the constant passing of horses, till, at this hour of the day, there was hardly at that spot anything of a fence to be jumped. 'We must cross with them again, Cox,' said the Squire. At that moment he was nearest to the gap, and close to him were Ralph and George Morris, as well as the huntsman. But Mr. Newton's horse was standing sideways to the hedge, and was not facing the passage. He, nevertheless, prepared to pass it first, and turned his horse sharply at it; as he did so, some bush or stick caught the animal in the flank, and he, in order to escape the impediment, clambered up the bank sideways, not taking the gap, and then balanced himself to make his jump over the ditch. But he was entangled among the sticks and thorns and was on broken ground, and jumping short, came down into the ditch. The Squire fell heavily headlong on to the field, and the horse, with no further effort of his own, but unable to restrain himself, rolled over his master. It was a place as to which any horseman would say that a child might ride through if on a donkey without a chance of danger, and yet the three men who saw it knew at once that the Squire had had a bad fall. Ralph was first through the gap, and was off his own horse as the old Irish hunter, with a groan, collected himself and got upon his legs. In rising, the animal was very careful not to strike his late rider with his feet; but it was too evident to Cox that the beast, in his attempt to rise, had given a terrible squeeze to the prostrate Squire with his saddle.

In a moment the three men were on their knees, and it was clear that Mr. Newton was insensible. 'I'm afraid he's hurt,' said Morris. Cox merely shook his head, as he gently attempted to raise the Squire's shoulder against his own. Ralph, as pale as death, held his father's hand in one of his own, and with the other endeavoured to feel the pulse of the heart. Presently, before any one else came up to them, a few drops of blood came from between the sufferer's lips. Cox again shook his head. 'We'd better get him on to a gate, Mr. Ralph, and into a house,' said the huntsman. They were quickly surrounded by others, and the gate was soon there, and within twenty minutes a surgeon was standing over our poor old friend. 'No; he wasn't dead,' the surgeon said; 'but—' 'What is it?' asked Ralph, impetuously. The surgeon took the master of the hunt aside and whispered into his ear that Mr. Newton was a dead man.

# Clergy

## Diocese of Barchester

BEFORE I TAKE MY LEAVE of the diocese of Barchester for ever, which I purpose to do in the succeeding paragraph, I desire to be allowed to say one word of apology for myself, in answer to those who have accused me,—always without bitterness, and generally with tenderness,—of having forgotten, in writing of clergymen, the first and most prominent characteristic of the ordinary English clergyman's life. I have described many clergymen, they say, but have spoken of them all as though their professional duties, their high calling, their daily workings for the good of those around them, were matters of no moment, either to me, or in my opinion, to themselves. I would plead, in answer to this, that my object has been to paint the social and not the professional lives of clergymen; and that I have been led to do so, firstly, by a feeling that as no men affect more strongly, by their own character, the society of those around than do country clergymen, so, therefore, their social habits have been worth the labour necessary for painting them; and secondly, by a feeling that though I, as a novelist, may feel myself entitled to write of clergymen out of their pulpits, as I may also write of lawyers and doctors, I have no such liberty to write of them in their pulpits. When I have done so, if I have done so, I have so far transgressed. There are those who have told me that I have made all my clergymen bad, and none good. I must venture to hint to such judges that they have taught their eyes to love a colouring higher than nature justifies. We are, most of us, apt to love Raphael's madonnas better than

Rembrandt's matrons. But, though we do so, we know that Rembrandt's matrons existed; but we have a strong belief that no such woman as Raphael painted ever did exist. In that he painted, as he may be surmised to have done, for pious purposes,—at least for Church purposes,—Raphael was justified; but had he painted so for family portraiture he would have been false. Had I written an epic about clergymen, I would have taken St. Paul for my model; but describing, as I have endeavoured to do, such clergymen as I see around me, I could not venture to be transcendental. For myself I can only say that I shall always be happy to sit, when allowed to do so, at the table of Archdeacon Grantly, to walk through the High Street of Barchester arm in arm with Mr. Robarts of Framley, and to stand alone and shed a tear beneath the modest black stone in the north transept of the cathedral on which is inscribed the name of Septimus Harding.

## An American View

IT WAS A VERY WET MORNING and the curate had ridden over from Dillsborough on a little pony which the rector kept for him in addition to the £100 per annum paid for his services. That he should have got over his service quickly was not a matter of surprise, nor was it wonderful that there should have been no soul-stirring matter in his discourse, as he had two sermons to preach every week and to perform singlehanded all the other clerical duties of a parish lying four miles distant from his lodgings. Perhaps had he expected the presence of so distinguished a critic as the Senator from Mikewa he might have done better. As it was, being nearly wet through and muddy up to his knees, he did not do the work very well. When Morton and his friends left the church and got into the carriage for their half-mile drive home across the park, Mrs. Morton was the first to speak. 'John,' she said, 'that church is enough to give any woman her death. I won't go there any more.'

'They don't understand warming a church in the country,' said John apologetically.

'Is it not a little too large for the congregation?' asked the Senator.

The church was large and straggling and ill-arranged, and on this particular Sunday had been almost empty. There was in it an harmonium, which Mrs. Puttock played when she was at home, but in her absence the attempt made by a few rustics to sing the hymns had not been a musical success. The whole affair had been very sad, and so the Paragon had felt it, who knew,—and was remembering through the whole service,—how these things are done in transatlantic cities.

'The weather kept the people away, I suppose,' said Morton.

'Does that gentleman generally draw large congregations?' asked the persistent Senator.

'We don't go in for drawing congregations here.' Under the cross-examination of his guest, the Secretary of Legation almost lost his diplomatic good temper. 'We have a church in every parish for those who choose to attend it.'

'And very few do choose,' said the Senator. 'I can't say that they're wrong.' There seemed at the moment to be no necessity to carry the disagreeable conversation any further as they had now reached the house. Mrs. Morton immediately went upstairs, and the two gentlemen took themselves to the fire in the so-called library, which room was being used as more commodious than the big drawing-room. Mr. Gotobed placed himself on the rug with his back to the fire and immediately reverted to the church. 'That gentleman is paid by tithes, I suppose.'

'He's not the rector. He's a curate.'

'Ah;—just so. He looked like a curate. Doesn't the rector do anything?' Then Morton, who was by this time heartily sick of explaining, explained the unfortunate state of Mr. Puttock's health, and the conversation was carried on till gradually the Senator learned that Mr. Puttock received £800 a year and a house for doing nothing, and that he paid his deputy £100 a year with the use of a pony. 'And how long will that be allowed to go on, Mr. Morton?' asked the Senator.

To all these inquiries Morton found himself compelled not only to answer, but to answer the truth. Any prevarication or attempt at mystification fell to the ground at once under the Senator's tremendous powers of inquiry. It had been going on for four years and would probably go on now till Mr. Puttock died. 'A man of his age with the asthma may live for twenty years,' said the Senator, who had already learned that Mr. Puttock was only fifty. Then he ascertained that Mr. Puttock had not been presented to, or selected for, the living on account of any peculiar fitness;—but that he had been a fellow of Rufford at Oxford till he was forty-five, when he had thought it well to marry and take a living. 'But he must have been asthmatic then?' said the Senator.

'He may have had all the ailments endured by the human race, for anything I know,' said the unhappy host.

'And for anything the bishop cared, as far as I can see,' said the Senator. 'Well now, I guess, that couldn't occur in our country. A minister may turn out badly with us as well as with you. But we don't appoint a man without inquiry as to his fitness,—and if a man can't do his duty he has to give way to some one who can. If the sick gentleman took the small portion of the stipend and the working man the larger, would not better justice be done, and the people better served?'

'Mr. Puttock has a freehold in the parish.'

'A freehold possession of men's souls! The fact is, Mr. Morton, that the spirit of conservatism in this country is so strong that you cannot bear to part with a shred of the barbarism of the Middle Ages. And when a rag is sent to the winds you shriek with agony at the disruption, and think that the wound will be mortal.' As Mr. Gotobed said this he extended his right hand and laid his left on his breast, as though he were addressing the Senate from his own chair. Morton, who had offered to entertain the gentleman for ten days, sincerely wished that he were doing so.

## Mrs. Proudie's Abstinence

ONE OTHER MARKED PECULIARITY in the character of the bishop's wife must be mentioned. Though not averse to the society and manners of the world, she is in her own way a religious woman; and the form in which this tendency shows itself in her is by a strict observance of Sabbatarian rule. Dissipation and low dresses during the week are, under her control, atoned for by three services, an evening sermon read by herself, and a perfect abstinence from any cheering employment on the Sunday. Unfortunately for those under her roof to whom the dissipation and low dresses are not extended, her servants namely and her husband, the compensating strictness of the Sabbath includes all. Woe betide the recreant housemaid who is found to have been listening to the honey of a sweetheart in the Regent's park, instead of the soul-stirring evening discourse of Mr. Slope. Not only is she sent adrift, but she is so sent with a character which leaves her little hope of a decent place. Woe betide the six-foot hero who escorts Mrs. Proudie to her pew in red plush breeches, if he slips away to the neighbouring beer-shop, instead of falling into the back seat appropriated to his use. Mrs. Proudie has the eyes of Argus for such offenders. Occasional drunkenness in the week may be overlooked, for six feet on low wages are hardly to be procured if the morals are always kept at a high pitch; but not even for grandeur or economy will Mrs. Proudie forgive a desecration of the Sabbath.

## Mr. Slope's Anathemas

IN HIS SERMONS he deals greatly in denunciations, excites the minds of his weaker hearers with a not unpleasant terror, and leaves an impression on their minds that all mankind are in a perilous state, and all womankind too, except those who attend regularly to the evening lectures in Baker Street. His looks and tones are extremely severe, so much so that one cannot but fancy that he regards the greater part of the world as being infinitely too bad for his care. As he walks through the streets, his very face denotes his horror of the world's wickedness; and there is always an anathema lurking in the corner of his eye.

In doctrine, he, like his patron, is tolerant of dissent, if so strict a mind can be called tolerant of anything. With Wesleyan-Methodists he has something in common, but his soul trembles in agony at the iniquities of the Puseyites. His aversion is carried to things outward as well as inward. His gall rises at a new church with a high pitched roof; a full-breasted black silk waistcoat is with him a symbol of Satan; and a profane jest-book would not, in his view, more foully desecrate the church seat of a Christian, than a book of prayer printed with red letters, and ornamented with a cross on the back. Most active clergymen have their hobby, and Sunday observances are his. Sunday, however, is a word which never pollutes his mouth—it is always 'the Sabbath.' The 'desecration of the Sabbath,' as he delights to call it, is to him meat and drink:—he thrives upon that as policemen do on the general evil habits of the community. It is the loved subject of all his evening discourses, the source of all his eloquence, the secret of all his power over the female heart.

### Rigour of Church Doctrine

Hitherto Barchester had escaped the taint of any extreme rigour of church doctrine. The clergymen of the city and neighbourhood, though very well inclined to promote high-church principles, privileges, and prerogatives, had never committed themselves to tendencies, which are somewhat too loosely called Puseyite practices. They all preached in their black gowns, as their fathers had done before them; they wore ordinary black cloth waistcoats; they had no candles on their altars, either lighted or unlighted; they made no private genuflexions, and were contented to confine themselves to such ceremonial observances as had been in vogue for the last hundred years. The services were decently and demurely read in their parish churches, chanting was confined to the cathedral, and the science of intoning was unknown. One young man who had come direct from Oxford as a curate to Plumstead had, after the lapse of two or three Sundays, made a faint attempt, much to the bewilderment of the poorer part of the congregation. Dr. Grantly had not been present on the occasion; but Mrs. Grantly, who had her own opinion on the subject, immediately after the service expressed a hope that the young gentleman had not been taken ill, and offered to send him all kinds of condiments supposed to be good for a sore throat. After that there had been no more intoning at Plumstead Episcopi.

## The Parson's Vice

After breakfast he followed his father into his study, and there, sitting in two easy-chairs opposite to each other, they lit each a cigar. Such was the reverend gentleman's custom in the afternoon, and such also in the morning. I do not know whether the smoking of four or five cigars daily by the parson of a parish may now-a-day be considered as a vice in him, but if so, it was the only vice with which Mr. Clavering could be charged. He was a kind, soft-hearted, gracious man, tender to his wife, whom he ever regarded as the angel of his house, indulgent to his daughters, whom he idolized, ever patient with his parishioners, and awake,—though not widely awake, —to the responsibilities of his calling. The world had been too comfortable for him, and also too narrow; so that he had sunk into idleness. The world had given him much to eat and drink, but it had given him little to do, and thus he had gradually fallen away from his early purposes, till his energy hardly sufficed for the doing of that little. His living gave him eight hundred a year; his wife's fortune nearly doubled that.

He had married early, and had got his living early, and had been very prosperous. But he was not a happy man. He knew that he had put off the day of action till the power of action had passed away from him. His library was well furnished, but he rarely read much else than novels and poetry; and of late years the reading even of poetry had given way to the reading of novels. Till within ten years of the hour of which I speak, he had been a hunting parson,—not hunting loudly, but followed his sport as it is followed by moderate sportsmen. Then there had come a new bishop, and the new bishop had sent for him,—nay, finally had come to him, and had lectured him with blatant authority. 'My lord,' said the parson of Clavering, plucking up something of his past energy, as the colour rose to his face, 'I think you are wrong in this. I think you are specially wrong to interfere with me in this way on your first coming among us. You feel it to be your duty, no doubt, but to me it seems that you mistake your duty. But, as the matter is one simply of my own pleasure, I shall give it up.' After that Mr. Clavering hunted no more, and never spoke a good word to any one of the bishop of his diocese. For myself, I think it as well that clergymen should not hunt; but had I been the parson of Clavering, I should, under those circumstances, have hunted double.

Mr. Clavering hunted no more, and probably smoked a greater number of cigars in consequence. He had an increased amount of time at his disposal, but did not, therefore, give more time to his duties. Alas! what time did he give to his duties? He kept a most energetic curate, whom he allowed to do almost what he would with the parish. Every-day services he did prohibit, declaring that he would not have the parish church made ridiculous; but in other respects his curate was the pastor. Once every Sunday he read the service, and once every Sunday he preached, and he resided in his parsonage ten months every year. His wife and daughters went among the poor,—and he smoked cigars in his library. Though not yet fifty, he was becoming fat and idle,—unwilling to walk, and not caring much even for such riding as the bishop had left to him. And to make matters worse,—far worse,—he knew all this of himself, and understood it thoroughly. 'I see a better path, and know how good it is, but I follow ever the worse.' He was saying that to himself daily, and was saying it always without hope.

## High Church and Matrimony

Mr. Oriel was a man of family and fortune, who, having gone to Oxford with the usual views of such men, had become inoculated there with very High-Church principles, and had gone into orders influenced by a feeling of enthusiastic love for the priesthood. He was by no means an ascetic—such men, indeed, seldom are—nor was he a devotee. He was a man well able, and certainly willing, to do the work of a parish clergyman; and when he became one, he was efficacious in his profession. But it may perhaps be said of him, without speaking slanderously, that his original calling, as a young man, was rather to the outward and visible signs of religion than to its inward and spiritual graces.

He delighted in lecterns and credence-tables, in services at dark hours of winter mornings when no one would attend, in high waistcoats and narrow white neckties, in chanted services and intoned prayers, and in all the paraphernalia of Anglican formalities which have given such offence to those of our brethren who live in daily fear of the scarlet lady. Many of his friends declared that Mr. Oriel would sooner or later deliver himself over body and soul to that lady; but there was no need to fear for him: for though sufficiently enthusiastic to get out of bed at five a.m. on winter mornings—he did so, at least, all through his first winter at Greshamsbury—he was not made of that stuff which is necessary for a staunch, burning, self-denying convert. It was not in him to change his very sleek black coat for a Capuchin's filthy cassock, nor his pleasant parsonage for some dirty hole in Rome. And it was better so both for him and others. There are but few, very few, to whom it is given to be a Huss, a Wickliffe, or a Luther; and a man gains but little by being a false Huss, or a false Luther,—and his neighbours gain less.

But certain lengths in self-privation Mr. Oriel did go; at any rate, for some time. He eschewed matrimony, imagining that it became him as a priest to do so; he fasted rigorously on Fridays; and the neighbours declared that he scourged himself.

Mr. Oriel was, as it has been said, a man of fortune; that is to say, when he came of age he was master of thirty thousand pounds. When he took it into his head to go into the Church, his friends bought for him the next presentation to the living of Greshamsbury; and, a year after his ordination, the living falling in, Mr. Oriel brought himself and his sister to the rectory.

Mr. Oriel soon became popular. He was a dark-haired, good-looking man, of polished manners, agreeable in society, not given to monkish austerities—except in the matter of Fridays—nor yet to the Low-Church severity of demeanour. He was thoroughly a gentleman, good-humoured, inoffensive, and sociable. But he had one fault: he was not a marrying man.

On this ground there was a feeling against him so strong as almost at one time to throw him into serious danger. It was not only that he should be sworn against matrimony in his individual self—he whom fate had made so able to sustain the weight of a wife and family; but what an example was he setting! If other clergymen all around should declare against wives and families, what was to become of the country? What was to be done with the rural districts? The religious observances, as regards women, of a Brigham Young were hardly so bad as this!

There were around Greshamsbury very many unmarried ladies—I believe there generally are so round most such villages... There was Miss Gushing,—a young thing. Miss Gushing had a great advantage over the other competitors for the civilization of Mr. Oriel, namely, in this—that she was able to attend his morning services. If Mr. Oriel was to be reached in any way, it was probable that he might be reached in this way. If anything could civilize him, this would do it. Therefore, the young thing, through all one long, tedious winter, tore herself from her warm bed, and was to be seen—no, not seen, but heard—entering Mr. Oriel's church at six o'clock. With indefatigable assiduity the responses were made, uttered from under a close bonnet, and out of a dark corner, in an enthusiastically feminine voice, through the whole winter.

Nor did Miss Gushing altogether fail in her object. When a clergyman's daily audience consists of but one person, and that person is a young lady, it is hardly possible that he should not become personally intimate with her; hardly possible that he should not be in some measure grateful. Miss Gushing's responses came from her with such fervour, and she begged for ghostly advice with such eager longing to have her scruples satisfied, that Mr. Oriel had nothing for it but to give way to a certain amount of civilization.

By degrees it came to pass that Miss Gushing could never get her final prayer said, her shawl and boa adjusted, and stow away her nice new Prayer-Book with the red letters inside, and the cross on the back, till Mr. Oriel had been into his vestry and got rid of his surplice. And then they met at the church-porch, and naturally walked together till Mr. Oriel's cruel gateway separated them. The young thing did sometimes think that, as the parson's civilization progressed, he might have taken the trouble to walk with her as far as Mr. Yates Umbleby's hall door; but she had hope to sustain her, and a firm resolve to merit success, even though she might not attain it.

'Is it not ten thousand pities,' she once said to him, 'that none here should avail themselves of the inestimable privilege which your coming has conferred upon us? Oh, Mr. Oriel, I do so wonder at it! To me it is so delightful! The morning service in the dark church is so beautiful, so touching!'

'I suppose they think it is a bore getting up so early,' said Mr. Oriel.

'Ah, a bore!' said Miss Gushing, in an enthusiastic tone of deprecation. 'How insensate they must be! To me it gives a new charm to life. It quiets one for the day; makes one so much fitter for one's daily trials and daily troubles. Does it not, Mr. Oriel?'

'I look upon morning prayer as an imperative duty, certainly.'

'Oh, certainly, a most imperative duty; but so delicious at the same time. I spoke to Mrs. Umbleby about it, but she said she could not leave the children.'

'No: I dare say not,' said Mr. Oriel.

'And Mr. Umbleby said his business kept him up so late at night.'

'Very probably. I hardly expect the attendance of men of business.'

'But the servants might come, mightn't they, Mr. Oriel?'

'I fear that servants seldom can have time for daily prayers in church.'

'Oh, ah, no; perhaps not.' And then Miss Gushing began to bethink herself of whom should be composed the congregation which it must be presumed Mr. Oriel wished to see around him. But on this matter he did not enlighten her.

Then Miss Gushing took to fasting on Fridays, and made some futile attempts to induce her priest to give her the comfort of confessional absolution. But, unfortunately, the zeal of the master waxed cool as that of the pupil waxed hot; and, at last, when the young thing returned to Greshamsbury from an autumn excursion which she had made with Mrs. Umbleby to Weston-super-Mare, she found that the delicious morning services had died a natural death. Miss Gushing did not on that account give up the game, but she was bound to fight with no particular advantage in her favour.

Miss Oriel, though a good Churchwoman, was by no means a convert to her brother's extremist views, and perhaps gave but scanty credit to the Gushings, Athelings, and Opie Greens for the sincerity of their religion. But, nevertheless, she and her brother were staunch friends; and she still hoped to see the day when he might be induced to think that an English parson might get through his parish work with the assistance of a wife better than he could do so without such feminine encumbrance. The girl whom she selected for his bride was not the young thing, but Beatrice Gresham.

And at last it seemed probable to Mr. Oriel's nearest friends that he was in a fair way to be overcome. Not that he had begun to make love to Beatrice, or committed himself by the utterance of any opinion as to the propriety of clerical marriages; but he daily became looser about his peculiar tenets, raved less immoderately than heretofore as to the atrocity of the Greshamsbury church pews, and was observed to take some opportunities of conversing alone with Beatrice. Beatrice had always denied the imputation—this had usually been made by Mary in their happy days—with vehement asseverations of anger; and Miss Gushing had tittered, and expressed herself as supposing that great people's daughters might be as barefaced as they pleased. . .

Mr. Oriel gradually got himself into a way of sauntering up to the great house, sauntering into the drawing-room for the purpose, as I am sure he thought, of talking to Lady Arabella, and then of sauntering home again, having usually found an opportunity for saying a few words to Beatrice during the visit. . . And then one morning, about a month before the date fixed for Frank's return, Mr. Oriel found himself engaged to Miss Beatrice Gresham.

From the day that Miss Gushing heard of it—which was not however for some considerable time after this—she became an Independent Methodist.

## The Hunting Parson

'I am told that he hunts two or three times a week. Everybody round us is talking about it.'

'No, Mr. Crawley; not two or three times a week; very seldom above once, I think. And then I do believe he does it more with the view of being with Lord Lufton than anything else.'

'I cannot see that that would make the matter better,' said Mr. Crawley.

'It would show that he was not strongly imbued with a taste which I cannot but regard as vicious in a clergyman.'

'It must be vicious in all men,' said Mr. Crawley. 'It is in itself cruel, and leads to idleness and profligacy.' Again Lady Lufton made a gulp... She did not like to be told that her son's amusement was idle and profligate. She had always regarded hunting as a proper pursuit for a country gentleman. It was, indeed, in her eyes one of the peculiar institutions of country life in England, and it may be almost said that she looked upon the Barsetshire Hunt as something sacred. She could not endure to hear that a fox was trapped, and allowed her turkeys to be purloined without a groan. Such being the case, she did not like being told that it was vicious, and had by no means wished to consult Mr. Crawley on that matter. But nevertheless she swallowed down her wrath.

'It is at any rate unbecoming in a clergyman,' she said; 'and as I know that Mr. Robarts places a high value on your opinion, perhaps you will not object to advise him to discontinue it.'

## Parson's Memories

'Fill your glass, Henry,' said the archdeacon. 'You'd better, I tell you, for there is no more of it left.' Then the major filled his glass and sipped the wine... 'Pity it should be all gone; isn't it, sir?' said the archdeacon to his father-in-law.

'It has lasted my time,' said Mr. Harding, 'and I'm very much obliged to it. Dear, dear; how well I remember your father giving the order for it! There were two pipes, and somebody said it was a heady wine. "If the prebendaries and rectors can't drink it," said your father, "the curates will."'

'Curates indeed!' said the archdeacon. 'It's too good for a bishop, unless one of the right sort.'

'Your father used to say those things, but with him the poorer the guest the better the cheer. When he had a few clergymen round him, how he loved to make them happy!'

'Never talked shop to them,—did he?' said the archdeacon.

'Not after dinner, at any rate. Goodness gracious, when one thinks of it! Do you remember how we used to play cards?'

'Every night regularly;—threepenny points, and sixpence on the rubber,' said the archdeacon.

'Dear, dear! How things are changed! And I remember when the clergymen did more of the dancing in Barchester than all the other young men in the city put together.'

'And a good set they were;—gentlemen every one of them. It's well that some of them don't dance now;—that is, for the girls' sake.'

'I sometimes sit and wonder,' said Mr. Harding, 'whether your father's spirit ever comes back to the old house and sees the changes,—and if so whether he approves them.'

'Approves them!' said the archdeacon.

'Well;—yes. I think he would, upon the whole. I'm sure of this: he would not disapprove, because the new ways are changes from his ways. He never thought himself infallible. And do you know, my dear, I am not sure that it isn't all for the best. I sometimes think that some of us were very idle when we were young. I was, I know.'

'I worked hard enough,' said the archdeacon.

'Ah, yes; you. But most of us took it very easily. Dear, dear! When I think of it, and see how hard they work now, and remember what pleasant times we used to have,—I don't feel sometimes quite sure.'

'I believe the work was done a great deal better than it is now,' said the archdeacon. 'There wasn't so much fuss, but there was more reality. And men were men, and clergymen were gentlemen.'

'Yes;—they were gentlemen.'

'Such a creature as that old woman at the palace couldn't have held his head up among us. That's what has come from Reform. A reformed House of Commons makes Lord Brock Prime Minister, and then your Prime Minister makes Dr. Proudie a bishop! Well;—it will last my time, I suppose.'

'It has lasted mine,—like the wine,' said Mr. Harding.

## English Village Curate

The Rev. Montagu Blake was curate of Little Alresford, a parish, though hardly to be called a village, lying about three miles from the town. The vicar was a feeble old gentleman who had gone away to die in the Riviera, and Mr. Blake had the care of souls to himself. He was a man to whom his lines had fallen in pleasant places. There were about 250 men, women, and children, in his parish, and not a Dissenter among them. For looking after these folk he had £120 per annum, and as pretty a little parsonage as could be found in England. There was a squire with whom he was growing in grace and friendship, who, being the patron of the living, might probably bestow it upon him. It was worth only £250, and was not, therefore, too valuable to be expected. He had a modest fortune of his own, £300 a-year perhaps, and,—for the best of his luck shall be mentioned last,—he was engaged to the daughter of one of the prebendaries of Winchester, a pretty bright little girl, with a further sum of £5000 belonging to herself. He was thirty years of age, in the possession of perfect health, and not so strict in matters of religion as to make it necessary for him to abandon any of the innocent pleasures of this world. He could dine out, and play cricket, and read a novel. And should he chance, when riding his cob about the parish, or visiting some neighbouring parish, to come across the hounds, he would not scruple to see them over a field or two. So that the Rev. Montagu Blake was upon the whole a happy fellow.

## THE PARSON'S VIEW OF LIFE

ON EVERY SUCCEEDING DAY, Gregory, the parson, dined up at the large house... He was a tall, slender man, somewhat narrow-chested, bright-eyed, with a kind-looking sweet mouth, a small well-cut nose, dark but not black hair, and a dimple on his chin. He always went with his hands in his pockets, walking quick, but shuffling sometimes in step as though with hesitation, stooping somewhat, absent occasionally, going about with his chin stuck out before him, as though he were seeking something,—he knew not what. A more generous fellow, who delighted more in giving, hesitated more in asking, more averse to begging though a friend of beggars, less self-arrogant, or self-seeking, or more devoted to his profession, never lived. He was a man with prejudices,—kindly, gentlemanlike, amiable prejudices. He thought that a clergyman should be a graduate from one of the three universities,— including Trinity, Dublin; and he thought, also, that a clergyman should be a gentleman. He thought that Dissenters were,—a great mistake. He thought that Convocation should be potential. He thought that the Church had certain powers and privileges which Parliament could not take away except by spoliation. He thought that a parson should always be well-dressed,—according to his order. He thought that the bishop of his diocese was the purest, best, and noblest peer in England. He thought that Newton churchyard was, of all spots on earth, the most lovely. He thought very little of himself. And he thought that of all the delights given by God for the delectation of his creatures, the love of Clarissa Underwood would be the most delightful. In all these thinkings he was astray, carried away by prejudices which he was not strong enough to withstand. But the joint effect of so many faults in judgment was not disagreeable; and, as one result of that effect, Gregory Newton was loved and respected, and believed in by all men and women, poor and rich, who lived within knowledge of his name. His uncle Gregory, who was wont to be severe in his judgment on men, would declare that the Rev. Gregory,—as he was called,—was perfect. But then the Squire was a man who was himself very much subject to prejudices. . . In the little book-room of his parsonage he opened the window, and, crossing the garden, seated himself on a low brick wall, which divided his small domain from the churchyard. The night was bright with stars, but there was no moon in the heavens, and the gloom of the old ivy-coloured church tower was complete. But all the outlines of the place were so well known to him that he could trace them all in the dim light. After a while he got down among the graves, and with slow steps walked round and round the precincts of his church. Here, at least, in this spot, close to the house of God which was his own church, within this hallowed enclosure, which was his own freehold in a peculiar manner, he could, after a fashion, be happy, in spite of the misfortunes of himself and his family. His lines had been laid for him in very pleasant places. According to his ideas there was no position among the children of men more blessed, more diversified, more useful, more noble, than that which had been awarded to him,—if only, by God's help, he could perform with adequate zeal and ability the high duties which had been entrusted to him. Things outside were dark,—at least, so said the squires and parsons around him, with whom he was wont to associate. His uncle, Gregory, was sure that all things were going to the dogs, since a so-called Tory leader had become an advocate for household suffrage, and real Tory gentlemen had condescended to follow him. But to our parson it had always seemed that there was still a fresh running stream of water for him who would care to drink from a fresh stream. He heard much of unbelief, and of the professors of unbelief, both within and without the great Church; —but in that little church with which he was personally concerned there were more worshippers now than there had ever been before. And he heard, too, how certain well-esteemed preachers and prophets of the day talked loudly of the sins of the people, and foretold destruction such as was the destruction of Gomorrah;—but to him it seemed that the people of his village were more honest, less given to drink, and certainly better educated than their fathers. In all which thoughts he found matter for hope and encouragement in his daily life. And he set himself to work diligently, placing all this as a balance against his private sorrows, so that he might teach himself to take that world, of which he himself was the centre, as one whole,—and so to walk on rejoicing.

## Parson Smallbones

'But Parson Smallbones was a bit of a farmer?'

'Ay, ay. Parsons in them days warn't above a bit of farming. I warn't much more than a scrap of a boy, but I remember him. He wore a wig, and old black gaiters; and knew as well what was his'n and what wasn't as any parson in Wiltshire. Tithes was tithes then; and parson was cute enough in taking on 'em.'

'But these sheep of his were his own, I suppose?'

'Whose else would they be, sir?'

'And did he fence them in on that bit of ground?'

'There'd be a boy with 'em, I'm thinking, sir. There wasn't so much fencing of sheep then as there be now. Boys was cheaper in them days.'

'Just so; and the parson wouldn't allow other sheep there?'

'Muster Smallbones mostly took all he could get, sir.'

'Exactly. The parsons generally did, I believe. It was the way in which they followed most accurately the excellent examples set them by the bishops.'

## Clerical Pastimes

Mr. Harding's warmest admirers cannot say that he was ever an industrious man; the circumstances of his life have not called on him to be so; and yet he can hardly be called an idler. Since his appointment to his precentorship, he has published, with all possible additions of vellum, typography, and gilding, a collection of our ancient church music, with some correct dissertations on Purcell, Crotch, and Nares. He has greatly improved the choir of Barchester, which, under his dominion, now rivals that of any cathedral in England. He has taken something more than his fair share in the cathedral services, and has played the violoncello daily to such audiences as he could collect, or, *faute de mieux,* to no audience at all.

## Clerical Bed-Curtains

How much sweet solace, how much valued counsel has our archdeacon received within that sainted enclosure! 'Tis there alone that he unbends, and comes down from his high church pedestal to the level of a mortal man. In the world Dr. Grantly never lays aside that demeanour which so well becomes him. He has all the dignity of an ancient saint with the sleekness of a modern bishop; he is always the same; he is always the archdeacon; unlike Homer, he never nods. Even with his father-in-law, even with the bishop and dean, he maintains that sonorous tone and lofty deportment which strikes awe into the young hearts of Barchester, and absolutely cows the whole parish of Plumstead Episcopi. 'Tis only when he has exchanged that ever-new shovel hat for a tasselled nightcap, and those shining black habiliments for his accustomed *robe de nuit,* that Dr. Grantly talks, and looks, and thinks like an ordinary man. . .

Do we not all know some reverend, all but sacred, personage before whom our tongue ceases to be loud and our step

## WHISTLING

THE BISHOP DID NOT WHISTLE: we believe that they lose the power of doing so on being consecrated; and that in these days one might as easily meet a corrupt judge as a whistling bishop; but he looked as though he would have done so, but for his apron.

## THE ARCHDEACON SPEAKS

AS THE ARCHDEACON stood up to make his speech, erect in the middle of that little square, he looked like an ecclesiastical statue placed there, as a fitting impersonation of the church militant here on earth; his shovel hat, large, new, and well-pronounced, a churchman's hat in every inch, declared the profession as plainly as does the Quaker's broad brim; his heavy eyebrows, large open eyes, and full mouth and chin expressed the solidity of his order; the broad chest, amply covered with fine cloth, told how well to do was its estate; one hand ensconced within his pocket, evinced the practical hold which our mother church keeps on her temporal possessions; and the other, loose for action, was ready to fight if need be in her defence; and, below these, the decorous breeches, and neat black gaiters showing so admirably that well-turned leg, betokened the decency, the outward beauty and grace of our church establishment.

## SANCTUM SANCTORUM

THE CHURCH REFORMER soon found himself tête-à-tête with the archdeacon in that same room, in that sanctum sanctorum of the rectory, to which we have already been introduced. As he entered he heard the click of a certain patent lock, but it struck him with no surprise; the worthy clergyman was no doubt hiding from eyes profane his last much-studied sermon; for the archdeacon, though he preached but seldom, was famous for his sermons. No room, Bold thought, could have been more becoming for a dignitary of the church; each wall was loaded with theology; over each separate bookcase was printed in small gold letters the names of those great divines whose works were ranged beneath: beginning from the early fathers in due chronological order, there were to be found the precious labours of the chosen servants of the church down to the last pamphlet written in opposition to the consecration of Dr. Hampden; and raised above this were to be seen the busts of the greatest among the great: Chrysostom, St. Augustine, Thomas à Becket, Cardinal Wolsey, Archbishop Laud, and Dr. Philpotts.

Every appliance that could make study pleasant and give ease to the overtoiled brain was there; chairs made to relieve each limb and muscle; reading-desks and writing-desks to suit every attitude; lamps and candles mechanically contrived to throw their light on any favoured spot, as the student might desire; a shoal of newspapers to amuse the few leisure moments which might be stolen from the labours of the day; and then from the window a view right through a bosky vista along which ran a broad green path from the rectory to the church—at the end of which the tawny-tinted fine old tower was seen with all its variegated pinnacles and parapets.

## In Westminster Abbey

HE DETERMINED TO TAKE SANCTUARY in Westminster Abbey, so he again went thither in an omnibus, and finding that the doors were not open for morning service, he paid his twopence, and went in as a sightseer. It occurred to him that he had no definite place of rest for the day, and that he should be absolutely worn out before his interview if he attempted to walk about from 10 a.m. to 10 p.m., so he sat himself down on a stone step, and gazed up at the figure of William Pitt, who looks as though he had just entered the church for the first time in his life and was anything but pleased at finding himself there.

He had been sitting unmolested about twenty minutes when the verger asked him whether he wouldn't like to walk around. Mr. Harding didn't want to walk anywhere, and declined, merely observing that he was waiting for the morning service. The verger seeing that he was a clergyman, told him that the doors of the choir were now open, and showed him into a seat. This was a great point gained; the archdeacon would certainly not come to morning service at Westminster Abbey, even though he were in London; and here the warden could rest quietly, and, when the time came, duly say his prayers.

He longed to get up from his seat, and examine the music-books of the choristers, and the copy of the litany from which the service was chanted, to see how far the little details at Westminster corresponded with those at Barchester, and whether he thought his own voice would fill the church well from the Westminster precentor's seat. There would, however, be impropriety in such meddling, and he sat perfectly still, looking up at the noble roof, and guarding against the coming fatigues of the day.

By degrees two or three people entered; the very same damp old woman who had nearly obliterated him in the omnibus, or some other just like her; a couple of young ladies with their veils down, and gilt crosses conspicuous on their prayer-books; an old man on crutches; a party who were seeing the abbey, and thought they might as well hear the service for their twopence, as opportunity served; and a young woman with her prayer-book done up in her handkerchief, who rushed in late, and, in her hurried entry, tumbled over one of the forms, and made such a noise that every one, even the officiating minor canon, was startled, and she herself was so frightened by the echo of her own catastrophe that she was nearly thrown into fits by the panic.

Mr. Harding was not much edified by the manner of the service. The minor canon in question hurried in, somewhat late, in a surplice not in the neatest order, and was followed by a dozen choristers, who were also not as trim as they might have been: they all jostled into their places with a quick hurried step, and the service was soon commenced. Soon commenced and soon over—for there was no music, and time was not unnecessarily lost in the chanting. On the whole Mr. Harding was of opinion that things were managed better at Barchester, though even there he knew that there was room for improvement.

It appears to us a question whether any clergyman can go through our church service with decorum, morning after morning, in an immense building, surrounded by not more than a dozen listeners. The best actors cannot act well before empty benches, and though there is, of course, a higher motive in one case than the other, still even the best of clergymen cannot but be influenced by their audience; and to expect that a duty should be well done under such circumstances, would be to require from human nature more than human power.

When the two ladies with the gilt crosses, the old man with his crutch, and the still palpitating housemaid were going, Mr. Harding found himself obliged to go too. The verger stood in his way, and looked at him and looked at the door, and so he went. But he returned again in a few minutes, and re-entered with another twopence. There was no other sanctuary so good for him.

## At the Cigar Divan

As HE PAID HIS BILL to the woman in the shop, he asked her if there was any place near where he could get a cup of coffee. Though she did keep a shell-fish supper-house, she was very civil, and directed him to the cigar divan on the other side of the street.

Mr. Harding had not a much correcter notion of a cigar divan than he had of a London dinner-house, but he was desperately in want of rest, and went as he was directed. He thought he must have made some mistake when he found himself in a cigar shop, but the man behind the counter saw immediately that he was a stranger, and understood what he wanted. 'One shilling, sir—thank ye, sir—cigar, sir?—ticket for coffee, sir—you'll only have to call the waiter. Up those stairs, if you please, sir. Better take the cigar, sir—you can always give it to a friend you know. Well, sir, thank ye, sir—as you are so good, I'll smoke it myself.' And so Mr. Harding ascended to the divan, with his ticket for coffee, but minus the cigar.

The place seemed much more suitable to his requirements than the room in which he had dined: there was, to be sure, a strong smell of tobacco, to which he was not accustomed; but after the shell-fish, the tobacco did not seem disagreeable. There were quantities of books, and long rows of sofas. What on earth could be more luxurious than a sofa, a book, and a cup of coffee? An old waiter came up to him, with a couple of magazines and an evening paper. Was ever anything so civil? Would he have a cup of coffee, or would he prefer sherbet? Sherbet! Was he absolutely in an Eastern divan, with the slight addition of all the London periodicals? He had, however, an idea that sherbet should be drunk sitting crosslegged, and as he was not quite up to this, he ordered the coffee.

The coffee came, and was unexceptionable. Why, this divan was a paradise! The civil old waiter suggested to him a game of chess: though a chess player he was not equal to this, so he declined, and, putting up his weary legs on the sofa, leisurely sipped his coffee, and turned over the pages of his Blackwood. He might have been so engaged for about an hour, for the old waiter enticed him to a second cup of coffee, when a musical clock began to play. Mr. Harding then closed his magazine, keeping his place with his finger, and lay, listening with closed eyes to the clock. Soon the clock seemed to turn into a violoncello, with piano accompaniments, and Mr. Harding began to fancy the old waiter was the Bishop of Barchester; he was inexpressibly shocked that the bishop should have brought him his coffee with his own hands; then Dr. Grantly came in, with a basket full of lobsters, which he would not be induced to leave downstairs in the kitchen; and then the warden couldn't quite understand why so many people would smoke in the bishop's drawing-room; and so he fell asleep, and his dreams wandered away to his accustomed stall in Barchester Cathedral, and the twelve old men he was so soon about to leave for ever.

He was fatigued, and slept soundly for some time. Some sudden stop in the musical clock woke him at length, and he jumped up with a start, surprised to find the room quite full: it had been nearly empty when his nap began. With nervous anxiety he pulled out his watch, and found that it was half-past nine. He seized his hat, and, hurrying downstairs, started at a rapid pace for Lincoln's Inn.

# Doctors, Lawyers, and Others

## On Choosing a Profession

'You have decided, then, to be a clergyman?'

'Oh, no, not decided. Indeed, I really think that if a man will work, he may do better at the bar.'

'Very well indeed, if he have the peculiar kind of talent necessary.'

'But then, I doubt whether a practising barrister can ever really be an honest man.'

'What?'

'They have such dirty work to do. They spend their days in making out that black is white, or, worse still, that white is black.'

'Pshaw! Have a little more charity, Master George, and do not be so over-righteous. Some of the greatest men of your country have been lawyers.'

'But their being great men won't alter the fact, nor will my being charitable. When two clear-headed men take money to advocate the different sides of a case, each can not think that his side is true.'

'Fiddlestick! But mind, I do not want you to be a lawyer. You must choose for yourself. If you don't like that way of earning your bread there are others.'

'A man may be a doctor, to be sure; but I have no taste that way.'

'And is that the end of the list?'

'There is literature. But literature, though the grandest occupation in the world for a man's leisure, is, I take it, a slavish profession.'

'Grub Street, eh? Yes, I should think so. You never heard of commerce, I suppose?'

'Commerce! Yes, I have heard of it. But I doubt whether I have the necessary genius.'

The old man looked at him as though he doubted whether or no he were being laughed at.

'The necessary kind of genius, I mean,' continued George.

'Very likely not. Your genius is adapted to dispersing, perhaps, rather than collecting.'

'I dare say it is, sir.'

'And I suppose you never heard of a man with a—what is it you call your degree? a double-first—going behind a counter. What sort of men are the double-lasts, I wonder?'

'It is they, I rather think, who go behind the counters,' said George, who had no idea of allowing his uncle to have all the raillery on his side.

'Is it, sir? But I rather think they don't come out last when the pudding is to be proved by the eating. Success in life is not to be won by writing Greek verses—not though you write ever so many. A ship-load of them would not fetch you the value of this glass of wine at any market in the world.'

'Commerce is a grand thing,' said George, with an air of conviction.

'It is the proper work for men,' said his uncle, proudly.

'But I have always heard,' replied the nephew, 'that a man in this country has no right to look to commerce as a profession unless he possesses capital.' Mr. Bertram, feeling that the tables had been turned against him, finished his glass of wine and poked the fire.

A few days afterward the same subject was again raised between them. 'You must choose for yourself, George,' said the old man, 'and you should choose quickly.'

'If I could choose for myself—which I am aware that I can not do, for circumstances, after all, will have the decision—but, if I could choose, I would go into Parliament.'

'Go where?' said Mr. Bertram, who would have thought

it as reasonable if his nephew had proposed to take a house in Belgrave Square with a view of earning his livelihood.

'Into Parliament, sir.'

'Is Parliament a profession? I never knew it before.'

'Perhaps not, ordinarily, a money-making profession; nor would I wish to make it so.'

'And what county or what borough do you intend to honour by representing it? Perhaps the University will return you.'

'Perhaps it may, some of these days.'

'And, in the meantime, you mean to live on your fellowship, I suppose?'

'On that and anything else that I can get.'

Mr. Bertram sat quiet for some time without speaking, and George also seemed inclined to muse a while upon the subject. 'George,' said the uncle, at last, 'I think it will be better that we should thoroughly understand each other. You are a good fellow in your way, and I like you well enough. But you must not get into your head any idea that you are to be my heir.'

'No, sir, I won't.'

'Because it would only ruin you. My idea is that a man should make his own way in the world as I made mine. If you were my son, it may be presumed that I should do as other men do, and give you my money. And, most probably, you would make no better use of it than the sons of other men, who, like me, have made money. But you are not my son.'

## Country Doctor

AND THUS DR. THORNE became settled for life in the little village of Greshamsbury. As was then the wont with many country practitioners, and as should be the wont with them all if they consulted their own dignity a little less and the comforts of their customers somewhat more, he added the business of a dispensing apothecary to that of physician. In doing so, he was of course much reviled. Many people around him declared that he could not truly be a doctor, or, at any rate, a doctor to be so called; and his brethren in the art living around him, though they knew that his diplomas, degrees, and certificates were all *en règle,* rather countenanced the report. There was much about this new-comer which did not endear him to his own profession. In the first place he was a new-comer, and, as such, was of course to be regarded by other doctors as being *de trop.* Greshamsbury was only fifteen miles from Barchester, where there was a regular dépôt of medical skill, and but eight from Silverbridge, where a properly established physician had been in residence for the last forty years. Dr. Thorne's predecessor at Greshamsbury had been a humble-minded general practitioner, gifted with a due respect for the physicians of the county; and he, though he had been allowed to physic the servants, and sometimes the children at Greshamsbury, had never had the presumption to put himself on a par with his betters.

Then, also, Dr. Thorne, though a graduated physician, though entitled beyond all dispute to call himself a doctor, according to all the laws of all the colleges, made it known to the East Barsetshire world, very soon after he had seated himself at Greshamsbury, that his rate of pay was to be seven-and-sixpence a visit within a circuit of five miles, with a proportionally increased charge at proportionally increased distances. Now there was something low, mean, unprofessional, and democratic in this; so, at least, said the children of Æsculapius gathered together in conclave at Barchester. In the first place, it showed that this Thorne was always thinking of his money, like an apothecary, as he was; whereas, it would have behoved him, as a physician, had he had the feelings of a physician under his hat, to have regarded his own pursuits in a purely philosophical spirit, and to have taken any gain which might have accrued as an accidental adjunct to his station in life. A physician should take his fee without letting his left hand know what his right hand was doing; it should be taken without a thought, without a look, without

## DOCTORS, LAWYERS, AND OTHERS

a move of the facial muscles; the true physician should hardly be aware that the last friendly grasp of the hand had been made more precious by the touch of gold. Whereas, that fellow Thorne would lug out half a crown from his breeches pocket and give it in change for a ten-shilling piece. And then it was clear that this man had no appreciation of the dignity of a learned profession. He might constantly be seen compounding medicines in the shop, at the left hand of his front door; not making experiments philosophically in materia medica for the benefit of coming ages—which, if he did, he should have done in the seclusion of his study, far from profane eyes—but positively putting together common powders for rural bowels, or spreading vulgar ointments for agricultural ailments. . .

Another misfortune was, that he was a bachelor. Ladies think, and I, for one, think that ladies are quite right in so thinking, that doctors should be married men. All the world feels that a man when married acquires some of the attributes of an old woman—he becomes, to a certain extent, a motherly sort of being; he acquires a conversance with women's ways and women's wants, and loses the wilder and offensive sparks of his virility. It must be easier to talk to such a one about Matilda's stomach, and the growing pains in Fanny's legs, than to a young bachelor. This impediment also stood much in Dr. Thorne's way during his first years at Greshamsbury.

But his wants were not at first great; and though his ambition was perhaps high, it was not of an impatient nature. The world was his oyster; but, circumstanced as he was, he knew it was not for him to open it with his lancet all at once. He had bread to earn, which he must earn wearily; he had a character to make, which must come slowly; it satisfied his soul that, in addition to his immortal hopes, he had a possible future in this world to which he could look forward with clear eyes, and advance with a heart that would know no fainting.

## The Doctors' Consultation

The carriage—or rather post-chaise—of Dr. Fillgrave was now frequent in Greshamsbury, passing him constantly in the street, among the lanes, and on the high roads. It seemed as though Dr. Fillgrave could never get to his patients at the big house without showing himself to his beaten rival, either on his way thither or on his return. This alone would, perhaps, not have hurt our doctor much; but it did hurt him to know that Dr. Fillgrave was attending the squire for a little incipient gout, and that dear Nina was in measles under those unloving hands.

And then, also, the old-fashioned phaeton of old-fashioned old Dr. Century was seen to rumble up to the big house, and it became known that Lady Arabella was not very well. 'Not very well,' when pronounced in a low, grave voice about Ladies Arabella, always means something serious. And, in this case, something serious was meant. Lady Arabella was not only ill, but frightened. It appeared, even to her, that Dr. Fillgrave himself hardly knew what he was about, that he was not so sure in his opinion, so confident in himself, as Dr. Thorne used to be. How should he be, seeing that Dr. Thorne had medically had Lady Arabella in his hands for the last ten years?

If sitting with dignity in his hired carriage, and stepping with authority up the big front steps, would have done anything, Dr. Fillgrave might have done much. Lady Arabella was greatly taken with his looks when he first came to her, and it was only when she by degrees perceived that the symptoms, which she knew so well, did not yield to him that she began to doubt those looks.

After a while Dr. Fillgrave himself suggested Dr. Century. 'Not that I fear anything, Lady Arabella,' said he,—lying hugely, for he did fear; fear both for himself and for her. 'But Dr. Century has great experience, and in such a matter,

[ 240 ]

when the interests are so important, one cannot be too safe.'

So Dr. Century came and toddled slowly into her ladyship's room. He did not say much; he left the talking to his learned brother, who certainly was able to do that part of the business. But Dr. Century, though he said little, looked very grave, and by no means quieted Lady Arabella's mind. She, as she saw the two putting their heads together, already felt misgivings that she had done wrong. She knew that she could not be safe without Dr. Thorne at her bedside, and she already felt that she had exercised a most injudicious courage in driving him away.

'Well, doctor?' said she, as soon as Dr. Century had toddled downstairs to see the squire.

'Oh! we shall be all right, Lady Arabella; all right, very soon. But we must be careful, very careful; I am glad I've had Century here, very; but there's nothing to alter; little or nothing.'

There were but few words spoken between Dr. Century and the squire; but few as they were, they frightened Mr. Gresham. When Dr. Fillgrave came down the grand stairs, a servant waited at the bottom to ask him also to go to the squire. Now there never had been much cordiality between the squire and Dr. Fillgrave, though Mr. Gresham had consented to take a preventative pill from his hands, and the little man therefore swelled himself out somewhat more than ordinarily as he followed the servant.

'Dr. Fillgrave,' said the squire, at once beginning the conversation, 'Lady Arabella is, I fear, in danger.'

'Well, no; I hope not in danger, Mr. Gresham. I certainly believe I may be justified in expressing a hope that she is not in danger. Her state is, no doubt, rather serious—rather serious—as Dr. Century has probably told you;' and Dr. Fillgrave made a bow to the old man, who sat quiet in one of the dining-room armchairs.

'Well, doctor,' said the squire, 'I have not any grounds on which to doubt your judgment.'

Dr. Fillgrave bowed, but with the stiffest, slightest inclination which a head could possibly make. He rather thought that Mr. Gresham had no ground for doubting his judgment.

'Nor do I.'

The doctor bowed, and a little, a very little less stiffly.

'But, doctor, I think that something ought to be done.'

The doctor this time did his bowing merely with his eyes and mouth. The former he closed for a moment, the latter he pressed; and then decorously rubbed his hands one over the other.

'I am afraid, Dr. Fillgrave, that you and my friend Thorne are not the best friends in the world.'

'No, Mr. Gresham, no; I may go so far as to say we are not.'

'Well, I am sorry for it—'

'Perhaps, Mr. Gresham, we need hardly discuss it; but there have been circumstances—'

'I am not going to discuss anything, Dr. Fillgrave; I say I am sorry for it, because I believe that prudence will imperatively require Lady Arabella to have Doctor Thorne back again. Now, if you would not object to meet him—'

'Mr. Gresham, I beg pardon; I beg pardon, indeed; but you must really excuse me. Doctor Thorne has, in my estimation—'

'But, Doctor Fillgrave—'

'Mr. Gresham, you really must excuse me; you really must, indeed. Anything else that I could do for Lady Arabella, I should be most happy to do; but after what has passed, I cannot meet Doctor Thorne; I really cannot. You must not ask me to do so, Mr. Gresham. And, Mr. Gresham,' continued the doctor, 'I did understand from Lady Arabella that his— that is, Doctor Thorne's—conduct to her ladyship had been such—so very outrageous, I may say, that—that—that—of course, Mr. Gresham, you know best; but I did think that Lady Arabella herself was quite unwilling to see Doctor

## DOCTORS, LAWYERS, AND OTHERS

Thorne again;' and Dr. Fillgrave looked very big, and very dignified, and very exclusive.

The squire did not again ask him. He had no warrant for supposing that Lady Arabella would receive Dr. Thorne if he did come; and he saw that it was useless to attempt to overcome the rancour of a man so pig-headed as the little Galen now before him. Other propositions were then broached, and it was at last decided that assistance should be sought for from London, in the person of the great Sir Omicron Pie.

Sir Omicron came, and Drs. Fillgrave and Century were there to meet him. When they all assembled in Lady Arabella's room, the poor woman's heart almost sank within her, —as well it might, at such a sight. If she could only reconcile it with her honour, her consistency, with her high De Courcy principles, to send once more for Dr. Thorne... Sir Omicron and the lesser provincial lights had their consultation, and the lesser lights went their way to Barchester and Silverbridge, leaving Sir Omicron to enjoy the hospitality of Greshamsbury.

'You should have Thorne back here, Mr. Gresham,' said Sir Omicron, almost in a whisper, when they were quite alone. 'Doctor Fillgrave is a very good man, and so is Dr. Century; very good, I am sure. But Thorne has known her ladyship so long.' And then, on the following morning, Sir Omicron also went his way.

### Junior Law Partner

But Mr. Gazebee was a very different sort of gentleman; he was the junior partner in the firm of Gumption, Gazebee & Gazebee, of Mount Street, a house that never defiled itself with any other business than the agency business, and that in the very highest line. They drew out leases, and managed property both for the Duke of Omnium and Lord de Courcy; and ever since her marriage, it had been one of the objects dearest to Lady Arabella's heart, that the Greshamsbury acres

## HE CONSIDERS ITS PATTERNS

should be superintended by the polite skill and polished legal ability of that all but elegant firm in Mount Street. . .

It must not be supposed that Messrs. Gumption, Gazebee & Gazebee were in the least like the ordinary run of attorneys. They wrote no letters for six-and-eightpence each: they collected no debts, filed no bills, made no charge per folio for 'whereases' and 'as aforesaids;' they did no dirty work, and probably were as ignorant of the interior of a court of law as any young lady living in their Mayfair vicinity. No; their business was to manage the property of great people, draw up leases, make legal assignments, get the family marriage settlements made, and look after the wills. Occasionally, also, they had to raise money; but it was generally understood that this was done by proxy.

The firm had been going on for a hundred and fifty years, and the designation had often been altered; but it always consisted of Gumptions and Gazebees differently arranged, and no less hallowed names had ever been permitted to appear. It had been Gazebee, Gazebee & Gumption; then Gazebee & Gumption; then Gazebee, Gumption & Gumption; then Gumption, Gumption & Gazebee; and now it was Gumption, Gazebee & Gazebee.

Mr. Gazebee, the junior member of this firm, was a very elegant young man. While looking at him riding in Rotten Row, you would hardly have taken him for an attorney; and had he heard that you had so taken him, he would have been very much surprised indeed. He was rather bald; not being, as people say, quite so young as he was once. His exact age was thirty-eight. But he had a really remarkable pair of jet-black whiskers, which fully made up for any deficiency as to his head; he had also dark eyes, and a beaked nose, what may be called a distinguished mouth, and was always dressed in fashionable attire. The fact was, that Mr. Mortimer Gazebee, junior partner in the firm of Gumption, Gazebee & Gazebee, by no means considered himself to be made of that very disagreeable material which mortals call small beer.

## Law Business in London

Mr. Bidewhile got up from his large wooden-seated Windsor chair, and, with a soft smile, in which, however, was mingled some slight dash of the attorney's acuteness, put out his hand to his young client; not, indeed, as though he were going to shake hands with him, but as though the hand were some ripe fruit all but falling, which his visitor might take and pluck if he thought proper. Frank took hold of the hand, which returned him no pressure, and then let it go again, not making any attempt to gather the fruit.

'I have come up to town, Mr. Bidewhile, about this mortgage,' commenced Frank.

'Mortgage—ah, sit down, Mr. Gresham; sit down. I hope your father is quite well.'

'Quite well, thank you.'

'I have a great regard for your father. So I had for your grandfather; a very good man indeed. You, perhaps, don't remember him, Mr. Gresham?'

'He died when I was only a year old.'

'Oh, yes; no, you of course can't remember him; but I do, well: he used to be very fond of some port wine I had. I think it was "11"; and if I don't mistake, I have a bottle or two of it yet; but it is not worth drinking now. Port wine, you know, won't keep beyond a certain time. That was very good wine. I don't exactly remember what it stood me a dozen then; but such wine can't be had now. As for the Madeira, you know there's an end of that. Do you drink Madeira, Mr. Gresham?'

'No,' said Frank, 'not very often.'

'I'm sorry for that, for it's a fine wine; but then there's none of it left, you know. I have a few dozen. I'm told they're growing pumpkins where the vineyards were. I wonder what they do with all the pumpkins they grow in Switzerland! You've been in Switzerland, Mr. Gresham?'

# HE CONSIDERS ITS PATTERNS

Frank said he had been in Switzerland.

'It's a beautiful country; my girls made me go there last year. They said it would do me good; but then, you know, they wanted to see it themselves; ha! ha! ha! However, I believe I shall go again this autumn. That is to Aix, or some of those places; just for three weeks. I can't spare any more time, Mr. Gresham. Do you like that dining at the *tables d'hôte?*'

'Pretty well, sometimes.'

'One would get tired of it—eh! But they gave us capital dinners at Zurich. I don't think much of their soup. But they had fish, and about seven kinds of meats and poultry, and three or four puddings, and things of that sort. Upon my word, I thought we did very well, and so did my girls, too. You see a great many ladies travelling now.'

'Yes,' said Frank; 'a great many.'

'Upon my word, I think they are right; that is, if they can afford time. I can't afford time. I'm here every day till five, Mr. Gresham; then I go out and dine in Fleet Street, and then back to work till nine.'

'Dear me! that's very hard.'

'Well, yes, it is hard work. My boys don't like it; but I manage it somehow. I get down to my little place in the country on Saturday. I shall be most happy to see you there next Saturday.'

Frank, thinking it would be outrageous on his part to take up much of the time of a gentleman who was constrained to work so unreasonably hard, began again to talk about his mortgages. . .

And so Mr. Bideawhile went on for two hours, and Frank found no opportunity of saying one word about the business which had brought him up to town. What wonder that such a man as this should be obliged to stay at his office every night till nine o'clock?

During these two hours, a clerk had come in three or four times, whispering something to the lawyer, who, on the last of such occasions, turned to Frank, saying, 'Well, perhaps that

[ 246 ]

will do for to-day. If you'll manage to call to-morrow, say about two, I will have the whole thing looked up; or, perhaps, Wednesday or Thursday would suit you better.' Frank, declaring that the morrow would suit him very well, took his departure, wondering much at the manner in which business was done at the house of Messrs. Slow & Bidewhile.

## Preparing a Defence

'In preparing a defence we have to rummage about and get up what we can. If we can't find anything that suits us exactly, we are obliged to use what we do find as well as we can. I remember, when I was a young man, an ostler was to be tried for stealing some oats in the Borough; and he did steal them too, and sold them at a rag-shop regularly. The evidence against him was as plain as a pike-staff. All I could find out was that on a certain day a horse had trod on the fellow's foot. So we put it to the jury whether the man could walk as far as the rag-shop with a bag of oats when he was dead lame;—and we got him off.'

'Did you though?' said Mr. Harding.

'Yes, we did.'

'And he was guilty?'

'He had been at it regularly for months.'

'Dear, dear, dear! Wouldn't it have been better to have had him punished for the fault,—gently; so as to warn him of the consequences of such doings?'

'Our business was to get him off,—and we got him off.'

## The Embassy in Brussels

There were Lady Mountjoy, and Miss Abbott, and Mr. Anderson, and Mr. Montgomery Arbuthnot, the two attachés. Mr. Montgomery Arbuthnot was especially proud of his name, but was otherwise rather a humble young man as an attaché, having as yet been only three months with Sir Magnus, and desirous of perfecting himself in Foreign Office manners under the tuition of Mr. Anderson. Mr. Blow, the Secretary of Legation, was not there. He was a married man of austere manners, who, to tell the truth, looked down from a considerable height as regarded Foreign Office knowledge upon his chief. It was Mr. Blow who did the 'grinding' on behalf of the Belgian Legation, and who sometimes did not hesitate to let it be known that such was the fact. Neither he nor Mrs. Blow were popular at the embassy; or it may perhaps be said with more truth that the embassy was not popular with Mr. and Mrs. Blow. It may be stated also that there was a clerk attached to the establishment, Mr. Bunderdown, who had been there for some years, and who was good-naturedly regarded by the English inhabitants as a third attaché. Mr. Montgomery Arbuthnot did his best to let it be understood that this was a mistake. . . There was Sir Thomas Tresham, with his wife, who had been sent over to inquire into the iron trade of Belgium. He was a learned free-trader, who could not be got to agree with the old familiar views of Sir Magnus,—who thought that the more iron that was produced in Belgium the less would be forthcoming from England. But Sir Thomas knew better; and as Sir Magnus was quite unable to hold his own with the political economist, he gave him many dinners, and was civil to his wife. Sir Thomas no doubt felt that in doing so Sir Magnus did all that could be expected from him. Lady Tresham was a quiet little woman, who could endure to be patronised by Lady Mountjoy without annoyance. And there was M. Grascour, from the Belgian Foreign Office, who spoke English so much better than the other gentlemen present, that a stranger might have supposed him to be a schoolmaster, whose mission it was to instruct the English Embassy in their own language.

## Barrister's Career

Mr. Furnival was a lawyer—I mean a barrister—belonging to Lincoln's Inn, and living at the time at which our story is supposed to commence in Harley Street. But he had not been long a resident in Harley Street, having left the less fashionable neighbourhood of Russell Square only two or three years before that period. On his marriage he had located himself in a small house in Keppel Street, and had there remained till professional success, long waited for, enabled him to move further west, and indulge himself with the comforts of larger rooms and more servants. At the time of which I am now speaking Mr. Furnival was known, and well known, as a successful man; but he had struggled long and hard before that success had come to him, and during the earliest years of his married life had found the work of keeping the wolf from the door to be almost more than enough for his energies.

Mr. Furnival practised at the common law bar, and early in life had attached himself to the home circuit. I cannot say why he obtained no great success till he was nearer fifty than forty years of age. At that time I fancy that barristers did not come to their prime till a period of life at which other men are supposed to be in their decadence. Nevertheless, he had married on nothing, and had kept the wolf from the door. To do this he had been constant at his work in season and out of season, during the long hours of day and the long hours of night. Throughout his term times he had toiled in court, and during the vacations he had toiled out of court. He had reported volumes of cases, having been himself his own short-hand writer,—as it is well known to most young lawyers, who as a rule always fill an upper shelf in their law libraries with Furnival and Staples' seventeen volumes in calf. He had worked for the booksellers, and for the newspapers, and for the attorneys,—always working, however, with reference to the law; and though he had worked for years with the lowest pay, no man had heard him complain. That no woman had heard him do so, I will not say; as it is more than probable that into the sympathizing ears of Mrs. Furnival he did pour forth plaints as to the small wages which the legal world meted out to him in return for his labours. He was a constant, hard, patient man, and at last there came to him the full reward of all his industry. What was the special case by which Mr. Furnival obtained his great success no man could say. In all probability there was no special case. Gradually it began to be understood that he was a safe man, understanding his trade, true to his clients, and very damaging as an opponent. Legal gentlemen are, I believe, quite as often bought off as bought up. Sir Richard and Mr. Furnival could not both be required on the same side, seeing what a tower of strength each was in himself; but then Sir Richard would be absolutely neutralized if Mr. Furnival were employed on the other side. This is a system well understood by attorneys, and has been found to be extremely lucrative by gentlemen leading at the bar.

## The Income-tax Office

Mr. Dale was civil, and even kind, to his own young friend, asking a question here and there as to his life in London, and saying something about the work at the Income-tax Office.

'It is hard work,' said Eames. 'If you're under the line, they make a great row about it, send for you, and look at you as though you'd been robbing the bank; but they think nothing of keeping you till five.'

'But how long do you have for lunch and reading the papers?' said the earl.

'Not ten minutes. We take a paper among twenty of us for half the day. That's exactly nine minutes to each; and as for lunch, we only have a biscuit dipped in ink.'

'Dipped in ink!' said the squire.

'It comes to that, for you have to be writing while you munch it.'

'I hear all about you,' said the earl; 'Sir Raffle Buffle is a crony of mine.'

'I don't suppose he ever heard my name as yet,' said Johnny. 'But do you really know him well, Lord De Guest?'

'Haven't seen him these thirty years; but I did know him.'

'We call him old Huffle Scuffle.'

'Huffle Scuffle! Ha, ha, ha! He always was Huffle Scuffle; a noisy, pretentious, empty-headed fellow. But I oughtn't to say so before you, young man. Come, we'll go into the drawing-room.'

## Bureau of Internal Navigation

THERE IS ONE BRANCH of the Civil Service located in Somerset House, which has little else to redeem it from the lowest depths of official vulgarity than the ambiguous respectability of its material position. This is the office of the Commissioners of Internal Navigation. The duties to be performed have reference to the preservation of canal banks, the tolls to be levied at locks, and disputes with the Admiralty as to points connected with tidal rivers. The rooms are dull and dark, and saturated with the fog which rises from the river, and their only ornament is here and there some dusty model of an improved barge. Bargees not unfrequently scuffle with hobnailed shoes through the passages, and go in and out, leaving behind them a smell of tobacco, to which the denizens of the place are not unaccustomed.

Indeed, the whole office is apparently infected with a leaven of bargedom. Not a few of the men are employed from time to time in the somewhat lethargic work of inspecting the banks and towing-paths of the canals which intersect the country. This they generally do seated on a load of hay, or perhaps of bricks, in one of those long, ugly, shapeless boats, which are to be seen congregating in the neighbourhood of

Brentford. So seated, they are carried along at the rate of a mile and a half an hour, and usually while away the time in gentle converse with the man at the rudder, or in silent abstraction over a pipe.

But the dullness of such a life as this is fully atoned for by the excitement of that which follows it in London. The men of the Internal Navigation are known to be fast, nay, almost furious in their pace of living; not that they are extravagant in any great degree, a fault which their scale of salaries very generally forbids; but they are one and all addicted to Coal Holes and Cider Cellars; they dive at midnight hours into Shades, and know all the back parlours of all the public-houses in the neighbourhood of the Strand. Here they leave messages for one another, and call the girl at the bar by her Christian name. They are a set of men endowed with sallow complexions, and they wear loud clothing, and spend more money in gin-and-water than in gloves.

The establishment is not unusually denominated the 'Infernal Navigation,' and the gentlemen employed are not altogether displeased at having it so called. The 'Infernal Navvies,' indeed, rather glory in the name. The navvies of Somerset House are known all over London, and there are those who believe that their business has some connexion with the rivers or railroads of that bourne from whence no traveller returns.

### Chaffanbrass, Trial Lawyer

As he spoke, Mr. Chaffanbrass, carrying in his hand a huge old blue bag, which, as he entered, he took from his clerk's hands, and bearing on the top of his head a wig that apparently had not been dressed for the last ten years, made his way in among the barristers, caring little on whose toes he trod, whose papers he upset, or whom he elbowed on his road. Mr. Chaffanbrass was the cock of this dunghill, and well he knew how to make his crowing heard there.

'And now, pray, let us lose no more time,' said the judge.

## DOCTORS, LAWYERS, AND OTHERS

'My lord, if time has been lost through me, I am very sorry; but if your lordship's horse had fallen down in the street as mine did just now—'

'My horse never falls down in the street, Mr. Chaffanbrass.'

'Some beasts, my lord, can always keep their legs under them, and others can't; and men are pretty much in the same condition. I hope the former may be the case with your lordship and your lordship's cob for many years.' The judge, knowing of old that nothing could prevent Mr. Chaffanbrass from having the last word, now held his peace, and the trial began. . .

He was one of an order of barristers by no means yet extinct, but of whom it may be said that their peculiarities are somewhat less often seen than they were when Mr. Chaffanbrass was in his prime. He confined his practice almost entirely to one class of work, the defence, namely, of culprits arraigned for heavy crimes, and in this he was, if not unrivalled, at least unequalled. Rivals he had, who, thick as the skins of such men may be presumed to be, not unfrequently writhed beneath the lashes which his tongue could inflict. To such a perfection had he carried his skill and power of fence, so certain was he in attack, so invulnerable when attacked, that few men cared to come within the reach of his forensic flail. To the old stagers who were generally opposed to him, the gentlemen who conducted prosecutions on the part of the Crown, and customarily spent their time and skill in trying to hang those marauders on the public safety whom it was the special business of Mr. Chaffanbrass to preserve unhung, to these he was, if not civil, at least forbearing; but when any barrister, who was comparatively a stranger to him, ventured to oppose him, there was no measure to his impudent sarcasm and offensive sneers.

Those, however, who most dreaded Mr. Chaffanbrass, and who had most occasion to do so, were the witnesses. A rival lawyer could find a protection on the bench when his powers of endurance were tried too far; but a witness in a court of law has no protection. He comes there unfeed, without hope of guerdon, to give such assistance to the State in repressing crime and assisting justice as his knowledge in this particular case may enable him to afford; and justice, in order to ascertain whether his testimony be true, finds it necessary to subject him to torture. One would naturally imagine that an undisturbed thread of clear evidence would be best obtained from a man whose position was made easy and whose mind was not harassed; but this is not the fact: to turn a witness to good account, he must be badgered this way and that till he is nearly mad; he must be made a laughingstock for the court; his very truths must be turned into falsehoods, so that he may be falsely shamed; he must be accused of all manner of villany, threatened with all manner of punishment; he must be made to feel that he has no friend near him, that the world is all against him; he must be confounded till he forget his right hand from his left, till his mind be turned into chaos, and his heart into water; and then let him give his evidence. What will fall from his lips when in this wretched collapse must be of special value, for the best talents of practised forensic heroes are daily used to bring it about; and no member of the Humane Society interferes to protect the wretch. Some sorts of torture are, as it were, tacitly allowed even among humane people. Eels are skinned alive, and witnesses are sacrificed, and no one's blood curdles at the sight, no soft heart is sickened at the cruelty.

To apply the thumbscrew, the boot, and the rack to the victim before him was the work of Mr. Chaffanbrass's life. And it may be said of him that the labour he delighted in physicked pain. He was as little averse to this toil as the cat is to that of catching mice. And, indeed, he was not unlike a cat in his method of proceeding; for he would, as it were, hold his prey for a while between his paws, and pat him with gentle taps before he tore him. He would ask a few civil little questions in his softest voice, glaring out of his wicked old

## DOCTORS, LAWYERS, AND OTHERS

eye as he did so at those around him, and then, when he had his mouse well in hand, out would come his envenomed claw, and the wretched animal would feel the fatal wound in his tenderest part.

Mankind in general take pleasure in cruelty, though those who are civilized abstain from it on principle. On the whole Mr. Chaffanbrass is popular at the Old Bailey. Men congregate to hear him turn a witness inside out, and chuckle with an inward pleasure at the success of his cruelty. This Mr. Chaffanbrass knows, and, like an actor who is kept up to his high mark by the necessity of maintaining his character, he never allows himself to grow dull over his work. Therefore Mr. Chaffanbrass bullies when it is quite unnecessary that he should bully; it is a labour of love; and though he is now old, and stiff in his joints, though ease would be dear to him, though like a gladiator satiated with blood, he would as regards himself be so pleased to sheathe his sword, yet he never spares himself. He never spares himself, and he never spares his victim.

As a lawyer, in the broad and high sense of the word, it may be presumed that Mr. Chaffanbrass knows little or nothing. He has, indeed, no occasion for such knowledge. His business is to perplex a witness and bamboozle a jury, and in doing that he is generally successful. He seldom cares for carrying the judge with him: such tactics, indeed, as his are not likely to tell upon a judge. That which he loves is, that a judge should charge against him, and a jury give a verdict in his favour. When he achieves that he feels that he has earned his money. Let others, the young lads and spooneys of his profession, undertake the milk-and-water work of defending injured innocence; it is all but an insult to his practised ingenuity to invite his assistance to such tasteless business. Give him a case in which he has all the world against him; Justice with her sword raised high to strike; Truth with open mouth and speaking eyes to tell the bloody tale; outraged humanity shrieking for punishment; a case from which Mercy herself, with averted eyes, has loathing turned and bade her sterner sister do her work; give him such a case as this, and then you will see Mr. Chaffanbrass in his glory. Let him, by the use of his high art, rescue from the gallows and turn loose upon the world the wretch whose hands are reeking with the blood of father, mother, wife, and brother, and you may see Mr. Chaffanbrass, elated with conscious worth, rub his happy hands with infinite complacency. Then will his ambition be satisfied, and he will feel that in the verdict of the jury he has received the honour due to his genius. He will have succeeded in turning black into white, in washing the blackamoor, in dressing in the fair robe of innocence the foulest, filthiest wretch of his day; and as he returns to his home, he will be proudly conscious that he is no little man.

In person, however, Mr. Chaffanbrass is a little man, and a very dirty little man. He has all manner of nasty tricks about him, which make him a disagreeable neighbour to barristers sitting near to him. He is profuse with snuff, and very generous with his handkerchief. He is always at work upon his teeth, which do not do much credit to his industry. His wig is never at ease upon his head, but is poked about by him, sometimes over one ear, sometimes over the other, now on the back of his head, and then on his nose; and it is impossible to say in which guise he looks most cruel, most sharp, and most intolerable. His linen is never clean, his hands never washed, and his clothes apparently never new. He is about five feet six in height, and even with that stoops greatly. His custom is to lean forward, resting with both hands on the sort of desk before him, and then to fix his small brown basilisk eye on the victim in the box before him. In this position he will remain unmoved by the hour together, unless the elevation and fall of his thick eyebrows and the partial closing of his wicked eyes can be called motion. But his tongue! that moves; there is the weapon which he knows how to use!

## DOCTORS, LAWYERS, AND OTHERS

Such is Mr. Chaffanbrass in public life; and those who only know him in public life can hardly believe that at home he is one of the most easy, good-tempered, amiable old gentlemen that ever was pooh-poohed by his grown-up daughters, and occasionally told to keep himself quiet in a corner.

# Business

### 'Real Louey Catorse'

'And if you would allow me, sir, to have the pleasure of showing you a few of my patterns, I'm sure I should be delighted.' This he said observing that Mr. Moulder was sitting over his empty glass with the pipe in his hand, and his eyes fast closed. 'I think, sir, I could show you an article that would please you very much. You see, sir, that new ideas are coming in every day, and wood, sir, is altogether going out,—altogether going out as regards furniture. In another twenty years, sir, there won't be such a thing as a wooden table in the country, unless with some poor person that can't afford to refurnish. Believe me, sir, iron's the thing now-a-days.'

'And indian-rubber,' said Dockwrath.

'Yes; indian-rubber's wonderful too. Are you in that line, sir?'

'Well, no; not exactly.'

'It's not like iron, sir. You can't make a dinner-table for fourteen people out of indian-rubber, that will shut up into a box 3—6 by 2—4 deep, and 2—6 broad. Why, sir, I can let you have a set of drawing-room furniture for fifteen ten that you've never seen equalled in wood for three times the money;—ornamented in the tastiest way, sir, and fit for any lady's drawing-room or boodoor. The ladies of quality are all getting them now for their boodoors. There's three tables, eight chairs, easy rocking-chair, music-stand, stool to match, and pair of stand-up screens, all gilt in real Louey catorse; and it goes in three boxes 4—2 by 2—1 and 2—3. Think of that, sir. For fifteen ten and the boxes in.' Then there was a pause, after which Mr. Kantwise added—'If ready money, the carriage paid.' And then he turned his head very much away, and looked back very hard at his expected customer.

'I'm afraid the articles are not in my line,' said Mr. Dockwrath.

'It's the tastiest present for a gentleman to make to his lady that has come out since—since those sort of things have come out at all. You'll let me show you the articles, sir. It will give me the sincerest pleasure.' And Mr. Kantwise proposed to leave the room in order that he might introduce the three boxes in question.

'They would not be at all in my way,' said Mr. Dockwrath.

'The trouble would be nothing,' said Mr. Kantwise, 'and it gives me the greatest pleasure to make them known when I find any one who can appreciate such undoubted luxuries;' and so saying Mr. Kantwise skipped out of the room, and soon returned with James and Boots, each of the three bearing on his shoulder a deal box nearly as big as a coffin, all of which were deposited in different parts of the room. Mr. Moulder in the meantime snored heavily, his head falling on to his breast every now and again. But nevertheless he held fast by his pipe.

Mr. Kantwise skipped about the room with wonderful agility, unfastening the boxes, and taking out the contents, while Joe the boots and James the waiter stood by assisting. They had never yet seen the glories of these chairs and tables, and were therefore not unwilling to be present. It was singular to see how ready Mr. Kantwise was at the work, how recklessly he threw aside the whitey-brown paper in which the various pieces of painted iron were enveloped, and with what a practised hand he put together one article after another. First there was a round loo-table, not quite so large in its circumference as some people might think desirable, but, nevertheless, a round loo-table. The pedestal with its three claws was all together. With a knowing touch Mr. Kantwise separated the bottom of what looked like a yellow stick, and, lo! there were three legs, which he placed carefully on the ground. Then a small bar was screwed on to the top, and over the bar was screwed the leaf, or table itself, which consisted of three pieces unfolding with hinges. These, when the screw had been duly fastened in the centre, opened out upon the bar, and there was the table complete.

It was certainly a 'tasty' article, and the pride with which Mr. Kantwise glanced back at it was quite delightful. The top of the table was blue, with a red bird of paradise in the middle; and the edges of the table, to the breadth of a couple of inches, were yellow. The pillar also was yellow, as were the three legs. 'It's the real Louey catorse,' said Mr. Kantwise, stooping down to go on with table number two, which was, as he described it, a 'chess,' having the proper number of blue and light-pink squares marked upon it; but this also had been made Louey catorse with reference to its legs and edges. The third table was a 'sofa,' of proper shape, but rather small in size. Then, one after another, he brought forth and screwed up the chairs, stools, and sundry screens, and within a quarter of an hour he had put up the whole set complete. The red bird of paradise and the blue ground appeared on all, as did also the yellow legs and edgings which gave to them their peculiarly fashionable character. 'There,' said Mr. Kantwise, looking at them with fond admiration, 'I don't mind giving a personal guarantee that there's nothing equal to that for the money either in England or in France.'

'They are very nice,' said Mr. Dockwrath. When a man has had produced before him for his own and sole delectation any article or articles, how can he avoid eulogium? Mr. Dockwrath found himself obliged to pause, and almost feared that he should find himself obliged to buy.

'Nice! I should rather think they are,' said Mr. Kantwise, becoming triumphant,—'and for fifteen ten, delivered, boxes included. There's nothing like iron, sir, nothing; you may take my word for that. They're so strong, you know. Look here, sir.' And then Mr. Kantwise, taking two of the pieces of whitey-brown paper which had been laid aside, carefully spread one on the centre of the round table, and the other on the seat of one of the chairs. Then lightly poising himself on his toe, he stepped on to the chair, and from thence on to the table. In that position he skillfully brought his feet together, so that his weight was directly on the leg, and gracefully waved his hands over his head. James and Boots stood by admiring, with open mouths, and Mr. Dockwrath, with his hands in his pockets, was meditating whether he could not give the order without complying with the terms as to ready money.

'Look at that for strength,' said Mr. Kantwise from his exalted position. 'I don't think any lady of your acquaintance, sir, would allow you to stand on her rosewood or mahogany loo-table. And if she did, you would not like to adventure it yourself. But look at this for strength,' and he waved his arms abroad, still keeping his feet skillfully together in the same exact position.

At that moment Mr. Moulder awoke. 'So you've got your iron traps out, have you?' said he. 'What; you're there, are you? Upon my word I'd sooner you than me.'

'I certainly should not like to see you up here, Mr. Moulder. I doubt whether even this table would bear five-and-twenty stone. Joe, lend me your shoulder, there's a good fellow.' And then Mr. Kantwise, bearing very lightly on the chair, descended to the ground without accident.

'Now, that's what I call gammon,' said Moulder.

'What is gammon, Mr. Moulder?' said the other, beginning to be angry.

'It's all gammon. The chairs and tables is gammon, and so is the stools and the screens.'

'Mr. Moulder, I didn't call your tea and coffee and brandy gammon.'

'You can't; and you wouldn't do any harm if you did. Hubbles and Grease are too well known in Yorkshire for you to hurt them. But as for all that show-off and gimcrack-work,

## HE CONSIDERS ITS PATTERNS

I tell you fairly it aint what I call trade, and it aint fit for a commercial room. It's gammon, gammon, gammon! James, give me a bedcandle.' And so Mr. Moulder took himself off to bed.

'I think I'll go too,' said Mr. Dockwrath.

'You'll let me put you up the set, eh?' said Mr. Kantwise.

'Well; I'll think about it,' said the attorney. 'I'll not just give you an answer to-night. Good night, sir; I'm very much obliged to you.' And he too went, leaving Mr. Kantwise to repack his chairs and tables with the assistance of James the waiter.

### COMMERCIAL ROOM AT THE BULL INN

GROBY PARK is about seven miles from Leeds, and as Mr. Dockwrath had in the first instance to travel from Hamworth up to London, he did not reach Leeds till late in the evening. It was a nasty, cold, drizzling night, so that the beauties and marvels of the large manufacturing town offered him no attraction, and at nine o'clock he had seated himself before the fire in the commercial room at The Bull, had called for a pair of public slippers, and was about to solace all his cares with a glass of mahogany-coloured brandy and water and a cigar. The room had no present occupant but himself, and therefore he was able to make the most of all its comforts. He had taken the solitary arm-chair, and had so placed himself that the gas would fall direct from behind his head on to that day's Leeds and Halifax Chronicle, as soon as he should choose to devote himself to local politics.

The waiter had looked at him with doubtful eyes when he asked to be shown into the commercial room, feeling all but confident that such a guest had no right to be there. He had no bulky bundles of samples, nor any of those outward characteristics of a commercial 'gent' with which all men conversant with the rail and road are acquainted, and which the accustomed eye of a waiter recognizes at a glance...

BUSINESS

' 'Mercial, sir?' said the waiter at The Bull Inn, Leeds, to Mr. Dockwrath, in that tone of doubt which seemed to carry an answer to his own question. But Mr. Dockwrath was not a man to be put down by a waiter. 'Yes,' said he. 'Didn't you hear me say so?' And then the waiter gave way. None of those lords of the road were in the house at the moment, and it might be that none would come that night.

Mr. Dockwrath had arrived by the 8.22 P.M. down, but the 8.45 P.M. up from the north followed quick upon his heels, and he had hardly put his brandy and water to his mouth before a rush and a sound of many voices were heard in the hall. There is a great difference between the entrance into an inn of men who are not known there and of men who are known. The men who are not known are shy, diffident, doubtful, and anxious to propitiate the chambermaid by great courtesy. The men who are known are loud, jocular, and assured;—or else, in case of deficient accommodation, loud, angry, and full of threats. The guests who had now arrived were well known, and seemed at present to be in the former mood. 'Well, Mary, my dear, what's the time of day with you?' said a rough, bass voice, within the hearing of Mr. Dockwrath. 'Much about the old tune, Mr. Moulder,' said the girl at the bar. 'Time to look alive and keep moving. Will you have them boxes up stairs, Mr. Kantwise?' and then there were a few words about the luggage, and two real commercial gentlemen walked into the room.

Mr. Dockwrath resolved to stand upon his rights, so he did not move his chair, but looked up over his shoulder at the new comers. The first man who entered was short and very fat;—so fat that he could not have seen his own knees for some considerable time past. His face rolled with fat, as also did all his limbs. His eyes were large, and bloodshot. He wore no beard, and therefore showed plainly the triple bagging of his fat chin. In spite of his overwhelming fatness, there was something in his face that was masterful and almost vicious. His body had been overcome by eating, but not as yet his

[ 263 ]

spirit—one would be inclined to say. This was Mr. Moulder, well known on the road as being in the grocery and spirit line; a pushing man, who understood his business, and was well trusted by his firm in spite of his habitual intemperance. What did the firm care whether or no he killed himself by eating and drinking? He sold his goods, collected his money, and made his remittances. If he got drunk at night that was nothing to them, seeing that he always did his quota of work the next day. But Mr. Moulder did not get drunk. His brandy and water went into his blood, and into his eyes, and into his feet, and into his hands,—but not into his brain.

The other was a little square man in the hardware line, of the name of Kantwise. He disposed of fire-irons, grates, ovens, and kettles, and was at the present moment heavily engaged in the sale of certain newly-invented metallic tables and chairs lately brought out by the Patent Steel Furniture Company, for which Mr. Kantwise did business. He looked as though a skin rather too small for the purpose had been drawn over his head and face so that his forehead and cheeks and chin were tight and shiny. His eyes were small and green, always moving about in his head, and were seldom used by Mr. Kantwise in the ordinary way. At whatever he looked he looked sideways; it was not that he did not look you in the face, but he always looked at you with a sidelong glance, never choosing to have you straight in front of him. And the more eager he was in conversation—the more anxious he might be to gain his point, the more he averted his face and looked askance; so that sometimes he would prefer to have his antagonist almost behind his shoulder. And then as he did this, he would thrust forward his chin, and having looked at you round the corner till his eyes were nearly out of his head, he would close them both and suck in his lips, and shake his head with rapid little shakes, as though he were saying to himself, 'Ah, sir! you're a bad un, a very bad un.' His nose—for I should do Mr. Kantwise injustice if I did not mention this feature—seemed to have been compressed almost into nothing by that skin-squeezing operation. It was long enough, taking the measurement down the bridge, and projected sufficiently, counting the distance from the upper lip; but it had all the properties of a line; it possessed length without breadth. There was nothing in it from side to side. If you essayed to pull it, your fingers would meet. When I shall have also said that the hair on Mr. Kantwise's head stood up erect all round to the height of two inches, and that it was very red, I shall have been accurate enough in his personal description.

That Mr. Moulder represented a firm good business, doing tea, coffee, and British brandy on a well-established basis of capital and profit, the travelling commercial world in the north of England was well aware. No one entertained any doubt about his employers, Hubbles and Grease of Houndsditch. Hubbles and Grease were all right, as they had been any time for the last twenty years. But I cannot say that there was quite so strong a confidence felt in the Patent Steel Furniture Company generally, or in the individual operations of Mr. Kantwise in particular. The world in Yorkshire and Lancashire was doubtful about metallic tables, and it was thought that Mr. Kantwise was too eloquent in their praise.

Mr. Moulder when he had entered the room, stood still, to enable the waiter to peel off from him his greatcoat and the large shawl with which his neck was enveloped, and Mr. Kantwise performed the same operation for himself, carefully folding up the articles of clothing as he took them off. Then Mr. Moulder fixed his eyes on Mr. Dockwrath, and stared at him very hard. 'Who's the party, James?' he said to the waiter, speaking in a whisper that was plainly heard by the attorney.

'Gen'elman by the 8.22 down,' said James.

'Commercial?' asked Mr. Moulder, with angry frown.

'He says so himself, anyways,' said the waiter.

'Gammon!' replied Mr. Moulder, who knew all the bearings of a commercial man thoroughly, and could have put one together if he were only supplied with a little bit—say the mouth, as Professor Owen always does with the Dodoes. Mr. Moulder now began to be angry, for he was a stickler for the rights and privileges of his class, and had an idea that the world was not so conservative in that respect as it should be. Mr. Dockwrath, however, was not to be frightened, so he drew his chair a thought nearer to the fire, took a sup of brandy and water, and prepared himself for war if war should be necessary.

'Cold evening, sir, for the time of year,' said Mr. Moulder, walking up to the fireplace, and rolling the lumps of his forehead about in his attempt at a frown. In spite of his terrible burden of flesh, Mr. Moulder could look angry on occasions, but he could only do so when he was angry. He was not gifted with a command of his facial muscles.

'Yes,' said Mr. Dockwrath, not taking his eyes from off the Leeds and Halifax Chronicle. 'It is coldish. Waiter, bring me a cigar.'

This was very provoking, as must be confessed. Mr. Moulder had not been prepared to take any step towards turning the gentleman out, though doubtless he might have done so had he chosen to exercise his prerogative. But he did expect that the gentleman would have acknowledged the weakness of his footing, by moving himself a little towards one side of the fire, and he did not expect that he would have presumed to smoke without asking whether the practice was held to be objectionable by the legal possessors of the room. Mr. Dockwrath was free of any such pusillanimity. 'Waiter,' he said again, 'bring me a cigar, d'ye hear?'

The great heart of Moulder could not stand this unmoved. He had been an accustomed visitor to that room for fifteen years, and had always done his best to preserve the commercial code unsullied. He was now so well known, that no one else ever presumed to take the chair at the four o'clock commercial dinner if he were present. It was incumbent on him to stand forward and make a fight, more especially in the presence of Kantwise, who was by no means stanch to his order. Kantwise would at all times have been glad to have outsiders in the room, in order that he might puff his tables, and if possible effect a sale;—a mode of proceeding held in much aversion by the upright, old-fashioned, commercial mind.

'Sir,' said Mr. Moulder, having become very red about the cheeks and chin, 'I and this gentleman are going to have a bit of supper, and it aint accustomed to smoke in commercial rooms during meals. You know the rules no doubt if you're commercial yourself;—as I suppose you are, seeing you in this room.'

Now Mr. Moulder was wrong in his law, as he himself was very well aware. Smoking is allowed in all commercial rooms when the dinner has been some hour or so off the table. But then it was necessary that he should hit the stranger in some way, and the chances were that the stranger would know nothing about commercial law. Nor did he; so he merely looked Mr. Moulder hard in the face. But Mr. Kantwise knew the laws well enough, and as he saw before him a possible purchaser of metallic tables, he came to the assistance of the attorney.

'I think you are a little wrong there, Mr. Moulder; eh; aint you?' said he.

'Wrong about what?' said Moulder, turning very sharply upon his base-minded compatriot.

'Well, as to smoking. It's nine o'clock, and if the gentleman—'

'I don't care a brass farthing about the clock,' said the other, 'but when I'm going to have a bit of steak with my tea, in my own room, I chooses to have it comfortable.'

'Goodness me, Mr. Moulder, how many times have I seen you sitting there with a pipe in your mouth, and half a dozen gents eating their teas the while in this very room? The rule of the case I take it to be this; when—'

'Bother your rules.'

'Well; it was you spoke of them.'

## HE CONSIDERS ITS PATTERNS

'The question I take to be this,' said Moulder, now emboldened by the opposition he had received. 'Has the gentleman any right to be in this room at all, or has he not? Is he commercial, or is he—miscellaneous? That's the chat, as I take it.'

'You're on the square there, I must allow,' said Kantwise.

'James,' said Moulder, appealing with authority to the waiter, who had remained in the room during the controversy; —and now Mr. Moulder was determined to do his duty and vindicate his profession, let the consequences be what they might. 'James, is that gentleman commercial, or is he not?'

It was clearly necessary now that Mr. Dockwrath himself should take his own part, and fight his own battle. 'Sir,' said he, turning to Mr. Moulder, 'I think you'll find it extremely difficult to define that word;—extremely difficult. In this enterprising country all men are more or less commercial.'

'Hear! hear!' said Mr. Kantwise.

'That's gammon,' said Mr. Moulder.

'Gammon it may be,' said Mr. Dockwrath, 'but nevertheless it's right in law. Taking the word in its broadest, strictest, and most intelligible sense, I am a commercial gentleman; and as such I do maintain that I have a full right to the accommodation of this public room.'

'That's very well put,' said Mr. Kantwise.

'Waiter,' thundered out Mr. Moulder, as though he imagined that that functionary was down the yard at the taproom instead of standing within three feet of his elbow. 'Is this gent a commercial, or is he not? Because if not,—then I'll trouble you to send Mr. Crump here. My compliments to Mr. Crump, and I wish to see him.' Now Mr. Crump was the landlord of the Bull Inn.

'Master's just stepped out, down the street,' said James.

'Why don't you answer my question, sir?' said Moulder, becoming redder and still more red about his shirt-collars.

'The gent said as how he was 'mercial,' said the poor man.

'Was I to go to contradict a gent and tell him he wasn't when he said as how he was?'

'If you please,' said Mr. Dockwrath, 'we will not bring the waiter into this discussion. I asked for the commercial room, and he did his duty in showing me to the door of it. The fact I take to be this; in the south of England the rules to which you refer are not kept so strictly as in these more mercantile localities.'

'I've always observed that,' said Kantwise.

'I travelled for three years in Devonshire, Somersetshire, and Wiltshire,' said Moulder, 'and the commercial rooms were as well kept there as any I ever see.'

'I alluded to Surrey and Kent,' said Mr. Dockwrath.

'They're uncommonly miscellaneous in Surrey and Kent,' said Kantwise. 'There's no doubt in the world about that.'

'If the gentleman means to say that he's come in here because he didn't know the custom of the country, I've no more to say, of course,' said Moulder. 'And in that case, I, for one, shall be very happy if the gentleman can make himself comfortable in this room as a stranger, and I may say guest;— paying his own shot, of course.'

'And as for me, I shall be delighted,' said Kantwise. 'I never did like too much exclusiveness. What's the use of bottling oneself up? that's what I always say. Besides, there's no charity in it. We gents as are always on the road should show a little charity to them as ain't so well accustomed to the work.'

At this allusion to charity Mr. Moulder snuffled through his nose to show his great disgust, but he made no further answer. Mr. Dockwrath, who was determined not to yield, but who had nothing to gain by further fighting, bowed his head, and declared that he felt very much obliged. Whether or no there was any touch of irony in his tone, Mr. Moulder's ears were not fine enough to discover. So they now sat round the fire together, the attorney still keeping his seat in the middle. And then Mr. Moulder ordered his little bit of steak with his tea. 'With the gravy in it, James,' he said, solemnly.

'And a bit of fat, and a few slices of onion, thin mind, put on raw, not with all the taste fried out; and tell the cook if she don't do it as it should be done, I'll be down into the kitchen and do it myself. You'll join me, Kantwise, eh?'

'Well, I think not; I dined at three, you know.'

'Dined at three! What of that? a dinner at three won't last a man for ever. You might as well join me.'

'No, I think not. Have you got such a thing as a nice red herring in the house, James?'

'Get one round the corner, sir.'

'Do, there's a good fellow; and I'll take it for a relish with my tea. I'm not so fond of your solids three times a day. They heat the blood too much.'

'Bother,' grunted Moulder; and then they went to their evening meal, over which we will not disturb them. The steak, we may presume, was cooked aright, as Mr. Moulder did not visit the kitchen, and Mr. Kantwise no doubt made good play with his unsubstantial dainty, as he spoke no further till his meal was altogether finished.

## Tricks of the Trade

THOUGH THINGS SOMETIMES looked very bad, yet money always 'turned up.' Some of their buyings and sellings had answered pretty well. Some had been great failures. No great stroke had been made as yet, but then the great stroke was always being expected. Sexty's fears were greatly exaggerated by the feeling that the coffee and guano were not always real coffee and guano. His partner, indeed, was of opinion that in such a trade as this they were following there was no need at all of real coffee and real guano, and explained his theory with considerable eloquence. 'If I buy a ton of coffee and keep it six weeks, why do I buy it and keep it, and why does the seller sell it instead of keeping it? The seller sells it because he thinks he can do best by parting with it now at a certain price. I buy it because I think I can make money by keeping it. It is just the same as though we were to back our opinions. He backs the fall. I back the rise. You needn't have coffee and you needn't have guano to do this. Indeed the possession of the coffee or the guano is only a very clumsy addition to the trouble of your profession. I make it my study to watch the markets;—but I needn't buy everything I see in order to make money by my labour and intelligence.' Sexty Parker before his lunch always thought that his partner was wrong, but after that ceremony he almost daily became a convert to the great doctrine. Coffee and guano still had to be bought because the world was dull and would not learn the tricks of trade as taught by Ferdinand Lopez,—also possibly because somebody might want such articles,—but our enterprising hero looked for a time in which no such dull burden should be imposed on him.

## Money-Making

'But them men, when they get on at money-making,—or money-losing, which makes 'em worse,—are like tigers clawing one another. They don't care how many they kills, so that they has the least bit for themselves. There ain't no fear of God in it, nor yet no mercy, nor ere a morsel of heart. It ain't what I call manly,—not that longing after other folks' money. When it's come by hard work, as I tell Sexty,—by the very sweat of his brow,—oh,—it's sweet as sweet. When he'd tell me that he'd made his three pound, or his five pound, or, perhaps, his ten pound in a day, and'd calculate it up, how much it'd come to if he did that every day, and where we could go to, and what we could do for the children, I loved to hear him talk about his money. But now—! why, it's altered the looks of the man altogether. It's just as though he was a-thirsting for blood.'

## The Billboards

IF A CERTAIN NEW SPIRIT which had just been concocted from the bark of trees in Central Africa, and which was called Bios, could only be made to go up in the market, everything might be satisfactorily arranged. The hoardings of London were already telling the public that if it wished to get drunk without any of the usual troubles of intoxication it must drink Bios. The public no doubt does read the literature of the hoardings, but then it reads so slowly! This Bios had hardly been twelve months on the boards as yet! But they were now increasing the size of the letters in the advertisements and the jocundity of the pictures,—and the thing might be done.

## Sharp Dealing

WHEN, THEREFORE, LOPEZ called one day at the little house in the little street he was not an unwelcome visitor. Mrs. Leslie was in the drawing-room, but soon left it after his arrival. He had of late been often there, and when he at once introduced the subject on which he was himself intent it was not unexpected. 'Seven thousand five hundred pounds!' said Lizzie, after listening to the proposition which he had come to make. 'That is a very large sum of money!'

'Yes;—it's a large sum of money. It's a large affair. I'm in it to rather more than that, I believe.'

'How are you to get people to drink it?' she asked after a pause.

'By telling them that they ought to drink it. Advertise it. It has become a certainty now that if you will only advertise sufficiently you may make a fortune by selling anything. Only the interest on the money expended increases in so large a ratio in accordance with the magnitude of the operation! If you spend a few hundreds in advertising you throw them

BUSINESS

away. A hundred thousand pounds well laid out makes a certainty of anything.'

'What am I to get to show for my money;—I mean immediately, you know?'

'Registered shares in the Company.'

'The Bios Company?'

'No;—we did propose to call ourselves Parker and Co., limited. I think we shall change the name. They will probably use my name. Lopez and Co., limited.'

'But it's all for Bios?'

'Oh, yes;—all for Bios.'

'And it's to come from Central Africa?'

'It will be rectified in London, you know. Some English spirit will perhaps be mixed. But I must not tell you the secrets of the trade till you join us. That Bios is distilled from the bark of the Duffertree is a certainty.'

'Have you drank any?'

'I've tasted it.'

'Is it nice?'

'Very nice;—rather sweet, you know, and will be the better for mixing.'

'Gin?' suggested her ladyship.

'Perhaps so,—or whisky. I think I may say that you can't do very much better with your money. You know I would not say this to you were it not true. In such a matter I treat you just as if,—as if you were my sister.'

'I know how good you are,—but seven thousand five hundred! I couldn't raise so much as that just at present.'

'There are to be six shares,' said Lopez, 'making £45,000 capital. Would you consent to take a share jointly with me? That would be three thousand seven hundred and fifty.'

'But you have a share already,' said Lizzie suspiciously.

'I should then divide that with Mr. Parker. We intend to register at any rate as many as nine partners. Would you object to hold it with me?' Lopez, as he asked the question, looked at her as though he were offering her half his heart.

'No,' said Lizzie, slowly, 'I don't suppose I should object to that.'

'I should be doubly eager about the affair if I were in partnership with you.'

'It's such a venture.'

'Nothing venture nothing have.'

'But I've got something as it is, Mr. Lopez, and I don't want to lose it all.'

'There's no chance of that if you join us.'

'You think Bios is so sure!'

'Quite safe,' said Lopez.

'You must give me a little more time to think about it,' said Lady Eustace at last, panting with anxiety, struggling with herself, anxious for the excitement which would come to her from dealing in Bios, but still fearing to risk her money.

## Messrs. Bungall and Tappitt, Brewers

It is not to be supposed that they were great men like the mighty men of beer known of old,—such as Barclay and Perkins, or Reid and Co. Nor were they new, and pink, and prosperous, going into Parliament for this borough or that just as they pleased, like the modern heroes of the bitter cask. When the student at Oxford was asked what man had most benefited humanity, and when he answered 'Bass,' I think that he should not have been plucked. It was a fair average answer: but no student at any university could have said as much for Bungall and Tappitt without deserving utter disgrace.—It was a sour and muddy stream that flowed from their vats; a beverage disagreeable to the palate and very cold and uncomfortable to the stomach. Who drank it I could never learn. It was to be found at no respectable inn. It was admitted at no private gentleman's table. The farmers knew nothing of it. The labourers drenched themselves habitually with cider. Nevertheless the brewery of Messrs. Bungall and Tappitt was kept going, and the large ugly square brick house in which the Tappitt family lived was warm and comfortable. There is something in the very name of beer that makes money.

## Advertising

THERE ARE THOSE—men of the old school—who cannot rouse themselves to see and read the signs of the time, men who would have been in the last ranks, let them have lived when they would,—who object to it that it is untrue,—who say that advertisements do not keep the promises which they make...

Well; I say again and again to all young tradesmen—Advertise, advertise, advertise;—and don't stop to think too much about capital. It is a bugbear. Capital is a bugbear; and it is talked about by those who have it,—and by some that have not so much of it neither,—for the sake of putting down competition, and keeping the market to themselves...

But there must be some *nous* in your advertisements; there must be a system, and there must be some wit in your system. It won't suffice now-a-days to stick up on a black wall a simple placard to say that you have forty thousand best new hose just arrived. Any wooden-headed fellow can do as much as that. That might have served in the olden times that we hear of, twenty years since; but the game to be successful in these days must be played in another sort of fashion. There must be some finish about your advertisements, something new in your style, something that will startle in your manner. If a man can make himself a real master of this art, we may say that he has learnt his trade, whatever his trade may be. Let him know how to advertise, and the rest will follow.

## How to Play the Market

IF A MAN intends to make a fortune in the share-market he will never do it by being bold one day and timid the next. No turf betting-book can be made up safely except on consistent principles. Half-measures are always ruinous. In mat-

## HE CONSIDERS ITS PATTERNS

ters of speculation one attempt is made safe by another. No man, it is true, can calculate accurately what may be the upshot of a single venture; but a sharp fellow may calculate with a fair average of exactness what will be the aggregate upshot of many ventures. All mercantile fortunes have been made by the knowledge and understanding of this rule. If a man speculates but once and again, now and then, as it were, he must of course be a loser. He will be playing a game which he does not understand, and playing it against men who do understand it. Men who so play always lose. But he who speculates daily puts himself exactly in the reversed position. He plays a game which experience teaches him to play well, and he plays generally against men who have no such advantage. Of course he wins.

*HE DISTILLS ITS IDEAS AND THEORIES*

*Social Ideas*

---

On England
'Bush Inn, Dillsborough,
'Ufford County, England,
'December 16, 187–.

'MY DEAR SIR,

'Since my last I have enjoyed myself very well, and I am, I trust, beginning to understand something of the mode of thinking of this very peculiar people. That there should be so wide a difference between us Americans and these English, from whom we were divided, so to say, but the other day, is one of the most peculiar physiological phenomena that the history of the world will have afforded. As far as I can hear, a German or even a Frenchman thinks much more as an Englishman thinks than does an American. Nor does this come mainly from the greater prevalence with us of democratic institutions. I do not think that any one can perceive in half an hour's conversation the difference between a Swiss and a German; but I fancy, and I may say I flatter myself, that an American is as easily distinguished from an Englishman, as a sheep from a goat, or a tall man from one who is short.

'And yet there is a pleasure in associating with those here of the highest rank which I find it hard to describe, and which perhaps I ought to regard as a pernicious temptation to useless luxury. There is an ease of manner with them which recalls with unfavourable reminiscences the hard self-consciousness of the better class of our citizens. There is a story of an old hero who with his companions fell among beautiful women and luscious wine, but the hero had been warned in time that they would all be turned into filthy animals should they yield to the allurements around them. The temptation here is perhaps the same. I am not a hero; and, though I too have been warned by the lessons I have learned under our happy Constitution, I feel that I might easily become one of the animals in question.

'And, to give them their due, it is better than merely beautiful women and luscious wine. There is a reality about them, and a desire to live up to their principles, which is very grand. Their principles are no doubt very bad, utterly antagonistic to all progress, unconscious altogether of the demand for progressive equality which is made by the united voices of suffering mankind. The man who is born a lord, and who sees a dozen serfs around him who have been born to be half-starved ploughmen, thinks that God arranged it all, and that he is bound to maintain a state of things so comfortable to himself, as being God's vicegerent here on earth. But they do their work as vicegerents with an easy grace, and with sweet pleasant voices and soft movements, which almost make a man doubt whether the Almighty has not, in truth, intended that such injustice should be permanent. That one man should be rich and another poor is a necessity in the present imperfect state of civilization;—but that one man should be born to be a legislator, born to have everything, born to be a tyrant,—and should think it all right, is to me miraculous. But the greatest miracle of all is that they who are not so born,—who have been born to suffer the reverse side,—should also think it to be all right.

'With us it is necessary that a man, to shine in society, should have done something, or should, at any rate, have the capacity of doing something. But here the greatest fool that you meet will shine, and will be admitted to be brilliant, simply because he has possessions. Such a one will take his part in conversation though he knows nothing, and, when

SOCIAL IDEAS

inquired into, he will own that he knows nothing. To know anything is not in his line in life. But he can move about, and chatter like a child of ten, and amuse himself from morning to night with various empty playthings,—and be absolutely proud of his life!

'I have lately become acquainted with a certain young lord here of this class, who has treated me with great kindness, although I have taken it into my head to oppose him as to a matter in which he is very keen. I ventured to inquire of him as to the pursuits of his life. He is a lord, and therefore a legislator, but he made no scruple to tell me that he never went near the Chamber in which it is his privilege to have a seat. But his party does not lose his support. Though he never goes near the place he can vote and is enabled to trust his vote to some other more ambitious lord who does go there. It required the absolute evidence of personal information from those who are themselves concerned to make me believe that legislation in Great Britain could be carried on after such a fashion as this! Then he told me what he did do. All the winter he hunts and shoots, going about to other rich men's houses when there is no longer sufficient for him to shoot left on his own estate. That lasts him from the 1st of September to the end of March, and occupies all his time. August he spends in Scotland, also shooting other animals. During the other months he fishes, and plays cricket and tennis, and attends races, and goes about to parties in London. His evenings he spends at a card table when he can get friends to play with him. It is the employment of his life to fit in his amusements so that he may not have a dull day. Wherever he goes he carries his wine with him and his valet and his grooms;— and if he thinks there is anything to fear, his cook also. He very rarely opens a book. He is more ignorant than a boy of fifteen with us, and yet he manages to have something to say about everything. When his ignorance has been made as clear as the sun at noon-day, he is no whit ashamed. One would say that such a life would break the heart of any man, but, upon my word, I doubt whether I ever came across a human being so self-satisfied as this young lord.

'I have come down here to support the case of a poor man who is, I think, being trampled on by this do-nothing legislator. But I am bound to say that the lord in his kind is very much better than the poor man in his. Such a wretched, squalid, lying, cowardly creature I did not think that even England could produce. And yet the man has a property in land on which he ought to be able to live in humble comfort. I feel sure that I have leagued myself with a rascal, whereas I believe the lord, in spite of his ignorance and his idleness, to be honest. But yet the man is being hardly used, and has had the spirit, or rather perhaps has been instigated by others, to rebel. His crops have been eaten up by the lord's pheasants, and the lord, exercising plenary power as though he were subject to no laws, will only pay what compensation he himself chooses to award. The whole country here is in arms against the rebel, thinking it monstrous that a man living in a hovel should contest such a point with the owner of half-a-dozen palaces. I have come forward to help the man for the sake of seeing how the matter will go; and I have to confess that though those under the lord have treated me as though I were a miscreant, the lord himself and his friends have been civil enough.

'I say what I think wherever I go, and I do not find it taken in bad part. In that respect we might learn something from them. When a Britisher over in the States says what he thinks about us, we are apt to be a little rough with him. I have, indeed, known towns in which he couldn't speak out with personal safety. Here there is no danger of that kind. I am getting together the materials for a lecture on British institutions in general, in which I shall certainly speak my mind plainly, and I think I shall venture to deliver it in London before I leave for New York in the course of next spring.

I will, however, write to you again before that time comes.

'Believe me to be,
'Dear sir,
'With much sincerity,
'Yours truly,
'ELIAS GOTOBED.'

'The Honble. Josiah Scroome,
'125, Q Street,
'Minnesota Avenue,
'Washington.'

## ENGLAND IN THE EYES OF AMERICA

IN HIS OWN COUNTRY he had heard vehement abuse of the old country from the lips of politicians, and had found at the same time almost on all sides great social admiration for the people so abused. He had observed that every Englishman of distinction was received in the States as a demigod, and that some who were not very great in their own land had been converted into heroes in his. English books were read there; English laws were obeyed there; English habits were cultivated, often at the expense of American comfort. And yet it was the fashion among orators to speak of the English as a wornout, stupid, and enslaved people. He was a thoughtful man, and all this had perplexed him.

## ON AN ENGLISH MODEL FARM

THE TWO STARTED ABOUT THREE with the object of walking round the park and the home farm,—the Senator intent on his duty of examining the ways of English life to the very bottom. . .

'Here we get out of the park on to the home farm. Rufford does it very well,—very well indeed.'

'Looks after it altogether himself?'

'I cannot quite say that. He has a land-bailiff, who lives in the house there.'

'With a salary?'

[ 283 ]

'Oh yes; £120 a year I think the man has.'

'And that house?' asked the Senator. 'Why, the house and garden are worth £50 a year.'

'I dare say they are. Of course it costs money. It's near the park, and had to be made ornamental.'

'And does it pay?'

'Well, no; I should think not. In point of fact, I know it does not. He loses about the value of the ground.'

The Senator asked a great many more questions, and then began his lecture. 'A man who goes into trade, and loses by it, cannot be doing good to himself or to others. You say, Sir George, that it is a model farm; but it's a model of ruin. If you want to teach a man any other business, you don't specially select an example in which the proprietors are spending all their capital without any return. And if you would not do this in shoemaking, why in farming?'

'The neighbours are able to see how work should be done.'

'Excuse me, Sir George, but it seems to me that they are enabled to see how work should not be done. If his lordship would stick up over his gate a notice to the effect that everything seen there was to be avoided, he might do some service. If he would publish his accounts half-yearly in the village newspaper—'

'There isn't a village newspaper.'

'In the *Rufford Gazette*. There is a *Rufford Gazette*, and Rufford isn't much more than a village. If he would publish his accounts half-yearly in the *Rufford Gazette*, honestly showing how much he had lost by his system, how much capital had been misapplied and how much labour wasted, he might serve as an example, like the pictures of "The Idle Apprentice." I don't see that he can do any other good,—unless it be to the estimable gentleman who is allowed to occupy the pretty house. I don't think you'd see anything like that model farm in our country, sir.'

'Your views, Mr. Gotobed, are utilitarian rather than picturesque.'

## SOCIAL IDEAS

'Oh! if you say that it is done for the picturesque, that is another thing. Lord Rufford is a wealthy lord, and can afford to be picturesque. A green sward I should have thought handsomer, as well as less expensive, than a ploughed field; but that is a matter of taste. Only why call a pretty toy a model farm? You might mislead the British rustics.'

They had by this time passed through a couple of fields which formed part of the model farm, and had come to a stile leading into a large meadow. 'This, I take it,' said the Senator, looking about him, 'is beyond the limits of my lord's plaything.'

'This is Shugborough,' said Sir George, 'and there is John Runce, the occupier, on his pony. He, at any rate, is a model farmer.'

### AT THE FÊTE CHAMPÊTRE

THE ORDER OF THE DAY was to be as follows. The quality, as the upper classes in rural districts are designated by the lower with so much true discrimination, were to eat a breakfast, and the non-quality were to eat a dinner. Two marquees had been erected for these two banquets, that for the quality on the esoteric or garden side of a certain deep ha-ha; and that for the non-quality on the exoteric or paddock side of the same. Both were of huge dimensions; that on the outer side was, one may say, on an egregious scale; but Mr. Plomacy declared that neither would be sufficient. To remedy this, an auxiliary banquet was prepared in the dining-room, and a subsidiary board was to be spread *sub dio* for the accommodation of the lower class of yokels on the Ullathorne property. . .

In the first place there was a dreadful line to be drawn. Who were to dispose themselves within the ha-ha, and who without? To this the unthinking will give an off-hand answer, as they will to every ponderous question. Oh, the bishop and such like within the ha-ha; and Farmer Greenacre and such like without. True, my unthinking friend; but who shall de-

[ 285 ]

fine these such-likes? It is in such definitions that the whole difficulty of society consists. To seat the bishop on an arm chair on the lawn and place Farmer Greenacre at the end of a long table in the paddock is easy enough; but where will you put Mrs. Lookaloft, whose husband, though a tenant on the estate, hunts in a red coat, whose daughters go to a fashionable seminary in Barchester, who calls her farm house Rosebank, and who has a pianoforte in her drawing-room? The Misses Lookaloft, as they call themselves, won't sit contented among the bumpkins. Mrs. Lookaloft won't squeeze her fine clothes on a bench and talk familiarly about cream and ducklings to good Mrs. Greenacre. And yet Mrs. Lookaloft is no fit companion and never has been the associate of the Thornes and the Grantlys. And if Mrs. Lookaloft be admitted within the sanctum of fashionable life, if she be allowed with her three daughters to leap the ha-ha, why not the wives and daughters of other families also? Mrs. Greenacre is at present well contented with the paddock, but she might cease to be so if she saw Mrs. Lookaloft on the lawn. And thus poor Miss Thorne had a hard time of it.

And how was she to divide her guests between the marquee and the parlour? She had a countess coming, an Honourable John and an Honourable George, and a whole bevy of Ladies Amelia, Rosina, Margaretta, &c.; she had a leash of baronets with their baronnettes; and, as we all know, she had a bishop. If she put them on the lawn, no one would go into the parlour; if she put them into the parlour, no one would go into the tent. She thought of keeping the old people in the house, and leaving the lawn to the lovers. She might as well have seated herself at once in a hornet's nest.

## Is the World Progressing?

'THERE IS SOMETHING about old-fashioned mansions, built as this is, and old-fashioned gardens, that to me is especially delightful.'

'I like everything old-fashioned,' said Eleanor; 'old-fashioned things are so much the honestest.'

'I don't know about that,' said Mr. Arabin, gently laughing. 'That is an opinion on which very much may be said on either side. It is strange how widely the world is divided on a subject which so nearly concerns us all, and which is so close beneath our eyes. Some think that we are quickly progressing towards perfection, while others imagine that virtue is disappearing from the earth.'

## GLORY OF OWNERSHIP

THERE IS MUCH in the glory of ownership,—of the ownership of land and houses, of beeves and woolly flocks, of wide fields and thick-growing woods, even when that ownership is of late date, when it conveys to the owner nothing but the realization of a property on the soil; but there is much more in it when it contains the memories of old years; when the glory is the glory of race as well as the glory of power and property. There had been Beltons of Belton living there for many centuries, and now he was the Belton of the day, standing on his own ground,—the descendant and representative of the Beltons of old,—Belton of Belton without a flaw in his pedigree! He felt himself to be proud of his position,—prouder than he could have been of any other that might have been vouchsafed to him. And yet amidst it all he was somewhat ashamed of his pride. 'The man who can do it for himself is the real man after all,' he said.

## AMERICANS

'BUT YOU ARE NOT AMERICAN, I hope. I do hate the Americans. It's the only strong political feeling I have. I went there once, and found I couldn't live with them on any terms.'

'But they please themselves. I don't see they are to be hated because they don't live after our fashion.'

'Oh; it's jealousy of course. I know that. I didn't come across a cab-driver who wasn't a much better educated man than I am. And as for their women, they know everything. But I hated them, and I intend to hate them. You haven't been there?'

'Oh no.'

'Then I will make bold to say that any English lady who spent a month with them and didn't hate them would have very singular tastes. I begin to think they'll eat each other up, and then there'll come an entirely new set of people of a different sort. I always regarded the States as a Sodom and Gomorrah, prospering in wickedness, on which fire and brimstone were sure to fall sooner or later.'

## WEALTH AND PROGRESS

'THERE IS NO VULGAR ERROR so vulgar,—that is to say, common or erroneous,—as that by which men have been taught to say that mercenary tendencies are bad. A desire for wealth is the source of all progress. Civilization comes from what men call greed. Let your mercenary tendencies be combined with honesty and they cannot take you astray.' This the future Chancellor of the Exchequer said with much of that air and tone of wisdom which a Chancellor of the Exchequer ought to possess.

## AGAINST THE IRISH

I WONDER WHETHER the novel-reading world—that part of it, at least, which may honour my pages, will be offended if I lay the plot of this story in Ireland. That there is a strong feeling against things Irish it is impossible to deny. Irish servants need not apply; Irish acquaintances are treated with limited confidence; Irish cousins are regarded as being decidedly dangerous; and Irish stories are not popular with the booksellers.

For myself, I may say that if I ought to know anything about any place, I ought to know something about Ireland;

SOCIAL IDEAS

and I do strongly protest against the injustice of the above conclusions. Irish cousins I have none. Irish acquaintances I have by dozens; and Irish friends also, by twos and threes, whom I can love and cherish—almost as well, perhaps, as though they had been born in Middlesex. Irish servants I have had some in my house for years, and never had one that was faithless, dishonest, or intemperate. I have travelled all over Ireland, closely as few other men can have done, and have never had my portmanteau robbed, or my pocket picked. At hotels I have seldom locked up my belongings, and my carelessness has never been punished. I doubt whether as much can be said for English inns.

## Young Democrat

'What can I do? Where can I turn? Oriel, if there be an empty, lying humbug in the world, it is the theory of high birth and pure blood which some of us endeavour to maintain. Blood, indeed! If my father had been a baker, I should know by this time where to look for my livelihood. As it is, I am told of nothing but my blood. Will my blood ever get me half a crown?'

And then the young democrat walked on again in solitude, leaving Mr. Oriel in doubt as to the exact line of argument which he had meant to inculcate.

## The Squire at Church

There was a separate door opening from the Greshamsbury pew out into the Greshamsbury grounds, so that the family were not forced into unseemly community with the village multitude in going to and from their prayers; for the front door of the church led out into a road which had no connexion with the private path. It was not unusual with Frank and his father to go round, after the service, to the chief entrance, so that they might speak to their neighbours, and get rid of some of the exclusiveness which was intended for them.

## The Peerage

THE DUKE WAS STRUCK with awe when he thought of all the circumstances. 'The brother of a marquis!' he said to his nephew's wife. 'It's such a disgrace to the peerage!'

'As for that, duke,' said Lady Glencora, 'the peerage is used to it by this time.'

'I never heard of such an affair as this before.'

'I don't see why the brother of a marquis shouldn't turn thief as well as anybody else. They say he hasn't got anything of his own;—and I suppose that is what makes men steal other people's property. Peers go into trade, and peeresses gamble on the Stock Exchange. Peers become bankrupt, and the sons of peers run away;—just like other men.'

## Rural Charity

SHE DESIRED THAT all the farmers round her should be able to pay their rents without trouble, that all the old women should have warm flannel petticoats, that the working men should be saved from rheumatism by healthy food and dry houses, that they should all be obedient to their pastors and masters—temporal as well as spiritual. That was her idea of loving her country. She desired also that the copses should be full of pheasants, the stubble-field of partridges, and the gorse covers of foxes; in that way, also, she loved her country.

## The Radical

'YOU WON'T TAKE TO WRITING for penny newspapers, will you, Brooke?' As she asked the question she put one of her hands softly on his shoulder.

'I certainly shan't offend in that way.'

'And you won't be a Radical?'

'No, not a Radical.'

'I mean a man to follow Beales and Bright, a republican, a putter-down of the Church, a hater of the Throne. You won't take up that line, will you, Brooke?'

'It isn't my way at present, Aunt Stanbury. But a man shouldn't promise.'

'Ah me! It makes me sad when I think what the country is coming to. I'm told there are scores of members of Parliament who don't pronounce their h's. When I was young, a member of Parliament used to be a gentleman;—and they've taken to ordaining all manner of people. It used to be the case that when you met a clergyman you met a gentleman.'

## The American Level

'In going among us, Mr. Glascock, you must not look for luxury or refinement, for you will find them not. Nor must you hope to encounter the highest order of erudition. The lofty summits of acquired knowledge tower in your country with an altitude we have not reached yet.'

'It's very good of you to say so,' said Mr. Glascock.

'No, sir. In our new country and in our new cities we still lack the luxurious perfection of fastidious civilisation. But, sir, regard our level. That is what I say to every unprejudiced Britisher that comes among us;—look at our level. And when you have looked at our level, I think that you will confess that we live on the highest table-land that the world has yet afforded to mankind. You follow my meaning, Mr. Glascock?' Mr. Glascock was not sure that he did, but the minister went on to make that meaning clear. 'It is the multitude that with us is educated. Go into their houses, sir, and see how they thumb their books. Look at the domestic correspondence of our helps and servants, and see how they write and spell. We haven't got the mountains, sir, but our table-lands are the highest on which the bright sun of our Almighty God has as yet shone with its illuminating splendour in this improving world of ours! It is because we are a young people, sir,—with nothing as yet near to us of the decrepitude of age. The weakness of age, sir, is the penalty paid by the folly of youth. We are not so wise, sir, but what we too shall suffer from its effects as years roll over our heads.' There was a great deal more, but at last Mr. Glascock did escape into the drawing-room.

## WOMEN'S RIGHTS

'I SHOULD BE SO PROUD if you would come with me to the Institute, Lady George.'

'I am sure I should be delighted. But what Institute?'

'Don't you know?—in the Marylebone Road,—for relieving females from their disabilities.'

'Do you mean Rights of Women? I don't think papa likes that,' said Mary, looking round at her father.

'You haven't got to mind what papa likes and dislikes any more,' said the Dean, laughing. 'Whether you go in for the rights or the wrongs of women is past my caring for now. Lord George must look after that.'

'I am sure Lord George could not object to your going to the Marylebone Institute,' said Aunt Ju. 'Lady Selina Protest is there every week, and Baroness Banmann, the delegate from Bavaria, is coming next Friday.'

'You'd find the Disabilities awfully dull, Lady George,' said Guss.

'Everybody is not so flighty as you are, my dear. Some people do sometimes think of serious things. And the Institute is not called the Disabilities.'

'What is it all about?' said Mary.

'Only to empower women to take their own equal places in the world,—places equal to those occupied by men,' said Aunt Ju eloquently. 'Why should one-half of the world be ruled by the *ipse dixit* of the other?'

'Or fed by their labours?' said the Dean.

'That is just what we are not. There are 1,133,500 females in England—'

'You had better go and hear it all at the Disabilities, Lady George,' said Guss. Lady George said that she would like to go for once, and so that matter was settled.

## Socialist

But Daniel Thwaite was a thoughtful man who had read many books. More's Utopia and Harrington's Oceana, with many a tale written in the same spirit, had taught him to believe that a perfect form of government, or rather of policy, under which all men might be happy and satisfied, was practicable on earth, and was to be achieved,—not merely by the slow amelioration of mankind under God's fostering ordinances,—but by the continued efforts of good and wise men who, by their goodness and wisdom, should be able to make the multitude believe in them. To diminish the distances, not only between the rich and the poor, but between the high and the low, was the grand political theory upon which his mind was always running. His father was ever thinking of himself and of Earl Lovel; while Daniel Thwaite was considering the injustice of the difference between ten thousand aristocrats and thirty million of people, who were for the most part ignorant and hungry.

## 'Democracy' for Ireland

The tuition had come from America! That, no doubt, was true; but it had come by Irish hearts and Irish voices, by Irish longings and Irish ambition. Nothing could be more false than to attribute the evil to America, unless that becomes American which has once touched American soil. But there does grow up in New York, or thereabouts, a mixture of Irish poverty with American wealth, which calls itself 'Democrat,' and forms as bad a composition as any that I know from which either to replenish or to create a people.

## How Sir Raffle Keeps His Hold

AND JOHN GAVE THEM an elaborate description of Sir Raffle Buffle, standing up with his back to the fire with his hat on his head, and speaking with a loud harsh voice, to show them the way in which he declared that that gentleman received his inferiors; and then bowing and scraping and rubbing his hands together and simpering with would-be softness,—declaring that after that fashion Sir Raffle received his superiors. And they were very merry. . .

'How can you consent to serve him if he's such a man as that?' said Lily, speaking of Sir Raffle.

'I do not serve him. I serve the Queen,—or rather the public. I don't take his wages, and he does not play his tricks with me. He knows that he can't. He has tried it, and has failed. And he only keeps me where I am because I've had some money left me. He thinks it fine to have a private secretary with a fortune. I know that he tells people all manner of lies about it, making it out to be five times as much as it is. Dear old Huffle Snuffle. He is such an ass; and yet he's had wit enough to get to the top of the tree, and to keep himself there. He began the world without a penny. Now he has got a handle to his name, and he'll live in clover all his life. It's very odd, isn't it, Mrs. Dale?'

'I suppose he does his work?'

'When men get so high as that, there's no knowing whether they work or whether they don't. There isn't much for them to do, as far as I can see. They have to look beautiful, and frighten the young ones.'

'And does Sir Raffle look beautiful?' Lily asked.

'After a fashion, he does. There is something imposing about such a man till you're used to it, and can see through it. Of course it's all padding. There are men who work, no doubt. But among the bigwigs, and bishops and cabinet ministers, I fancy that the looking beautiful is the chief part of it.'

## Success

'THE WORLD IS BECOMING a great deal too fond of what you call excitement and success. Of course it is a good thing for a man to make money by his profession, and a very hard thing when he can't do it,' added Mrs. Furnival, thinking of the olden days. 'But if success in life means rampaging about, and never knowing what it is to sit quiet over his own fireside, I for one would as soon manage to do without it.'

'But, mamma, I don't see why success should always be rampageous.'

'Literary women who have achieved a name bear their honours quietly,' said Lucius.

'I don't know,' said Mrs. Furnival. 'I am told that some of them are as fond of gadding as the men. As regards the old maids, I don't care so much about it; people who are not married may do what they like with themselves, and nobody has anything to say to them. But it is very different for married people. They have no business to be enticed away from their homes by any success.'

'Mamma is all for a Darby and Joan life,' said Sophia, laughing.

'No I am not, my dear; and you should not say so. I don't advocate anything that is absurd. But I do say that life should be lived at home. That is the best part of it. What is the meaning of home if it isn't that?'

## International Conventions

TO PRACTICAL ENGLISHMEN most of these international congresses seem to arrive at nothing else. Men will not be talked out of the convictions of their lives. No living orator would convince a grocer that coffee should be sold without chicory;

and no amount of eloquence will make an English lawyer think that loyalty to truth should come before loyalty to his client. And therefore our own pundits, though on this occasion they went to Birmingham, summoned by the greatness of the occasion, by the dignity of foreign names, by interest in the question, and by the influence of such men as Lord Boanerges, went there without any doubt on their minds as to the rectitude of their own practice, and fortified with strong resolves to resist all idea of change.

And indeed one cannot understand how the bent of any man's mind should be altered by the sayings and doings of such a congress.

'Well, Johnson, what have you all been doing to-day?' asked Mr. Furnival of a special friend whom he chanced to meet at the club which had been extemporized at Birmingham.

'We have had a paper read by Von Bauhr. It lasted three hours.'

'Three hours! heavens! Von Bauhr is, I think, from Berlin.'

'Yes; he and Dr. Slotacher. Slotacher is to read his paper the day after to-morrow.'

'Then I think I shall go to London again. But what did Von Bauhr say to you during those three hours?'

'Of course it was all in German, and I don't suppose that any one understood him,—unless it was Boanerges. But I believe it was the old story, going to show that the same man might be judge, advocate, and jury.'

'No doubt;—if men were machines, and if you could find such machines perfect at all points in their machinery.'

'And if the machines had no hearts?'

'Machines don't have hearts,' said Mr. Furnival; 'especially those in Germany. And what did Boanerges say? His answer did not take three hours more, I hope.'

'About twenty minutes; but what he did say was lost on Von Bauhr, who understands as much English as I do German. He said that the practice of the Prussian courts had always been to him a subject of intense interest, and that the general justice of their verdicts could not be impugned.'

'Nor ought it, seeing that a single trial for murder will occupy a court for three weeks. He should have asked Von Bauhr how much work he usually got through in the course of a sessions. I don't seem to have lost much by being away...'

On the whole the meeting was rather dull, as such meetings usually are. It must not be supposed that any lawyer could get up at will, as the spirit moved him, and utter his own ideas; or that all members of the congress could speak if only they could catch the speaker's eye. Had this been so, a man might have been supported by the hope of having some finger in the pie, sooner or later. But in such case the congress would have lasted for ever. As it was, the names of those who were invited to address the meeting were arranged, and of course men from each country were selected who were best known in their own special walks of their profession. But then these best-known men took an unfair advantage of their position, and were ruthless in the lengthy cruelty of their addresses. Von Bauhr at Berlin was no doubt a great lawyer, but he should not have felt so confident that the legal proceedings of England and of the civilized world in general could be reformed by his reading that book of his from the rostrum in the hall at Birmingham! The civilized world in general, as there represented, had been disgusted, and it was surmised that poor Dr. Slotacher would find but a meagre audience when his turn came...

'I confess I am getting rather tired of it,' said Felix Graham that evening to his friend young Staveley, as he stood outside his bedroom door at the top of a narrow flight of stairs in the back part of a large hotel at Birmingham.

'Tired of it! I should think you are too.'

'But nevertheless I am as sure as ever that good will come from it. I am inclined to think that the same kind of thing must be endured before any improvement is made in anything.'

'That all reformers have to undergo Von Bauhr?'

'Yes, all of them that do any good. Von Bauhr's words were very dry, no doubt.'

'You don't mean to say that you understood them?'

'Not many of them. A few here and there, for the first half-hour, came trembling home to my dull comprehension, and then—'

'You went to sleep.'

'The sounds became too difficult for my ears; but dry and dull and hard as they were, they will not absolutely fall to the ground. He had a meaning in them, and that meaning will reproduce itself in some shape.'

'Heaven forbid that it should ever do so in my presence! All the iniquities of which the English bar may be guilty cannot be so intolerable to humanity as Von Bauhr.'

'Well, good-night, old fellow; your governor is to give us his ideas to-morrow, and perhaps he will be as bad to the Germans as your Von Bauhr was to us.'

'Then I can only say that my governor will be very cruel to the Germans.' And so they two went to their dreams.

In the mean time Von Bauhr was sitting alone looking back on the past hours with ideas and views very different from those of the many English lawyers who were at that time discussing his demerits. To him the day had been one long triumph, for his voice had sounded sweet in his own ears as, period after period, he had poured forth in full flowing language the gathered wisdom and experience of his life. Public men in England have so much to do that they cannot give time to the preparation of speeches for such meetings as these, but Von Bauhr had been at work on his pamphlet for months. Nay, taking it in the whole, had he not been at work on it for years? And now a kind Providence had given him the opportunity of pouring it forth before the assembled pundits gathered from all the nations of the civilized world.

As he sat there, solitary in his bedroom, his hands dropped down by his side, his pipe hung from his mouth on to his breast, and his eyes, turned up to the ceiling, were lighted almost with inspiration. Men there at the congress, Mr. Chaffanbrass, young Staveley, Felix Graham, and others, had regarded him as an impersonation of dullness; but through his mind and brain, as he sat there wrapped in his old dressing-gown, there ran thoughts which seemed to lift him lightly from the earth into an elysium of justice and mercy. And at the end of this elysium, which was not wild in its beauty, but trim and orderly in its gracefulness—as might be a beer-garden at Munich—there stood among flowers and vases a pedestal, grand above all other pedestals in that garden; and on this there was a bust with an inscription:—'To Von Bauhr, who reformed the laws of nations.'

It was a grand thought; and though there was in it much of human conceit, there was in it also much of human philanthropy. If a reign of justice could be restored through his efforts—through those efforts in which on this hallowed day he had been enabled to make so great a progress—how beautiful would it be! And then as he sat there, while the smoke still curled from his unconscious nostrils, he felt that he loved all Germans, all Englishmen, even all Frenchmen, in his very heart of hearts, and especially those who had travelled wearily to this English town that they might listen to the results of his wisdom. He said to himself, and said truly, that he loved the world, and that he would willingly spend himself in these great endeavours for the amelioration of its laws and the perfection of its judicial proceedings. And then he betook himself to bed in a frame of mind that was not unenviable.

I am inclined, myself, to agree with Felix Graham that such efforts are seldom absolutely wasted. A man who strives honestly to do good will generally do good, though seldom perhaps as much as he has himself anticipated. Let Von Bauhr have his pedestal among the flowers, even though it be small and humble!

## The Successful Man

Nothing makes a man so cross as success, or so soon turns a pleasant friend into a captious acquaintance. Your successful man eats too much and his stomach troubles him; he drinks too much and his nose becomes blue. He wants pleasure and excitement, and roams about looking for satisfaction in places where no man ever found it. He frets himself with his banker's book, and everything tastes amiss to him that has not on it the flavour of gold. The straw of an omnibus always stinks; the linings of the cabs are filthy. There are but three houses round London at which an eatable dinner may be obtained. And yet a few years since how delicious was that cut of roast goose to be had for a shilling at the eating-house near Golden Square. Mrs. Jones and Mrs. Green, Mrs. Walker and all the other mistresses, are too vapid and stupid and humdrum for endurance. The theatres are dull as Lethe, and politics have lost their salt. Success is the necessary misfortune of life, but it is only to the very unfortunate that it comes early.

## A Trade-Union Man

Mr. Bunce was a copying journeyman, who spent ten hours a day in Carey Street with a pen between his fingers; and after that he would often spend two or three hours of the night with a pen between his fingers in Marlborough Street. He was a thoroughly hard-working man, doing pretty well in the world, for he had a good house over his head, and always could find raiment and bread for his wife and eight children; but, nevertheless, he was an unhappy man because he suffered from political grievances, or, I should more correctly say, that his grievances were semi-political and semi-social. He had no vote, not being himself the tenant of the house in Great Marlborough Street. The tenant was a tailor who occupied the shop, whereas Bunce occupied the whole of the remainder of the premises. He was a lodger, and lodgers were not as yet trusted with the franchise. And he had ideas, which he himself admitted to be very raw, as to the injustice of the manner in which he was paid for his work. So much a folio, without reference to the way in which his work was done, without regard to the success of his work, with no questions asked of himself, was, as he thought, no proper way of remunerating a man for his labours. He had long since joined a Trade Union, and for two years past had paid a subscription of a shilling a week towards its funds. He longed to be doing some battle against his superiors, and to be putting himself in opposition to his employers;—not that he objected personally to Messrs. Foolscap, Margin, and Vellum, who always made much of him as a useful man;—but because some such antagonism would be manly, and the fighting of some battle would be the right thing to do. 'If Labour don't mean to go to the wall himself,' Bunce would say to his wife, 'Labour must look alive, and put somebody else there.'

### Radical Peer

There's nobody on earth I pity so much as a radical peer who is obliged to work like a nigger with a spade to shovel away the ground from under his own feet.

### A Gentleman's Career

'But it is not about that, Oswald, that I would speak. What are your plans of life when you are married?'

'Plans of life?'

'Yes;—plans of life. I suppose you have some plans. I suppose you mean to apply yourself to some useful occupation?'

'I don't know really, sir, that I am of much use for any purpose.' Lord Chiltern laughed as he said this, but did not laugh pleasantly.

'You would not be a drone in the hive always?'

## HE DISTILLS ITS IDEAS AND THEORIES

'As far as I can see, sir, we who call ourselves lords generally are drones.'

'I deny it,' said the Earl, becoming quite energetic as he defended his order. 'I deny it utterly. I know no class of men who do work more useful or more honest. Am I a drone? Have I been so from my youth upwards? I have always worked, either in the one House or in the other, and those of my fellows with whom I have been most intimate have worked also. The same career is open to you.'

'You mean politics?'

'Of course I mean politics.'

'I don't care for politics. I see no difference in parties.'

'But you should care for politics, and you should see a difference in parties. It is your duty to do so. My wish is that you should go into Parliament.'

'I can't do that, sir.'

'And why not?'

'In the first place, sir, you have not got a seat to offer me. You have managed matters among you in such a way that poor little Loughton has been swallowed up. If I were to canvass the electors of Smotherem, I don't think that many would look very sweet on me.'

'There is the county, Oswald.'

'And whom am I to turn out? I should spend four or five thousand pounds, and have nothing but vexation in return for it. I had rather not begin that game, and indeed I am too old for Parliament. I did not take it up early enough to believe in it.'

All this made the Earl very angry, and from these things they went on to worse things. When questioned again as to the future, Lord Chiltern scowled, and at last declared that it was his idea to live abroad in the summer for his wife's recreation, and somewhere down in the shires during the winter for his own. He would admit of no purpose higher than recreation, and when his father again talked to him of a nobleman's duty, he said that he knew of no other special

SOCIAL IDEAS

duty than that of not exceeding his income. Then his father made a longer speech than before, and at the end of it Lord Chiltern simply wished him good night. 'It's getting late, and I've promised to see Violet before I go to bed. Good-bye.' Then he was off, and Lord Brentford was left there, standing with his back to the fire.

## Views of the Amateur

He believed of himself that he had gone rather deep into politics, and that he was entitled to call many statesmen asses because they did not see the things which he saw. He had the great question of labour, and all that refers to unions, strikes, and lock-outs, quite at his fingers' ends. He knew how the Church of England should be disestablished and recomposed. He was quite clear on questions of finance, and saw to a 't' how progress should be made towards communism, so that no violence should disturb that progress, and that in the due course of centuries all desire for personal property should be conquered and annihilated by a philanthropy so general as hardly to be accounted a virtue. In the meantime he could never contrive to pay his tailor's bill regularly out of the allowance of £400 a year which his father made him, and was always dreaming of the comforts of a handsome income.

## Wages and Work

'John is as hard upon the men as any one of the tenants,' said John's wife, Mrs. Fletcher of Longbarns.

'I'm not hard at all,' said John, 'and you understand nothing about it. I'm paying three shillings a week more to every man, and eighteen pence a week more to every woman, than I did three years ago.'

'That's because of the Unions,' said the barrister.

'I don't care a straw for the Unions. If the Unions interfered with my comfort I'd let the land and leave the place.'

'Oh, John!' ejaculated John's mother.

'I would not consent to be made a slave even for the sake of the country. But the wages had to be raised,—and having raised them I expect to get proper value for my money. If anything has to be given away, let it be given away,—so that the people should know what it is that they receive.'

'That's just what we don't want to do here,' said Lady Wharton, who did not often join in any of these arguments.

'You're wrong, my lady,' said her stepson. 'You're only breeding idleness when you teach people to think that they are earning wages without working for their money. Whatever you do with 'em let 'em know and feel the truth. It'll be the best in the long run.'

'I'm sometimes happy when I think that I shan't live to see the long run,' said the baronet.

## Amusements

'You shoot,' said the Duke. Phineas did shoot but cared very little about it. 'But you hunt.' Phineas was very fond of riding to hounds. 'I am beginning to think,' said the Duke, 'that I have made a mistake in not caring for such things. When I was very young I gave them up, because it appeared that other men devoted too much time to them. One might as well not eat because some men are gluttons.'

'Only that you would die if you did not eat.'

'Bread, I suppose, would keep me alive, but still one eats meat without being a glutton. I very often regret the want of amusements, and particularly of those which would throw me more among my fellow-creatures. A man is alone when reading, alone when writing, alone when thinking. Even sitting in Parliament he is very much alone, though there be a crowd around him. Now a man can hardly be thoroughly useful unless he knows his fellow-men, and how is he to know them

## SOCIAL IDEAS

if he shuts himself up? If I had to begin again I think I would cultivate the amusements of the time.'

### Radical or Conservative?

'Papa is beginning to be afraid that Everett is a Radical. But I'm sure he's not. He says he is as good a Conservative as there is in all Herefordshire, only that he likes to know what is to be conserved. Papa said after dinner yesterday that everything English ought to be maintained. Everett said that according to that we should have kept the Star Chamber. "Of course I would," said papa. Then they went at it, hammer and tongs. Everett had the best of it. At any rate he talked the longest. But I do hope he is not a Radical. No country gentleman ought to be a Radical. Ought he, dear?'

### Labour vs. Capital

'Labour is the salt of the earth, and Capital is the sworn foe to Labour.' Hear, hear, hear, with the clattering of many glasses, and the smashing of certain pipes! Then the orator went on. 'That Labour should be the salt of the earth has been the purpose of a beneficent Creator;—that Capital should be the foe to Labour has been man's handywork. The one is an eternal decree, which nothing can change,—which neither the good nor the evil done by man can affect. The other is an evil ordinance, the fruit of man's ignorance, and within the scope of man's intellect to annul.'

Mr. Ontario Moggs was the orator, and he was at this moment addressing a crowd of sympathising friends in the large front parlour of the Cheshire Cheese. Of all those who were listening to Ontario Moggs there was not probably one who had reached a higher grade in commerce than that of an artisan working for weekly wages;—but Mr. Moggs was especially endeared to them because he was not an artisan working for weekly wages, but himself a capitalist. His father was a master bootmaker on a great scale;—for none stood much higher in the West-end trade than Booby and Moggs; and it was known that Ontario was the only child and heir, and as it were sole owner of the shoulders on which must some day devolve the mantle of Booby and Moggs. Booby had long been gathered to his fathers, and old Moggs was the stern opponent of strikes. What he had lost by absolutely refusing to yield a point during the last strike among the shoemakers of London no one could tell. He had professed aloud that he would sooner be ruined, sooner give up his country residence at Shepherd's Bush, sooner pull down the honoured names of Booby and Moggs from over the shop-window in Old Bond Street, than allow himself to be driven half an inch out of his course by men who were attempting to dictate to him what he should do with his own. In these days of strikes Moggs would look even upon his own workmen with the eyes of a Coriolanus glaring upon the disaffected populace of Rome. Mr. Moggs senior would stand at his shop-door, with his hand within his waistcoat, watching the men out on strike who were picketing the streets round his shop, and would feel himself every inch a patrician, ready to die for his order. Such was Moggs senior. And Moggs junior, who was a child of Capital, but whose heirship depended entirely on his father's will, harangued his father's workmen and other workmen at the Cheshire Cheese, telling them that Labour was the salt of the earth, and that Capital was the foe to Labour! Of course they loved him. The demagogue who is of all demagogues the most popular, is the demagogue who is a demagogue in opposition to his apparent nature. The Radical Earl, the free-thinking parson, the squire who won't preserve, the tenant who defies his landlord, the capitalist with a theory for dividing profits, the Moggs who loves a strike,—these are the men whom the working men delight to follow. Ontario Moggs, who was at any rate honest in his philanthropy, and who did in truth believe that it was better that twenty real bootmakers should eat beef daily, than that one so-called bootmaker should live in a country residence,—who believed this and acted on his belief, though he was himself not of the twenty, but rather the one so-called bootmaker, who would suffer by the propagation of such a creed,—was beloved and almost worshipped by the denizens of the Cheshire Cheese. How far the real philanthropy of the man may have been marred by an uneasy and fatuous ambition; how far he was carried away by a feeling that it was better to make speeches at the Cheshire Cheese than to apply for payment of money due to his father, it would be very hard for us to decide. That there was an alloy even in Ontario Moggs is probable;—but of this alloy his hearers knew nothing. To them he was a perfect specimen of that combination, which is so grateful to them, of the rich man's position with the poor man's sympathies. Therefore they clattered their glasses, and broke their pipes, and swore that the words he uttered were the kind of stuff they wanted.

'The battle has been fought since man first crawled upon the earth,' continued Moggs, stretching himself to his full height, and pointing to the farthest confines of the inhabited globe;—'since man first crawled upon the earth.' There was a sound in that word 'crawl' typical of the abject humility to which working shoemakers were subjected by their employers, which specially aroused the feelings of the meeting. 'And whence comes the battle?' The orator paused, and the glasses were jammed upon the table. 'Yes,—whence comes the battle, in fighting which hecatombs of honest labourers have been crushed till the sides of the mountains are white with their bones, and the rivers run foul with their blood? From the desire of one man to eat the bread of two!' 'That's it,' said a lean, wizened, pale-faced little man in a corner, whose trembling hand was resting on a beaker of gin and water. 'Yes, and to wear two men's coats and trousers, and to take two men's bedses, and the wery witals out of two men's bodies. D—— them!' Ontario, who understood something of his trade as an orator, stood with his hand still stretched out, waiting till this ebullition should be over. 'No, my friend,' said he, 'we will not damn them. I for one will damn no man. I will simply rebel. Of all the sacraments given to us, the sacrament of rebellion is the most holy.' Hereupon the landlord of the Cheshire Cheese must have feared for his tables, so great was the applause and so tremendous the thumping;—but he knew his business, no doubt, and omitted to interfere. 'Of Rebellion, my friends,' continued Ontario, with his right hand now gracefully laid across his breast, 'there are two kinds,—or perhaps we may say three. There is the rebellion of arms, which can avail us nothing here.' 'Perhaps it might tho',' said the little wizened man in a corner, whose gin and water apparently did not comfort him. To this interruption Ontario paid no attention. 'And there is the dignified and slow rebellion of moral resistance;—too slow I fear for us.' This point was lost upon the audience, and though the speaker paused, no loud cheer was given. 'It's as true as true,' said one man; but he was a vain fellow, simply desirous of appearing wiser than his comrades. 'And then there is the rebellion of the Strike;' now the clamour of men's voices, and the kicking of men's feet, and the thumping with men's fists became more frantic than ever; '—the legitimate rebellion of Labour against its tyrant. Gentlemen, of all efforts this is the most noble. It is a sacrifice of self, a martyrdom, a giving up on the part of him who strikes of himself, his little ones, and his wife, for the sake of others who can only thus be rescued from the grasp of tyranny. Gentlemen, were it not for strikes, this would be a country in which no free man could live. By the aid of strikes we will make it the Paradise of the labourer, an Elysium of industry, an Eden of artizans.' There was much more of it,—but the reader might be fatigued were the full flood of Mr. Moggs's oratory to be let loose upon him. And through it all there was a germ of truth and a strong dash of true, noble feeling;—but the speaker had omitted as yet to learn how much thought must be given to a germ of truth before it can be made to produce fruit for

## SOCIAL IDEAS

the multitude. And then, in speaking, grand words come so easily, while thoughts,—even little thoughts,—flow so slowly!

But the speech, such as it was, sufficed amply for the immediate wants of the denizens of the Cheshire Cheese. There were men there who for the half-hour believed that Ontario Moggs had been born to settle all the difficulties between labourers and their employers, and that he would do so in such a way that the labourers, at least, should have all that they wanted. It would be, perhaps, too much to say that any man thought this would come in his own day,—that he so believed as to put a personal trust in his own belief; but they did think for a while that the good time was coming, and that Ontario Moggs would make it come. 'We'll have 'im in parl'ament any ways,' said a sturdy, short, dirty-looking artizan, who shook his head as he spoke to show that, on that matter, his mind was quite made up. 'I dunno no good as is to cum of sending sich as him to parl'ament,' said another. 'Parl'ament ain't the place. When it comes to the p'int they won't 'ave 'em. There was Odgers, and Mr. Beale. I don't b'lieve in parl'ament no more.' 'Kennington Oval's about the place,' said a third. 'Or Primrose 'ill,' said a fourth. 'Hyde Park!' screamed the little wizened man with the gin and water. 'That's the ticket;—and down with them gold railings. We'll let 'em see!' Nevertheless they all went away home in the quietest way in the world, and,—as there was no strike in hand,—got to their work punctually on the next morning. Of all those who had been loudest at the Cheshire Cheese there was not one who was not faithful, and, in a certain way, loyal to his employer.

As soon as his speech was over and he was able to extricate himself from the crowd, Ontario Moggs escaped from the public-house and strutted off through certain narrow, dark streets in the neighbourhood, leaning on the arm of a faithful friend. 'Mr. Moggs, you did pitch it rayther strong, to-night,' said his faithful friend.

'Pitch it rather strong;—yes. What good do you think can

ever come from pitching anything weak? Pitch it as strong as you will, and it don't amount to much.'

'But about rebellion, now, Mr. Moggs? Rebellion ain't a good thing, surely, Mr. Moggs?'

'Isn't it? What was Washington, what was Cromwell, what was Rienzi, what was,—was,—; but never mind,' said Ontario, who could not at the moment think of the name of his favourite Pole.

'And you think as the men should be rebels again' the masters?'

'That depends on who the masters are, Waddle.'

'What good 'd cum of it if I rebelled again' Mr. Neefit, and told him up to his face as I wouldn't make up the books? He'd only sack me. I find thirty-five bob a week, with two kids and their mother to keep on it, tight enough, Mr. Moggs. If I 'ad the fixing on it, I should say forty bob wasn't over the mark;—I should indeed. But I don't see as I should get it.'

'Yes you would;—if you earned it, and stuck to your purpose. But you're a single stick, and it requires a faggot to do this work.'

'I never could see it, Mr. Moggs. All the same I do like to hear you talk. It stirs one up, even though one don't just go along with it. You won't let on, you know, to Mr. Neefit as I was there.'

'And why not?' said Ontario, turning sharp upon his companion.

'The old gen'leman hates the very name of a strike. He's a'most as bad as your own father, Mr. Moggs.'

'You have done his work to-day. You have earned your bread. You owe him nothing.'

'That I don't, Mr. Moggs. He'll take care of that.'

'And yet you are to stay away from this place, or go to that, to suit his pleasure. Are you Neefit's slave?'

'I'm just the young man in his shop,—that's all.'

'As long as that is all, Waddle, you are not worthy to be called a man.'

'Mr. Moggs, you're too hard. As for being a man, I am a man. I've a wife and two kids. I don't think more of my governor than another;—but if he sacked me, where'd I get thirty-five bob a-week?'

'I beg your pardon, Waddle;—it's true. I should not have said it. Perhaps you do not quite understand me, but your position is one of a single stick, rather than of the faggot.'

## Heirs of the Body

As HE WENT, however, he leaned with his hand on Eames's shoulder, and the servants looking on saw that the young man was to be a favourite. 'He'll make him his heir,' said Vickers. 'I shouldn't wonder a bit if he don't make him his heir.' But to this the footman objected, endeavouring to prove to Mr. Vickers that, in accordance with the law of the land, his lordship's second cousin, once removed, whom the earl had never seen, but whom he was supposed to hate, must be his heir. 'A hearl can never choose his own heir, like you or me,' said the footman, laying down the law. 'Can't he though really, now? That's very hard on him; isn't it?' said the pretty housemaid. 'Psha,' said Vickers: 'you know nothing about it. My lord could make young Eames his heir to-morrow; that is, the heir of his property. He couldn't make him a hearl, because that must go to the heirs of his body. As to his leaving him the place here, I don't just know how that'd be; and I'm sure Richard don't.'

'But suppose he hasn't got any heirs of his body?' asked the pretty housemaid, who was rather fond of putting down Mr. Vickers.

'He must have heirs of his body,' said the butler. 'Everybody has 'em. If a man don't know 'em himself, the law finds 'em out.' And then Mr. Vickers walked away, avoiding further dispute.

## ELDEST SON

THAT ELDEST BROTHER, Lord Saint George, was in truth regarded at Turnover as being, of all persons in the world, the most august. The Marquis himself was afraid of his son, and held him in extreme veneration. To the mind of the Marquis the heir expectant of all the dignities of the House of Stowte was almost a greater man than the owner of them; and this feeling came not only from a consciousness on the part of the father that his son was a bigger man than himself, cleverer, better versed in the affairs of the world, and more thought of by those around them, but also to a certain extent from an idea that he who would have all these grand things thirty or perhaps even fifty years hence, must be more powerful than one with whom their possession would come to an end probably after the lapse of eight or ten years. His heir was to him almost divine. When things at the castle were in any way uncomfortable, he could put up with the discomfort for himself and his daughters; but it was not to be endured that Saint George should be incommoded. Old carriage-horses must be changed if he were coming; the glazing of the new greenhouse must be got out of the way, lest he should smell the paint; the game must not be touched till he should come to shoot it. And yet Lord Saint George himself was a man who never gave himself any airs; and who in his personal intercourse with the world around him demanded much less acknowledgment of his magnificence than did his father.

## LAND *vs.* WEALTH

ROGER CARBURY, OF CARBURY HALL, the owner of a small property in Suffolk, was the head of the Carbury family. The Carburys had been in Suffolk a great many years,—certainly from the time of the War of the Roses,—and had always held up their heads. But they had never held them very high. It

## SOCIAL IDEAS

was not known that any had risen ever to the honour of knighthood before Sir Patrick, going higher than that, had been made a baronet. They had, however, been true to their acres and their acres true to them through the perils of civil wars, Reformation, Commonwealth, and Revolution, and the head Carbury of the day had always owned, and had always lived at, Carbury Hall. At the beginning of the present century the squire of Carbury had been a considerable man, if not in his county, at any rate in his part of the county. The income of the estate had sufficed to enable him to live plenteously and hospitably, to drink port wine, to ride a stout hunter, and to keep an old lumbering coach for his wife's use when she went avisiting. He had an old butler who had never lived anywhere else, and a boy from the village who was in a way apprenticed to the butler. There was a cook, not too proud to wash up her own dishes, and a couple of young women;—while the house was kept by Mrs. Carbury herself, who marked and gave out her own linen, made her own preserves, and looked to the curing of her own hams. In the year 1800 the Carbury property was sufficient for the Carbury house. Since that time the Carbury property has considerably increased in value, and the rents have been raised. Even the acreage has been extended by the enclosure of commons. But the income is no longer comfortably adequate to the wants of an English gentleman's household. If a moderate estate in land be left to a man now, there arises the question whether he is not damaged unless an income also be left to him wherewith to keep up the estate. Land is a luxury, and of all luxuries is the most costly. Now the Carburys never had anything but land. Suffolk has not been made rich and great either by coal or iron. No great town had sprung up on the confines of the Carbury property. No eldest son had gone into trade or risen high in a profession so as to add to the Carbury wealth. No great heiress had been married. There had been no ruin,—no misfortune. But in the days of which we write the Squire of Carbury Hall had become a poor man simply through the wealth of others. His estate was supposed to bring him in £2,000 a year. Had he been content to let the Manor House, to live abroad, and to have an agent at home to deal with the tenants, he would undoubtedly have had enough to live luxuriously. But he lived on his own land among his own people, as all the Carburys before him had done, and was poor because he was surrounded by rich neighbours. The Longestaffes of Caversham,—of which family Dolly Longestaffe was the eldest son and hope,—had the name of great wealth, but the founder of the family had been a Lord Mayor of London and a chandler as lately as in the reign of Queen Anne. The Hepworths, who could boast good blood enough on their own side, had married into new money. The Primeros, —though the good nature of the country folk had accorded to the head of them the title of Squire Primero,—had been trading Spaniards fifty years ago, and had bought the Bundlesham property from a great duke. The estates of those three gentlemen, with the domain of the Bishop of Elmham, lay all around the Carbury property, and in regard to wealth enabled their owners altogether to overshadow our squire. The superior wealth of a bishop was nothing to him. He desired that bishops should be rich, and was among those who thought that the country had been injured when the territorial possessions of our prelates had been converted into stipends by Act of Parliament. But the grandeur of the Longestaffes and the too apparent wealth of the Primeros did oppress him, though he was a man who would never breathe a word of such oppression into the ear even of his dearest friend. It was his opinion,—which he did not care to declare loudly, but which was fully understood to be his opinion by those with whom he lived intimately,—that a man's standing in the world should not depend at all upon his wealth. The Primeros were undoubtedly beneath him in the social scale, although the young Primeros had three horses apiece, and killed legions of pheasants annually at about 10*s.* a head. Hepworth of Eardly was a very good fellow, who gave himself no airs and understood his duties as a country gentleman; but he could not be more than on a par with Carbury of Carbury, though he was supposed to enjoy £7,000 a year. The Longestaffes were altogether oppressive. Their footmen, even in the country, had powdered hair. They had a house in town,—a house of their own,—and lived altogether as magnates. The lady was Lady Pomona Longestaffe. The daughters, who certainly were handsome, had been destined to marry peers. The only son, Dolly, had, or had had, a fortune of his own. They were an oppressive people in a country neighbourhood. And to make the matter worse, rich as they were, they never were able to pay anybody anything that they owed. They continued to live with all the appurtenances of wealth. The girls always had horses to ride, both in town and country. The acquaintance of Dolly the reader has already made. Dolly, who certainly was a poor creature though good-natured, had energy in one direction. He would quarrel perseveringly with his father, who only had a life interest in the estate. The house at Caversham Park was during six or seven months of the year full of servants, if not of guests, and all the tradesmen in the little towns around, Bungay, Beccles, and Harlestone, were aware that the Longestaffes were the great people of that country. Though occasionally much distressed for money, they would always execute the Longestaffe orders with submissive punctuality, because there was an idea that the Longestaffe property was sound at the bottom. And, then, the owner of a property so managed cannot scrutinise bills very closely.

Carbury of Carbury had never owed a shilling that he could not pay, or his father before him. His orders to the tradesmen at Beccles were not extensive, and care was used to see that the goods supplied were neither overcharged nor unnecessary. The tradesmen, consequently, of Beccles did not care much for Carbury of Carbury;—though perhaps one or two of the elders among them entertained some ancient reverence for the family. Roger Carbury, Esq., was Carbury of Carbury,—a distinction of itself, which, from its nature, could not belong

## HE DISTILLS ITS IDEAS AND THEORIES

to the Longestaffes and Primeros, which did not even belong to the Hepworths of Eardly. The very parish in which Carbury Hall stood,—or Carbury Manor House, as it was more properly called,—was Carbury parish. And there was Carbury Chase, partly in Carbury parish.

# Women

## Women and Church Attendance

On the next morning Arabella went to church, as did of course a great many of the party. By remaining at home she could only have excited suspicion. The church was close to the house, and the family pew consisted of a large room screened off from the rest of the church, with a fire-place of its own,—so that the labour of attending divine service was reduced to a minimum. At two o'clock they lunched, and that amusement lasted nearly an hour. There was an afternoon service at three, in attending which the duchess was very particular. The duke never went at that time, nor was it expected that any of the gentlemen would do so; but ladies are supposed to require more church than men, and the duchess rather made it a point that, at any rate, the young ladies staying in the house should accompany her. Over the other young ladies there her authority could only be that of influence, but such authority generally sufficed. From her niece it might be supposed that she would exact obedience, and in this instance she tried it. 'We start in five minutes,' she said to Arabella as that young lady was loitering at the table.

'Don't wait for me, aunt; I'm not going,' said Arabella boldly.

'I hope you will come to church with us,' said the duchess sternly.

'Not this afternoon.'

'Why not, Arabella?'

'I never do go to church twice on Sundays. Some people do, and some people don't. I suppose that's about it.'

[ 317 ]

'I think that all young women ought to go to church on Sunday afternoon unless there is something particular to prevent them.' Arabella shrugged her shoulders and the duchess stalked angrily away.

## On Chaperones

It is generally understood that there are raging lions about the metropolis, who would certainly eat up young ladies whole if young ladies were to walk about the streets or even about the parks by themselves. There is, however, beginning to be some vacillation as to the received belief on this subject as regards London. In large continental towns, such as Paris and Vienna, young ladies would be devoured certainly. Such, at least, is the creed. In New York and Washington there are supposed to be no lions, so that young ladies go about free as air. In London there is a rising doubt, under which before long, probably, the lions will succumb altogether. Mrs. Dosett did believe somewhat in lions, but she believed also in exercise. And she was aware that the lions eat up chiefly rich people. Young ladies who must go about without mothers, brothers, uncles, carriages, or attendants of any sort, are not often eaten or even roared at. It is the dainty darlings for whom the roarings have to be feared. Mrs. Dosett, aware that daintiness was no longer within the reach of her and hers, did assent to these walkings in Kensington Gardens. At some hour in the afternoon Lucy would walk from the house by herself, and within a quarter of an hour would find herself on the broad gravel path which leads down to the Round Pond. From thence she would go by the back of the Albert Memorial, and then across by the Serpentine and return to the same gate, never leaving Kensington Gardens. Aunt Dosett had expressed some old-fashioned idea that lions were more likely to roar in Hyde Park than within the comparatively retired purlieus of Kensington.

## Diamonds

'EVERYBODY AGREES that diamonds will go further with a girl than anything else. When I told the governor he quite jumped at the idea.'

'Sir Thomas knows you are giving it?'

'Oh, dear, yes. I had to get the rhino from him. I don't go about with two hundred and fifty pounds always in my own pocket.'

'If he had sent the money to Ayala how much better it would have been,' said poor Mrs. Dosett.

'I don't think that at all. Who ever heard of making a present to a young lady in money? Ayala is romantic, and that would have been the most unromantic thing out. That would not have done me the least good in the world. It would simply have gone to buy boots and petticoats and such like. A girl would never be brought to think of her lover merely by putting on a pair of boots. When she fastens such a necklace as this round her throat he ought to have a chance. Don't you think so, Aunt Dosett?'

## Mrs. Proudie Rampant

NOT WITHOUT MANY MISGIVINGS did he find himself in Mrs. Proudie's boudoir. He had at first thought of sending for her. But it was not at all impossible that she might choose to take such a message amiss, and then also it might be some protection to him to have his daughters present at the interview. He found her sitting with her account books before her nibbling the end of her pencil evidently mersed in pecuniary difficulties, and harassed in mind by the multiplicity of palatial expenses, and the heavy cost of episcopal grandeur. Her daughters were around her. Olivia was reading a novel, Augusta was crossing a note to her bosom friend in Baker Street, and Netta was working diminutive coach wheels for the bottom of a petticoat. If the bishop could get the better of his wife in her present mood, he would be a man indeed. He might then consider the victory his own for ever. After all, in such cases the matter between husband and wife stands much the same as it does between two boys at the same school, two cocks in the same yard, or two armies on the same continent. The conqueror once is generally the conqueror for ever after. The prestige of victory is every thing.

'Ahem—my dear,' began the bishop, 'if you are disengaged, I wished to speak to you.' Mrs. Proudie put her pencil down carefully at the point to which she had dotted her figures, marked down in her memory the sum she had arrived at, and then looked up, sourly enough, into her helpmate's face. 'If you are busy, another time will do as well,' continued the bishop, whose courage like Bob Acres' had oozed out, now that he found himself on the ground of battle.

'What is it about, Bishop?' asked the lady.

'Well—it was about those Quiverfuls—but I see you are engaged. Another time will do just as well for me.'

'What about the Quiverfuls? It is quite understood I believe, that they are to come to the hospital. There is to be no doubt about that, is there?' and as she spoke she kept her pencil sternly and vigorously fixed on the column of figures before her.

### Feminine Intuition

Men hunt foxes by the aid of dogs, and are aware that they do so by the strong organ of smell with which the dog is endowed. They do not, however, in the least comprehend how such a sense can work with such acuteness. The organ by which women instinctively, as it were, know and feel how other women are regarded by men, and how also men are regarded by other women, is equally strong, and equally incomprehensible. A glance, a word, a motion, suffices.

## WOMEN IN POLITICS

'Women are not allowed to be politicians in this country.'

'Thank God, they can't do much in that way;—not directly, I mean. Only think where we should be if we had a feminine House of Commons, with feminine debates, carried on, of course, with feminine courtesy. My cousins Iphy and Phemy there would of course be members. You don't know them yet?'

'No; not yet. Are they politicians?'

'Not especially. They have their tendencies, which are decidedly Liberal. There has never been a Tory Palliser known, you know. But they are too clever to give themselves up to anything in which they can do nothing. Being women they live a depressed life, devoting themselves to literature, fine arts, social economy, and the abstract sciences. They write wonderful letters; but I believe their correspondence lists are quite full, so that you have no chance at present of getting on either of them.'

## WOMAN'S PLACE

'How I do wish I were a man!' his sister said to him when they were in the hansom together.

'You'd have a great deal more trouble.'

'But I'd have a hansom of my own, and go where I pleased. How would you like to be shut up at a place like The Horns?'

'You can go out if you like it.'

'Not like you. Papa thinks it's the proper place for me to live in, and so I must live there. I don't think a woman ever chooses how or where she shall live herself.'

'You are not going to take up woman's rights, I hope.'

'I think I shall if I stay at The Horns much longer. What would papa say if he heard that I was going to give a lecture at an Institute?'

## Double Standard

IN HER HEART OF HEARTS she approved of a different code of morals for men and women. That which merited instant, and as regarded this world, perpetual condemnation in a woman, might in a man be very easily forgiven. A sigh, a shake of the head, and some small innocent stratagem that might lead to a happy marriage and settlement in life with increased income, would have been her treatment of such sin for the heirs of the great and wealthy. She knew that the world could not afford to ostracise the men,—though happily it might condemn the women.

## Woman *vs.* Man

'I SUPPOSE MEN FRIENDS do listen to each other. They never seem to listen to women. Don't you think that, after all, they despise women? They look on them as dainty, foolish things.'

'Sometimes women despise men,' said Priscilla.

'Not very often;—do they? And then women are so dependent on men. A woman can get nothing without a man.'

'I manage to get on somehow,' said Priscilla.

'No, you don't, Miss Stanbury,—if you think of it. You want mutton. And who kills the sheep?'

'But who cooks it?'

'But the men-cooks are the best,' said Nora; 'and the men-tailors, and the men to wait at table, and the men-poets, and the men-painters, and the men-nurses. All the things that women do, men do better.'

'There are two things they can't do,' said Priscilla.

'What are they?'

'They can't suckle babies, and they can't forget themselves.'

'About the babies, of course not. As for forgetting themselves,—I am not quite so sure that I can forget myself.'

## WOMEN

### American Women

THEY WERE TWO MISS SPALDINGS, going on to Florence, at which place they had an uncle, who was minister from the States to the kingdom of Italy; and they were not at all unwilling to receive such little civilities as gentlemen can give to ladies when travelling. The whole party intended to sleep at Turin that night, and they were altogether on good terms with each other, when they started on the journey from St. Michael.

'Clever women those,' said Mr. Glascock, as soon as they had arranged their legs and arms in the banquette.

'Yes, indeed.'

'American women always are clever,—and are almost always pretty.'

'I do not like them,' said Trevelyan,—who in these days was in a mood to like nothing. 'They are exigeant;—and then they are so hard. They want the weakness that a woman ought to have.'

'That comes from what they would call your insular prejudice. We are accustomed to less self-assertion on the part of women than is customary with them. We prefer women to rule us by seeming to yield. In the States, as I take it, the women never yield, and the men have to fight their own battles with other tactics.'

'I don't know what their tactics are.'

'They keep their distance. The men live much by themselves, as though they knew they would not have a chance in the presence of their wives and daughters. Nevertheless they don't manage these things badly. You very rarely hear of an American being separated from his wife.'

## Female Artists

It had been arranged that on Friday evening Lady George should call for Aunt Ju in Green Street, and that they should go together to the Institute in the Marylebone Road. The real and full name of the college, as some ladies delighted to call it, was, though somewhat lengthy, placarded in big letters on a long black board on the front of the building, and was as follows, 'Rights of Women Institute; Established for the Relief of the Disabilities of Females.' By friendly tongues to friendly ears 'The College' or 'the Institute' was the pleasant name used; but the irreverent public was apt to speak of the building generally as the 'Female Disabilities.' And the title was made even shorter. Omnibuses were desired to stop at the 'Disabilities'; and it had become notorious that it was just a mile from King's Cross to the 'Disabilities.' There had been serious thoughts among those who were dominant in the Institute of taking down the big board and dropping the word. But then a change of a name implies such a confession of failure! It had on the whole been thought better to maintain the courage of the opinion which had first made the mistake. 'So you're going to the Disabilities, are you?' Mr. Houghton had said to Lady George.

'I'm to be taken by old Miss Mildmay.'

'Oh, yes; Aunt Ju is a sort of first-class priestess among them. Don't let them bind you over to belong to them. Don't go in for it.' Lady George had declared it to be very improbable that she should go in for it, but had adhered to her determination of visiting the Institute. . .

Aunt Ju was ready for her in the passage. 'I forgot to tell you that we ought to be a little early, as I have to take the chair. I daresay we shall do very well,' she added, 'if the man drives fast. But the thing is so important! One doesn't like to be flurried when one gets up to make the preliminary address.' The only public meetings at which Mary had ever been present had appertained to certain lectures at Brotherton, at which her father or some other clerical dignity had presided, and she could not as yet understand that such a duty should be performed by a woman. She muttered something expressing a hope that all would go right. 'I've got to introduce the Baroness, you know.'

'Introduce the Baroness?'

'The Baroness Banmann. Haven't you seen the bill of the evening? The Baroness is going to address the meeting on the propriety of patronising female artists,—especially in regard to architecture. A combined college of female architects is to be established in Posen and Chicago, and why should we not have a branch in London, which is the centre of the world?'

'Would a woman have to build a house?' asked Lady George.

'She would draw the plans, and devise the proportions, and —and—do the æsthetic part of it. An architect doesn't carry bricks on his back, my dear.'

## Spectacles and Slouch Hat

AND YET SHE WAS NOT, according to my idea, by any means an ill-favoured young woman. It is true that she wore spectacles; and, as she always desired to have her eyes about with her, she never put them off when out of bed. But how many German girls do the like, and are not accounted for that reason to be plain? She was tall and well made, we may almost say robust. She had the full use of all her limbs, and was never ashamed of using them. I think she was wrong when she would be seen to wheel the barrow about the garden, and that her hands must have suffered in her attempts to live down the conventional absurdities of the world. It is true that she did wear gloves during her gardening, but she wore them only in obedience to her father's request. She had bright eyes, somewhat far apart, and well-made, wholesome, regular features. Her nose was large, and her mouth was large; but they were singularly intelligent, and full of humour when she was pleased in conversation. As to her hair, she was too indifferent to enable one to say that it was attractive; but it was smoothed twice a day, was very copious, and always very clean. Indeed, for cleanliness from head to foot she was a model. 'She is very clean, but then it's second to nothing to her,' had said a sarcastic old lady, who had meant to imply that Miss Dorothy Grey was not constant at church. But the sarcastic old lady had known nothing about it. Dorothy Grey never stayed away from morning church unless her presence were desired by her father, and for once or twice that she might do so, she would take her father with her three or four times,—against the grain with him, it must be acknowledged.

But the most singular attribute of the lady's appearance has still to be mentioned. She always wore a slouch hat, which from motives of propriety she called her bonnet, which gave her a singular appearance, as though it had been put on to thatch her entirely from the weather. It was made generally of black straw, and was round, equal at all points of the circle, and was fastened with broad brown ribbons. It was supposed in the neighbourhood to be completely weather-tight. The unimaginative nature of Fulham did not allow the Fulham mind to gather in the fact that, at the same time, she might possess two or three such hats. But they were undoubtedly precisely similar, and she would wear them in London with exactly the same indifference as in the comparatively rural neighbourhood of her own residence. She would in truth go up and down in the omnibus, and would do so alone without the slightest regard to the opinion of any of her neighbours. The Carroll girls would laugh at her behind her back, but no Carroll girl had been seen ever to smile before her face, instigated to do so by their cousin's vagaries.

But I have not yet mentioned that attribute of Miss Grey's which is perhaps the most essential in her character. It is necessary at any rate that they should know it who wish to understand her nature. When it had once been brought home to her that duty required her to do this thing or the other, or to say this word or another, the thing would be done or the word said let the result be what it might. Even to the displeasure of her father, the word was said or the thing was done. Such a one was Dolly Grey.

## Sunday Magnificence

There were three or four factories there,—in and out of which troops of girls would be seen passing twice a day, in their ragged, soiled, dirty mill dresses, all of whom would come out on Sunday dressed with a magnificence that would lead one to suppose that trade at Loring was doing very well. Whether trade did well or ill, whether wages were high or low, whether provisions were cheap in price, whether there were peace or war between capital and labour, still there was the Sunday magnificence. What a blessed thing it is for women,—and for men too certainly,—that there should be a positive happiness to the female sex in the possession, and in exhibiting the possession of bright clothing! It is almost as good for the softening of manners, and the not permitting of them to be ferocious, as is the faithful study of the polite arts. At Loring the manners of the mill hands, as they were called, were upon the whole good,—which I believe was in a great degree to be attributed to their Sunday magnificence.

## Ageing

She went up to her room, disembarrassed herself of her finery, and wrapped herself in a white dressing-gown. As she sat opposite to her glass, relieving her head from its garniture of false hair, she acknowledged to herself that age was coming on her. She could hide the unwelcome approach by art,—hide it more completely than can most women of her age; but, there it was, stealing on her with short grey hairs over her ears and around her temples, with little wrinkles round her eyes easily concealed by objectionable cosmetics, and a look of weariness round the mouth which could only be removed by that self-assertion of herself which practice had made always possible to her in company, though it now so frequently deserted her when she was alone.

## Working Girls

THEY TOOK TOGETHER A BEDROOM in a very quiet street in Clerkenwell,—a street which might be described as genteel because it contained no shops; and here they began to keep house, as they called it. Now the nature of their work was such that they were not called upon to be in their office till noon, but that then they were required to remain there till eight in the evening. At two a short space was allowed them for dinner, which was furnished to them at a cheap rate in a room adjacent to that in which they worked. Here for eight-pence each they could get a good meal, or if they preferred it they could bring their food with them, and even have it cooked upon the premises. In the evening tea and bread and butter were provided for them by the officials; and then at eight or a few minutes after they left the building and walked home. The keeping of house was restricted in fact to providing tea and bread and butter for the morning meal, and perhaps when they could afford it for the repetition of such comfort later in the evening. There was the Sunday to be considered,—as to which day they made a contract with the keeper of the lodging-house to sit at her table and partake of her dishes. And so they were established.

# Politics

## COMFORTABLE CONSERVATIVE

MR. DIE himself of course regarded corn-law repeal as an invention of the devil. He had lived long enough to have regarded Catholic emancipation and parliamentary reform in the same light. Could you have opened his mind, you would probably have found there a settled conviction that the world was slowly coming to an end, that end being brought about by such devilish works as these. But you would also have found a conviction that the Three per Cents. would last his time, and that his fear for the future might with safety be thrown forward, so as to appertain to the fourth or fifth, or perhaps even to the tenth or twelfth coming generation. Mr. Die was not, therefore, personally wretched under his own political creed...

'In politics one should always look forward,' he said, as he held up to the light the glass of old port which he was about to sip; 'in real life it is better to look back—if one has any thing to look back at.' Mr. Die had something to look back at. He had sixty thousand pounds in the funds.

## ELECTIONEERING

LORD DE COURCY was now at home; but his presence did not add much hilarity to the claret-cup. The young men, however, were very keen about the election, and Mr. Nearthewinde, who was one of the party, was full of the most sanguine hopes.

## HE DISTILLS ITS IDEAS AND THEORIES

'I have done one good at any rate,' said Frank; 'I have secured the chorister's vote.'

'What! Bagley?' said Nearthewinde. 'The fellow kept out of my way, and I couldn't see him.'

'I haven't exactly seen him,' said Frank; 'but I've got his vote all the same.'

'What! by a letter?' said Mr. Moffat.

'No, not by a letter,' said Frank, speaking rather low as he looked at the bishop and the earl; 'I got a promise from his wife: I think he's a little in the henpecked line.'

'Ha—ha—ha!' laughed the good bishop, who, in spite of Frank's modulation of his voice, had overheard what had passed. 'Is that the way you manage electioneering matters in our cathedral city? Ha—ha—ha!' The idea of one of his choristers being in the henpecked line was very amusing to the bishop.

'Oh, I got a distinct promise,' said Frank, in his pride; and then added incautiously, 'but I had to order bonnets for the whole family.'

'Hush-h-h-h-h!' said Mr. Nearthewinde, absolutely flabbergasted by such imprudence on the part of one of his client's friends. 'I am quite sure that your order had no effect, and was intended to have no effect on Mr. Bagley's vote.'

'Is that wrong?' said Frank; 'upon my word I thought that it was quite legitimate.'

'One should never admit anything in electioneering matters, should one?' said George, turning to Mr. Nearthewinde.

'Very little, Mr. de Courcy; very little indeed—the less the better. It's hard to say in these days what is wrong and what is not. . .

'Who'll pay for the bonnets, Frank?' said George, whispering to him.

'Oh, I'll pay for them if Moffat won't. I think I shall keep an account there; they seem to have good gloves and those sort of things.'

'Very good, I have no doubt,' said George.

## POLITICS

### Bribery

THE LAWS AGAINST BRIBERY at elections are now so stringent that an unfortunate candidate may easily become guilty, even though actuated by the purest intentions. But not the less on that account does any gentleman, ambitious of the honour of serving his country in Parliament, think it necessary as a preliminary measure to provide a round sum of money at his banker's. A candidate must pay for no treating, no refreshments, no band of music; he must give neither ribbons to the girls nor ale to the men. If a huzza be uttered in his favour, it is at his peril; it may be necessary for him to prove before a committee that it was the spontaneous result of British feeling in his favour, and not the purchased result of British beer. He cannot safely ask any one to share his hotel dinner. Bribery hides itself now in the most impalpable shapes, and may be effected by the offer of a glass of sherry. But not the less on this account does a poor man find that he is quite unable to overcome the difficulties of a contested election.

We strain at our gnats with a vengeance, but we swallow our camels with ease. For what purpose is it that we employ those peculiarly safe men of business—Messrs. Nearthewinde and Closerstil—when we wish to win our path through all obstacles into that sacred recess, if all be so open, all so easy, all so much above board? Alas! the money is still necessary, is still prepared, or at any rate expended. The poor candidate of course knows nothing of the matter till the attorney's bill is laid before him, when all danger of petitions has passed away. He little dreamed till then, not he, that there had been banquetings and junketings, secret doings and deep drinkings at his expense. Poor candidate! Poor member! Who was so ignorant as he! 'Tis true he has paid such bills before; but 'tis equally true that he specially begged his managing friend, Mr. Nearthewinde, to be very careful that all was done according to law! He pays the bill, however, and on the next election will again employ Mr. Nearthewinde.

Now and again, at rare intervals, some glimpse into the inner sanctuary does reach the eyes of ordinary mortal men without; some slight accidental peep into those mysteries from whence all corruption has been so thoroughly expelled; and then, how delightfully refreshing is the sight, when, perhaps, some ex-member, hurled from his paradise like a fallen peri, reveals the secret of that pure heaven, and, in the agony of his despair, tells us all that it cost him to sit for —— through those few halcyon years!

But Mr. Nearthewinde is a safe man, and easy to be employed with but little danger. All these stringent bribery laws only enhance the value of such very safe men as Mr. Nearthewinde. To him, stringent laws against bribery are the strongest assurance of valuable employment. Were these laws of a nature to be evaded with ease, any indifferent attorney might manage a candidate's affairs and enable him to take his seat with security.

## Parliamentary Canvassing

Parliamentary canvassing is not a pleasant occupation. Perhaps nothing more disagreeable, more squalid, more revolting to the senses, more opposed to personal dignity, can be conceived. The same words have to be repeated over and over again in the cottages, hovels, and lodgings of poor men and women who only understand that the time has come round in which they are to be flattered instead of being the flatterers. 'I think I am right in supposing that your husband's principles are Conservative, Mrs. Bubbs.' 'I don't know nothing about it. You'd better call again and see Bubbs hissel.' 'Certainly I will do so. I shouldn't at all like to leave the borough without seeing Mr. Bubbs. I hope we shall have your influence, Mrs. Bubbs.' 'I don't know nothing about it. My folk at home allays vote buff; and I think Bubbs ought to go buff too. Only mind this; Bubbs don't never come home to his dinner. You must come arter six, and I hope he's to have some'at for his trouble. He won't have my word to vote unless he have some'at.' Such is the conversation in which the candidate takes a part, while his cortège at the door is criticising his very imperfect mode of securing Mrs. Bubbs' good wishes. Then he goes on to the next house, and the same thing with some variation is endured again. Some guide, philosopher, and friend, who accompanies him, and who is the chief of the cortège, has calculated on his behalf that he ought to make twenty such visitations an hour, and to call on two hundred constituents in the course of the day. As he is always falling behind in his number, he is always being driven on by his philosopher, till he comes to hate the poor creatures to whom he is forced to address himself, with a most cordial hatred.

## The Way to Office

'As far as I can understand the way of things in your Government, the aspirants to office succeed chiefly by making themselves uncommonly unpleasant to those who are in power. If a man can hit hard enough he is sure to be taken into the elysium of the Treasury bench,—not that he may hit others, but that he may cease to hit those who are there. I don't think men are chosen because they are useful.'

## No Free Agent

Now that Phineas had consented to join the Government . . . he could no longer be a free agent, or even a free thinker. He had been quite aware of this, and had taught himself to understand that members of Parliament in the direct service of the Government were absolved from the necessity of freethinking. Individual free-thinking was incompatible with the position of a member of the Government, and unless such abnegation were practised, no government would be possible.

It was of course a man's duty to bind himself together with no other men but those with whom, on matters of general policy, he could agree heartily;—but having found that he could so agree, he knew that it would be his duty as a subaltern to vote as he was directed.

## The Great American Model

'Government! Well; I suppose there must be government. But the less of it the better. I'm not against government;—nor yet against laws, Mr. Finn; though the less of them, too, the better. But what does these lords do in the Government? Lords indeed! I'll tell you what they do, Mr. Finn. They wotes; that's what they do! They wotes hard; black or white, white or black. Ain't that true? When you're a "lord," will you be able to wote against Mr. Mildmay to save your very soul?'

'If it comes to be a question of soul-saving, Mr. Bunce, I shan't save my place at the expense of my conscience.'

'Not if you knows it, you mean. But the worst of it is that a man gets so thick into the mud that he don't know whether he's dirty or clean. You'll have to wote as you're told, and of course you'll think it's right enough. Ain't you been among Parliament gents long enough to know that's the way it goes?'

'You think no honest man can be a member of the Government?'

'I don't say that, but I think honesty's a deal easier away from 'em. The fact is, Mr. Finn, it's all wrong with us yet, and will be till we get it nigher to the great American model. If a poor man gets into Parliament,—you'll excuse me, Mr. Finn, but I calls you a poor man.'

'Certainly,—as a member of Parliament I am a very poor man.'

'Just so,—and therefore what do you do? You goes and lays yourself out for government! I'm not saying as how you're anyways wrong. A man has to live. You has winning ways, and a good physognomy of your own, and are as big as a lifeguardsman.' Phineas as he heard this doubtful praise laughed and blushed. 'Very well; you makes your way with the big wigs, lords and earls and them like, and you gets returned for a rotten borough;—you'll excuse me, but that's about it, ain't it?—and then you goes in for government! . . .

'We've got to change a deal yet, Mr. Finn, and we'll do it. When a young man as has liberal feelings gets into Parliament, he shouldn't be snapped up and brought into the governing business just because he's poor and wants a salary. They don't do it that way in the States; and they won't do it that way here long. It's the system as I hates, and not you, Mr. Finn. Well, good-bye, sir. I hope you'll like the governing business, and find it suits your health.'

## The Peril of Change

IT IS THE NECESSARY NATURE of a political party in this country to avoid, as long as it can be avoided, the consideration of any question which involves a great change. There is a consciousness on the minds of leading politicians that the pressure from behind, forcing upon them great measures, drives them almost quicker than they can go, so that it becomes a necessity with them to resist rather than to aid the pressure which will certainly be at last effective by its own strength. The best carriage horses are those which can most steadily hold back against the coach as it trundles down the hill.

## The Political Club

ON THAT SAME DAY Lopez dined with his friend Everett Wharton at a new club called the Progress, of which they were both members. The Progress was certainly a new club, having as yet been open hardly more than three years; but still it was old enough to have seen many of the hopes of its early youth become dim with age and inaction. For the Progress had intended to do great things for the Liberal party,—or rather for political liberality in general,—and had in truth done little or nothing. It had been got up with considerable enthusiasm, and for a while certain fiery politicians had believed that through the instrumentality of this institution men of genius, and spirit, and natural power, but without wealth,— meaning always themselves,—would be supplied with sure seats in Parliament and a probable share in the Government. But no such results had been achieved. There had been a want of something,—some deficiency felt but not yet defined, —which had hitherto been fatal. The young men said it was because no old stager who knew the way of pulling the wires would come forward and put the club in the proper groove. The old men said it was because the young men were pretentious puppies. It was, however, not to be doubted that the party of Progress had become slack, and that the Liberal politicians of the country, although a special new club had been opened for the furtherance of their views, were not at present making much way. 'What we want is organization,' said one of the leading young men. But the organization was not as yet forthcoming.

The club, nevertheless, went on its way, like other clubs, and men dined and smoked and played billiards and pretended to read. Some few energetic members still hoped that a good day would come in which their grand ideas might be realised,—but as regarded the members generally, they were content to eat and drink and play billiards.

## Requisites for a Prime Minister

'I HAVE SEEN a good many Prime Ministers, Cantrip, and I've taught myself to think that they are not very different from other men. One wants in a Prime Minister a good many things, but not very great things. He should be clever but need not be a genius; he should be conscientious but by no means strait-laced; he should be cautious but never timid, bold but never venturesome; he should have a good digestion, genial manners, and, above all, a thick skin. These are the gifts we want, but we can't always get them, and have to do without them. For my own part, I find that though Smith be a very good Minister, the best perhaps to be had at the time, when he breaks down Jones does nearly as well.'

## Lady Glencora as Prime Minister

'They should have made me Prime Minister, and have let him be Chancellor of the Exchequer. I begin to see the ways of Government now. I could have done all the dirty work. I could have given away garters and ribbons, and made my bargains while giving them. I could select sleek, easy bishops who wouldn't be troublesome. I could give pensions or withhold them, and make the stupid men peers. I could have the big noblemen at my feet, praying to be Lieutenants of Counties. I could dole out secretaryships and lordships, and never a one without getting something in return. I could brazen out a job and let the "People's Banners" and the Slides make their worst of it. And I think I could make myself popular with my party, and do the high-flowing patriotic talk for the benefit of the Provinces. A man at a regular office has to work. That's what Plantagenet is fit for. He wants always to be doing something that shall be really useful, and a man has to toil at that and really to know things. But a Prime Minister should never go beyond generalities about commerce, agriculture, peace, and general philanthropy. Of course he should have the gift of the gab, and that Plantagenet hasn't got. He never wants to say anything unless he has got something to say. I could do a Mansion House dinner to a marvel!'

## CONSERVATIVES, LIBERALS, AND EQUALITY

'THE CONSERVATIVE who has had any idea of the meaning of the name which he carries, wishes, I suppose, to maintain the differences and the distances which separate the highly placed from their lower brethren. He thinks that God has divided the world as he finds it divided, and that he may best do his duty by making the inferior man happy and contented in his position, teaching him that the place which he holds is his by God's ordinance.'

'And it is so.'

'Hardly in the sense that I mean. But that is the great Conservative lesson. That lesson seems to me to be hardly compatible with continual improvement in the condition of the lower man. But with the Conservative all such improvement is to be based on the idea of the maintenance of those distances. I as a Duke am to be kept as far apart from the man who drives my horses as was my ancestor from the man who drove his, or who rode after him to the wars,—and that is to go on for ever. There is much to be said for such a scheme. Let the lords be, all of them, men with loving hearts, and clear intellect, and noble instincts, and it is possible that they should use their powers so beneficently as to spread happiness over the earth. It is one of the millenniums which the mind of man can conceive, and seems to be that which the Conservative mind does conceive.'

'But the other men who are not lords don't want that kind of happiness.'

'If such happiness were attainable it might be well to constrain men to accept it. But the lords of this world are fallible men; and though as units they ought to be and perhaps are better than those others who have fewer advantages, they are much more likely as units to go astray in opinion than the bodies of men whom they would seek to govern. We know that power does corrupt, and that we cannot trust kings to have loving hearts, and clear intellects, and noble instincts. Men as they come to think about it and to look forward, and to look back, will not believe in such a millennium as that.'

'Do they believe in any millennium?'

'I think they do after a fashion, and I think that I do myself. That is my idea of Conservatism. The doctrine of Liberalism is, of course, the reverse. The Liberal, if he have any fixed idea at all, must I think have conceived the idea of lessening distances,—of bringing the coachman and the Duke nearer together,—nearer and nearer, till a millennium shall be reached by—'

'By equality?' asked Phineas, eagerly interrupting the Prime Minister, and showing his dissent by the tone of his voice.

'I did not use the word, which is open to many objections. In the first place the millennium, which I have perhaps rashly named, is so distant that we need not even think of it as possible. Men's intellects are at present so various that we cannot even realise the idea of equality, and here in England we have been taught to hate the word by the evil effects of those absurd attempts which have been made elsewhere to proclaim it as a fact accomplished by the scratch of a pen or by a chisel on a stone. We have been injured in that, because a good word signifying a grand idea has been driven out of the vocabulary of good men. Equality would be a heaven, if we could attain it. How can we to whom so much has been given dare to think otherwise? How can you look at the bowed back and bent legs and abject face of that poor ploughman, who winter and summer has to drag his rheumatic limbs to his work, while you go a-hunting or sit in pride of place among the foremost few of your country, and say that it all is as it ought to be? You are a Liberal because you know that it is not all as it ought to be, and because you would still march on to some nearer approach to equality; though the thing itself is so great, so glorious, so godlike,—nay, so absolutely divine,—that you have been disgusted by the very promise of it, because its perfection is unattainable. Men have asserted a mock equality till the very idea of equality stinks in men's nostrils...'

'I shan't forget, Duke,' said Phineas, 'your definition of Conservatives and Liberals.'

'I don't think I ventured on a definition;—only a few loose ideas which had been troubling me lately. I say, Finn!'

'Your Grace?'

'Don't you go and tell Ramsden and Drummond that I have been preaching equality, or we shall have a pretty mess. I don't know that it would serve me with my dear friend, the Duke.'

'I will be discretion itself.'

'Equality is a dream. But sometimes one likes to dream,—especially as there is no danger that Matching will fly from me in a dream. I doubt whether I could bear the test that has been attempted in other countries.'

'That poor ploughman would hardly get his share, Duke.'

'No;—that's where it is. We can only do a little and a little to bring it nearer to us;—so little that it won't touch Matching in our day. Here is her ladyship and the ponies. I don't think her ladyship would like to lose her ponies by my doctrine.'

## A Thick Skin

BUT PERHAPS THE MOST WONDERFUL ministerial phenomenon,—though now almost too common to be longer called a phenomenon,—is he who rises high in power and place by having made himself thoroughly detested and also,—alas for parliamentary cowardice!—thoroughly feared. Given sufficient audacity, a thick skin, and power to bear for a few years the evil looks and cold shoulders of his comrades, and that is the man most sure to make his way to some high seat. But the skin must be thicker than that of any animal known, and the audacity must be complete. To the man who will once shrink at the idea of being looked at askance for treachery, or hated for his ill condition, the career is impossible. But let him be obdurate, and the bid will come. 'Not because I want him, do I ask for him,' says some groaning chief of a party,—to himself, and also sufficiently aloud for others' ears,—'but because he stings me and goads me, and will drive me to madness as a foe.' Then the pachydermatous one enters into the other's heaven, probably with the resolution already formed of ousting that unhappy angel.

## Reforming Campaigner

AT FIRST THE ROAR from the crowd was so great that it seemed that it was to be with him as it had been with the others. But by degrees, though there was still a roar,—as of the sea,— Moggs's words became audible. The voices of assent and dissent are very different, even though they be equally loud. Men desirous of interrupting, do interrupt. But cheers, though they be continuous and loud as thunder, are compatible with a hearing. Moggs by this time, too, had learned to pitch his voice for an out-of-door multitude. He preached his sermon, his old sermon, about the Rights of Labour and the Salt of the Earth, the Tyranny of Capital and the Majesty of the Workmen, with an enthusiasm that made him for the moment supremely happy. He was certainly the hero of the hour in Percycross, and he allowed himself to believe,—just for that hour,—that he was about to become the hero of a new doctrine throughout England. He spoke for over half an hour. . .

On that evening Moggs was called upon again to address his friends at the Mechanics' Institute, and to listen to the speeches of all the presidents and secretaries and chairmen; but by ten o'clock he was alone in his bedroom at the Cordwainers' Arms. Downstairs men were shouting, singing, and drinking,—shouting in his honour, though not drinking at his expense. He was alone in his little comfortless room, but felt it to be impossible that he should lie down and rest. His heart was swelling with the emotions of the day, and his mind was full of his coming triumph. It was black night, and there was a soft drizzling rain;—but it was absolutely necessary for his condition that he should go out. It seemed to him that his very bosom would burst, if he confined himself in that narrow space. His thoughts were too big for so small a closet. He crept downstairs and out, through the narrow passage, into the night. Then, by the light of the solitary lamp that stood before the door of the public-house, he could still see those glorious words, 'Moggs, Purity, and the Rights of Labour.' Noble words, which had sufficed to bind to him the whole population of that generous-hearted borough! Purity and the Rights of Labour! Might it not be that with that cry, well cried, he might move the very world! As he walked the streets of the town he felt a great love for the borough grow within his bosom. What would he not owe to the dear place which had first recognised his worth, and had enabled him thus early in life to seize hold of those ploughshares which it would be his destiny to hold for all his coming years? He had before him a career such as had graced the lives of the men whom he had most loved and admired,—of men who had dared to be independent, patriotic, and philanthropical, through all the temptations of political life. Would he be too vain if he thought to rival a Hume or a Cobden? . . . Who can rise but those who believe their wings strong enough for soaring? There might be shipwreck of course,— but he believed that he now saw his way. As to the difficulty of speaking in public,—that he had altogether overcome. Some further education as to facts, historical and political, might be necessary. That he acknowledged to himself;—but he would not spare himself in his efforts to acquire such education. He went pacing through the damp, muddy, dark streets, making speeches that were deliciously eloquent to his own ears. That night he was certainly the happiest man in Percycross, never doubting his success on the morrow, not questioning that. Had not the whole town greeted him with loudest acclamation as their chosen member? He was deliciously happy . . . but it may be doubted whether he slept a wink that night.

## POLITICS

And then there came the real day,—the day of the election. It was a foul, rainy, muddy, sloppy morning, without a glimmer of sun, with that thick, pervading, melancholy atmosphere which forces for the time upon imaginative men a conviction that nothing is worth anything. . .

Moggs, early in the morning, had been radiant with triumph, when he saw his name at the head of the lists displayed from the two inimical committee rooms. As he walked the streets, with a chairman on one side of him and a president on the other, it seemed as though his feet almost disdained to touch the mud. These were two happy hours, during which he did not allow himself to doubt of his triumph. When the presidents and the chairmen spoke to him, he could hardly answer them, so rapt was he in contemplation of his coming greatness. His very soul was full of his seat in Parliament! But when Griffenbottom approached him on the lists, and then passed him, there came a shadow upon his brow. He still felt sure of his election, but he would lose that grand place at the top of the poll to which he had taught himself to look so proudly. Soon after noon a cruel speech was made to him. 'We've about pumped our side dry,' said a secretary of a Young Men's Association.

'Do you mean we've polled all our friends?' asked Moggs.

'Pretty nearly, Mr. Moggs. You see our men have nothing to wait for, and they came up early.' Then Ontario's heart sank within him, and he began to think of the shop in Bond Street. . .

When the chairmen and presidents waited upon Moggs, telling him of the final result, and informing him that he must come to the hustings and make a speech, they endeavoured to console him by an assurance that he, and he alone, had fought the fight fairly. . . Moggs was not consoled, but he did make his speech. It was poor and vapid;—but still there was just enough of manhood left in him for that. As soon as his speech had been spoken he escaped up to London by the night mail train.

# The Press

## The Power of the Press

Mr. Slope had from his youth upwards been a firm believer in the public press. He had dabbled in it himself ever since he had taken his degree, and regarded it as the great arranger and distributor of all future British terrestrial affairs whatever. . . He delighted in the idea of wresting power from the hands of his country's magnates, and placing it in a custody which was at any rate nearer to his own reach. Sixty thousand broad sheets dispersing themselves daily among his reading fellow-citizens, formed in his eyes a better dépôt for supremacy than a throne at Windsor, a cabinet in Downing Street, or even an assembly at Westminster. And on this subject we must not quarrel with Mr. Slope, for the feeling is too general to be met with disrespect.

## Yellow Journalism

Those caterers for our morning repast, the staff of the Jupiter, had been sorely put to it for the last month to find a sufficiency of proper pabulum. Just then there was no talk of a new American president. No wonderful tragedies had occurred on railway trains in Georgia, or elsewhere. There was a dearth of broken banks, and a dead dean with the necessity for a live one was a godsend.

### 'Everybody's Business'

'Everybody's Business' was a paper which, in the natural course of things, did not find its way into the Bowick Rectory; and the Doctor, though he was no doubt acquainted with the title, had never even looked at its columns. It was the purpose of the periodical to amuse its readers, as its name declared, with the private affairs of their neighbours. It went boldly about its work, excusing itself by the assertion that Jones was just as well inclined to be talked about as Smith was to hear whatever could be said about Jones. As both parties were served, what could be the objection? It was in the main good-natured, and probably did most frequently gratify the Joneses, while it afforded considerable amusement to the listless and numerous Smiths of the world. If you can't read and understand Jones's speech in Parliament, you may at any rate have mind enough to interest yourself with the fact that he never composed a word of it in his own room without a ring on his finger and a flower in his button-hole. It may also be agreeable to know that Walker the poet always takes a mutton-chop and two glasses of sherry at half-past one. 'Everybody's Business' did this for everybody to whom such excitement was agreeable. But in managing everybody's business in that fashion, let a writer be as good-natured as he may and let the principle be ever so well-founded that nobody is to be hurt, still there are dangers. It is not always easy to know what will hurt and what will not. And then sometimes there will come a temptation to be, not spiteful, but specially amusing. There must be danger, and a writer will sometimes be indiscreet. Personalities will lead to libels even when the libeller has been most innocent. It may be that after all the poor poet never drank a glass of sherry before dinner in his life,—it may be that a little toast-and-water, even with his dinner, gives him all the refreshment that he wants, and that two glasses of alcoholic mixture in the middle of the day shall seem, when imputed to him, to convey a charge of downright inebriety. But the writer has perhaps learned to regard two glasses of meridian wine as but a moderate amount of sustentation. This man is much flattered if it be given to be understood of him that he falls in love with every pretty woman that he sees;—whereas another will think that he has been made subject to a foul calumny by such insinuation.

### Sensational Journalist

'I RATHER LIKE Mr. Supplehouse myself,' exclaimed Miss Dunstable. 'He never makes any bones about the matter. He has a certain work to do, and a certain cause to serve—namely, his own; and in order to do that work, and serve that cause, he uses such weapons as God has placed in his hands.'

'That's what the wild beasts do.'

'And where will you find men honester than they? The tiger tears you up because he is hungry and wants to eat you. That's what Supplehouse does. But there are so many among us tearing up one another without any excuse of hunger. The mere pleasure of destroying is reason enough.'

### Upholding Aristocratic Morale

'THE MORALE OF OUR ARISTOCRACY,—what you call the Upper Ten,—would be at a low ebb indeed if the public press didn't act as their guardians. Do you think that if the Duke of —— beats his wife black and blue, nothing is to be said about it unless the Duchess brings her husband into court? Did you ever know of a separation among the Upper Ten, that wasn't handled by the press one way or the other? It's my belief that there isn't a peer among 'em all as would live with his wife constant, if it was not for the press;—only some of the very old ones, who couldn't help themselves.'

## A Criminal Trial

As he passed by, a gleam of light fell on him from a window, and at the instant three different artists had him photographed, daguerreotyped, and bedevilled; four graphic members of the public press took down the details of his hat, whiskers, coat, trousers, and boots; and the sub-editor of the *Daily Delight* observed that 'there was a slight tremor in the first footstep which he took within the precincts of the prison, but in every other respect his demeanour was dignified and his presence manly; he had light-brown gloves, one of which was on his left hand, but the other was allowed to swing from his fingers. The court was extremely crowded, and some fair ladies appeared there to grace its customarily ungracious walls. On the bench we observed Lord Killtime, Sir Gregory Hardlines, and Mr. Whip Vigil. Mr. Undecimus Scott, who had been summoned as a witness by the prisoner, was also accommodated by the sheriffs with a seat.' Such was the opening paragraph of the seven columns which were devoted by the *Daily Delight* to the all-absorbing subject.

## On 'Writing to the Paper'

'Write to the *Jupiter*,' suggested the bishop.

'Yes,' said the archdeacon, more worldly wise than his father, 'yes, and be smothered with ridicule; tossed over and over again with scorn; shaken this way and that, as a rat in the mouth of a practised terrier. You will leave out some word or letter in your answer, and the ignorance of the cathedral clergy will be harped upon; you will make some small mistake, which will be a falsehood, or some admission, which will be self-condemnation; you will find yourself to have been vulgar, ill-tempered, irreverend, and illiterate, and the chances are ten to one, but that being a clergyman, you will have been guilty of blasphemy! A man may have the best of causes, the best of talents, and the best of tempers; he may write as well as Addison, or as strongly as Junius; but even with all this he cannot successfully answer, when attacked by the *Jupiter*. In such matters it is omnipotent. What the Czar is in Russia, or the mob in America, that the *Jupiter* is in England. Answer such an article! No, warden; whatever you do, don't do that.'

## Defrauding the Public

'Interference!' said Bold, 'I don't want to interfere.'

'Ah, but, my dear fellow, you do; what else is it? You think that I am able to keep certain remarks out of a newspaper. Your information is probably incorrect, as most public gossip on such subjects is; but, at any rate, you think I have such power, and you ask me to use it: now that is interference.'

'Well, if you choose to call it so.'

'And now suppose for a moment that I had this power, and used it as you wish: isn't it clear that it would be a great abuse? Certain men are employed in writing for the public press; and if they are induced either to write or to abstain from writing by private motives, surely the public press would soon be of little value. Look at the recognised worth of different newspapers, and see if it does not mainly depend on the assurance which the public feel that such a paper is, or is not, independent. You alluded to the *Jupiter*: surely you cannot but see that the weight of the *Jupiter* is too great to be moved by any private request, even though it should be made to a much more influential person than myself: you've only to think of this, and you'll see that I am right.'

The discretion of Tom Towers was boundless: there was no contradicting what he said, no arguing against such propositions. He took such high ground that there was no getting on it. 'The public is defrauded,' said he, 'whenever private considerations are allowed to have weight.' Quite true, thou greatest oracle of the middle of the nineteenth century, thou sententious proclaimer of the purity of the press—the public is defrauded when it is purposely misled. Poor public! how often is it misled! against what a world of fraud has it to contend!

## Newspaper Policy

The 'Evening Pulpit' was supposed to give daily to its readers all that had been said and done up to two o'clock in the day by all the leading people in the metropolis, and to prophesy with wonderful accuracy what would be the sayings and doings of the twelve following hours. This was effected with an air of wonderful omniscience, and not unfrequently with an ignorance hardly surpassed by its arrogance. But the writing was clever. The facts, if not true, were well invented; the arguments, if not logical, were seductive. The presiding spirit of the paper had the gift, at any rate, of knowing what the people for whom he catered would like to read, and how to get his subjects handled so that the reading should be pleasant. . .

A newspaper that wished to make its fortune should never waste its columns and weary its readers by praising anything. Eulogy is invariably dull,—a fact that Mr. Alf had discovered and had utilized.

Mr. Alf had, moreover, discovered another fact. Abuse from those who occasionally praise is considered to be personally offensive, and they who give personal offence will sometimes make the world too hot to hold them. But censure from those who are always finding fault is regarded so much as a matter of course that it ceases to be objectionable. The caricaturist, who draws only caricatures, is held to be justifiable, let him take what liberties he may with a man's face and person. It is his trade, and his business calls upon him to vilify all that he touches. But were an artist to publish a series of portraits, in which two out of a dozen were made to be hideous, he would certainly make two enemies, if not more. Mr. Alf never made enemies, for he praised no one, and, as far as the expression of his newspaper went, was satisfied with nothing.

# Education

## German Professors

'Talking of professors,' said a soft clear voice, close behind the chancellor's elbow; 'how much you Englishmen might learn from Germany; only you are all too proud.'

The bishop looking round, perceived that that abominable young Stanhope had pursued him. The dean stared at him, as though he were some unearthly apparition; so also did two or three prebendaries and minor canons. The archdeacon laughed.

'The German professors are men of learning,' said Mr. Harding, 'but—'

'German professors!' groaned out the chancellor, as though his nervous system had received a shock which nothing but a week of Oxford air could cure.

'Yes,' continued Ethelbert; not at all understanding why a German professor should be contemptible in the eyes of an Oxford don. 'Not but what the name is best earned at Oxford. In Germany the professors do teach; at Oxford, I believe they only profess to do so, and sometimes not even that. You'll have those universities of yours about your ears soon, if you don't consent to take a lesson from Germany.'

## An Oxford Tutor

Tom Staple was the Tutor of Lazarus, and moreover a great man at Oxford. Though universally known by a species of nomenclature so very undignified, Tom Staple was one who maintained a high dignity in the University. He was, as it were, the leader of the Oxford tutors, a body of men who consider themselves collectively as being by very little, if at all, second in importance to the heads themselves. It is not always the case that the master, or warden, or provost, or principal can hit it off exactly with his tutor. A tutor is by no means indisposed to have a will of his own. But at Lazarus they were great friends and firm allies at the time of which we are writing.

Tom Staple was a hale strong man of about forty-five; short in stature, swarthy in face, with strong sturdy black hair, and crisp black beard, of which very little was allowed to show itself in shape of whiskers. He always wore a white neckcloth, clean indeed, but not tied with that scrupulous care which now distinguishes some of our younger clergy. He was, of course, always clothed in a seemly suit of solemn black. Mr. Staple was a decent cleanly liver, not over addicted to any sensuality; but nevertheless a somewhat warmish hue was beginning to adorn his nose, the peculiar effect, as his friends averred, of a certain pipe of port introduced into the cellars of Lazarus the very same year in which the tutor entered it as a freshman. There was also, perhaps, a little redolence of port wine, as it were the slightest possible twang, in Mr. Staple's voice.

In these latter days Tom Staple was not a happy man; University reform had long been his bugbear, and now was his bane. It was not with him as with most others, an affair of politics, respecting which, when the need existed, he could for parties' sake or on behalf of principle, maintain a certain amount of necessary zeal; it was not with him a subject for dilettante warfare, and courteous common-place opposition. To him it was life and death. The *status quo* of the University was his only idea of life, and any reformation was as bad to him as death.

## Wild Oats

THE BAD MEN, said he, the weak and worthless, blunder into danger and burn their feet; but the good men, they who have any character, they who have that within them which can reflect credit on their Alma Mater, they come through scatheless. What merit will there be to a young man to get through safely, if he be guarded and protected and restrained like a school-boy? By so doing, the period of the ordeal is only postponed, and the manhood of the man will be deferred from the age of twenty to that of twenty-four. If you bind him with leading-strings at college, he will break loose while eating for the bar in London; bind him there, and he will break loose afterwards, when he is a married man. The wild oats must be sown somewhere. 'Twas thus that Tom Staple would argue of young men; not, indeed, with much consistency, but still with some practical knowledge of the subject gathered from long experience.

## On Seeming Not to Study

IT HAD ALWAYS BEEN Bertram's delight to study in such a manner that men should think he did not study. There was an affectation in this, perhaps not uncommon to men of genius, but which was deleterious to his character—as all affectations are. It was, however, the fact, that during the last year before his examination, he did study hard. There was a set round him at his college among whom he was esteemed as a great man—a little sect of worshippers, who looked for their idol to do great things; and it was a point of honour with them to assist this pretence of his. They gloried in Bertram's idleness; told stories, not quite veracious, of his doings at wine-parties; and proved, to the satisfaction of admiring freshmen, that he thought of nothing but his horse and his boating. He could do without study more than any other

## Dangers of Oxford

'Well, he has just come from Oxford, you know,' said Mr. Townsend: 'and at the present moment Oxford is the most dangerous place to which a young man can be sent.'

'And Sir Thomas would send him there, though I remember telling his aunt over and over again how it would be.' And Mrs. Townsend, as she spoke, shook her head sorrowfully.

'I don't mean to say, you know, that he's absolutely bitten.'

'Oh, I know—I understand. When they come to crossings and candlesticks, the next step to the glory of Mary is a very easy one. I would sooner send a young man to Rome than to Oxford. At the one he might be shocked and disgusted; but at the other he is cajoled, and cheated, and ruined.' And then Mrs. Townsend threw herself back in her chair, and threw her eyes up towards the ceiling.

But there was no hypocrisy or pretence in this expression of her feelings. She did in her heart of hearts believe that there was some college or club of papists at Oxford, emissaries of the Pope or of the Jesuits. In her moments of sterner thought the latter were the enemies she most feared; whereas, when she was simply pervaded by her usual chronic hatred of the Irish Roman Catholic hierarchy, she was wont to inveigh most against the Pope. And this college, she maintained, was fearfully successful in drawing away the souls of young English students. Indeed, at Oxford a man had no chance against the devil. Things were better at Cambridge; though even there there was great danger. Look at A—— and Z——; and she would name two perverts to the Church of Rome, of whom she had learned that they were Cambridge men. But, thank God, Trinity College still stood firm. Her idea was, that if there were left any real Protestant truth in the

Church of England, that Church should look to feed her lambs by the hands of shepherds chosen from that seminary, and from that seminary only.

## Dangers of a College Education

'I know well what such men are, and I know the evil that is done to them by the cramming they endure. They learn many names of things,—high-sounding names, and they come to understand a great deal about words. It is a knowledge that requires no experience and very little real thought. But it demands much memory; and when they have loaded themselves in this way, they think that they are instructed in all things. After all, what can they do that is of real use to mankind? What can they create?'

'I suppose they are of use.'

'I don't know it. A man will tell you, or pretend to tell you,—for the chances are ten to one that he is wrong,—what sort of lingo was spoken in some particular island or province six hundred years before Christ. What good will that do any one, even if he were right? And then see the effect upon the men themselves. At four-and-twenty a young fellow has achieved some wonderful success, and calls himself by some outlandish and conceited name—a 'double first,' or something of the kind. Then he thinks he has completed everything, and is too vain to learn anything afterwards. The truth is, that at twenty-four no man has done more than acquire the rudiments of his education. The system is bad from beginning to end. All that competition makes false and imperfect growth. Come, I'll go to bed.'

## Schools and Parents

There had, too, been some fighting between Dr. Wortle and the world about his school. He was, as I have said, a thoroughly generous man, but he required, himself, to be treated with generosity. Any question as to the charges made by him as schoolmaster was unendurable. He explained to all parents that he charged for each boy at the rate of two hundred a-year for board, lodging, and tuition, and that anything required for a boy's benefit or comfort beyond that ordinarily supplied would be charged for as an extra at such price as Dr. Wortle himself thought to be an equivalent. Now the popularity of his establishment no doubt depended in a great degree on the sufficiency and comfort of the good things of the world which he provided. The beer was of the best; the boys were not made to eat fat; their taste in the selection of joints was consulted. The morning coffee was excellent. The cook was a great adept at cakes and puddings. The Doctor would not himself have been satisfied unless everything had been plentiful, and everything of the best. He would have hated a butcher who had attempted to seduce him with meat beneath the usual price. But when he had supplied that which was sufficient according to his own liberal ideas, he did not give more without charging for it. Among his customers there had been a certain Honourable Mr. Stantiloup, and,—which had been more important,—an Honourable Mrs. Stantiloup. Mrs. Stantiloup was a lady who liked all the best things which the world could supply, but hardly liked paying the best price. Dr. Wortle's school was the best thing the world could supply of that kind, but then the price was certainly the very best. Young Stantiloup was only eleven, and as there were boys at Bowick as old as seventeen,—for the school had not altogether maintained its old character as being merely preparatory,—Mrs. Stantiloup had thought that her boy should be admitted at a lower fee. The correspondence which had ensued had been unpleasant. Then young Stantiloup had had the influenza, and Mrs. Stantiloup had sent her own doctor. Champagne had been ordered, and carriage exercise. Mr. Stantiloup had been forced by his wife to refuse to pay sums demanded for these undoubted extras. Ten shillings a day for a drive for a little boy seemed to her a great deal,—seemed so to Mrs. Stantiloup. Ought not the Doctor's wife to have been proud to take out her little boy in her own carriage? And then £2 10s. for champagne for the little boy! It was monstrous. Mr. Stantiloup remonstrated. Dr. Wortle said that the little boy had better be taken away and the bill paid at once. The little boy was taken away and the money was offered, short of £5. The matter was instantly put into the hands of the Doctor's lawyer, and a suit commenced. The Doctor, of course, got his money, and then there followed an acrimonious correspondence in the 'Times' and other newspapers. Mrs. Stantiloup did her best to ruin the school, and many very eloquent passages were written not only by her or by her own special scribe, but by others who took the matter up, to prove that two hundred a-year was a great deal more than ought to be paid for the charge of a little boy during three quarters of the year. But in the course of the next twelve months Dr. Wortle was obliged to refuse admittance to a dozen eligible pupils because he had not room for them.

## Sent Down

Our friend Peregrine had just been rusticated, and the head of his college had intimated to the baronet that it would be well to take the young man's name off the college books. This accordingly had been done, and the heir of The Cleeve was at present at home with his mother and grandfather. What special act of grace had led to this severity we need not inquire, but we may be sure that the frolics of which he had been guilty had been essentially young in their nature. He had assisted in driving a farmer's sow into the man's best parlour, or had daubed the top of the tutor's cap with white paint, or had perhaps given liberty to a bag full of rats in the college hall at dinner-time. Such were the youth's academical amusements, and as they were pursued with unremitting energy it was thought well that he should be removed from Oxford.

Then had come the terrible question of his university bills.

One after another, half a score of them reached Sir Peregrine, and then took place that terrible interview—such as most young men have had to undergo at least once,—in which he was asked how he intended to absolve himself from the pecuniary liabilities which he had incurred.

'I am sure I don't know,' said young Orme, sadly.

'But I shall be glad, sir, if you will favour me with your intentions,' said Sir Peregrine, with severity. 'A gentleman does not, I presume, send his orders to a tradesman without having some intention of paying him for his goods.'

'I intended that they should all be paid, of course.'

'And how, sir? by whom?'

'Well, sir,—I suppose I intended that you should pay them'; and the scapegrace as he spoke looked full up into the baronet's face with his bright blue eyes,—not impudently, as though defying his grandfather, but with a bold confidence which at once softened the old man's heart.

Sir Peregrine turned away and walked twice the length of the library; then, returning to the spot where the other stood, he put his hand on his grandson's shoulder. 'Well, Peregrine, I will pay them,' he said. 'I have no doubt that you did so intend when you incurred them;—and that was perhaps natural. I will pay them; but for your own sake, and for your dear mother's sake, I hope that they are not very heavy. Can you give me a list of all that you owe?'

Young Peregrine said that he thought he could, and sitting down at once he made a clean breast of it. With all his foibles, follies, and youthful ignorances, in two respects he stood on good ground. He was neither false nor a coward. He continued to scrawl down items as long as there were any of which he could think, and then handed over the list in order that his grandfather might add them up. It was the last he ever heard of the matter; and when he revisited Oxford some twelve months afterwards, the tradesmen whom he had honoured with his custom bowed to him as low as though he had already inherited twenty thousand a year.

## English Idea of Education

'I WONDER WHY the deuce you never learned Italian,' said the Marquis.

'We never were taught,' said Lord George.

'No;—nobody in England ever is taught anything but Latin and Greek,—with this singular result, that after ten or a dozen years of learning not one in twenty knows a word of either language. That is our English idea of education. In after life a little French may be picked up, from necessity; but it is French of the very worst kind. My wonder is that Englishmen can hold their own in the world at all.'

'They do,' said Lord George,—to whom all this was ear-piercing blasphemy. The national conviction that an Englishman could thrash three foreigners, and if necessary eat them, was strong with him.

'Yes; there is a ludicrous strength even in their pig-headedness. But I always think that Frenchmen, Italians, and Prussians must in dealing with us, be filled with infinite disgust. They must ever be saying, "pig, pig, pig," beneath their breath, at every turn.'

'They don't dare to say it out loud,' said Lord George.

'They are too courteous, my dear fellow.' Then he said a few words to his wife in Italian, upon which she left the room, again shaking hands with her brother-in-law, and again smiling.

## The Headmistress

SHE ASKED, THEREFORE, for an interview with Miss Prettyman, and was shown into the elder sister's room, at eleven o'clock on the Tuesday morning. The elder Miss Prettyman never came into the school herself till twelve, but was in the habit of having interviews with the young ladies,—which were sometimes very awful in their nature,—for the two previous hours. During these interviews an immense amount

## EDUCATION

of business was done, and the fortunes in life of some girls were said to have been there made or marred; as when, for instance, Miss Crimpton had been advised to stay at home with her uncle in England, instead of going out with her sisters to India, both of which sisters were married within three months of their landing in Bombay. The way in which she gave her counsel on such occasions was very efficacious. No one knew better than Miss Prettyman that a cock can crow most effectively in his own farmyard, and therefore all crowing intended to be effective was done by her within the shrine of her own peculiar room.

'Well, my dear, what is it?' she said to Grace. 'Sit in the arm-chair, my dear, and we can then talk comfortably.' The teachers, when they were closeted with Miss Prettyman, were always asked to sit in the arm-chair, whereas a small, straight-backed, uneasy chair was kept for the use of the young ladies. And there was, too, a stool of repentance, out against the wall, very uncomfortable indeed for young ladies who had not behaved themselves so prettily as young ladies generally do.

# Art and Letters

### Gothic Romances

I abhor a mystery. I would fain, were it possible, have my tale run through, from its little prologue to the customary marriage in its last chapter, with all the smoothness incidental to ordinary life. I have no ambition to surprise my reader. Castles with unknown passages are not compatible with my homely muse. I would as lief have to do with a giant in my book—a real giant, such as Goliath—as with a murdering monk with a scowling eye. The age for such delights is, I think, gone. We may say historically of Mrs. Radcliffe's time that there were mysterious sorrows in those days. They are now as much out of date as are the giants.

### Recipe for Letter-Writing

A pleasant letter I hold to be the pleasantest thing that this world has to give. It should be good-humoured; witty it may be, but with a gentle diluted wit. Concocted brilliancy will spoil it altogether. Not long, so that it be tedious in the reading; nor brief, so that the delight suffice not to make itself felt. It should be written specially for the reader, and should apply altogether to him, and not altogether to any other. It should never flatter. Flattery is always odious. But underneath the visible stream of pungent water there may be the slightest under-current of eulogy, so that it be not seen, but only understood. Censure it may contain freely, but censure which in arraigning the conduct implies no doubt as to the intellect. It should be legibly written, so that it may be read with comfort; but no more than that. Calligraphy betokens caution, and if it be not light in hand it is nothing. That it be fairly grammatical and not ill spelled the writer owes to his schoolmaster; but this should come of habit, not of care. Then let its page be soiled by no business; one touch of utility will destroy it all.

If you ask for examples, let it be as unlike Walpole as may be. If you can so write it that Lord Byron might have written it, you will not be very far from high excellence.

But, above all things, see that it be good-humoured.

## Country-House Library

'I HAVE HEARD that there is a library, but the clue to it has been lost, and nobody now knows the way. I don't believe in libraries. Nobody ever goes into a library to read, any more than you would into a larder to eat. But there is this difference;—the food you consume does come out of the larders, but the books you read never come out of the libraries.'

'Except Mudie's,' said Alice.

'Ah, yes; he is the great librarian.'

## Fashions in Novels

IRISH novels were once popular enough. But there is a fashion in novels, as there is in colours and petticoats; and now I fear they are drugs in the market. It is hard to say why a good story should not have a fair chance of success whatever may be its bent; why it should not be reckoned to be good by its own intrinsic merits alone; but such is by no means the case. I was waiting once, when I was young at the work, in the back parlour of an eminent publisher, hoping to see his eminence on a small matter of business touching a three-volumned manuscript which I held in my hand. The eminent publisher, having probably larger fish to fry, could not see me, but sent his clerk or foreman to arrange the business.

'A novel, is it, sir?' said the foreman.

'Yes,' I answered; 'a novel.'

'It depends very much on the subject,' said the foreman, with a thoughtful and judicious frown—'upon the name, sir, and the subject;—daily life, sir; that's what suits us; daily English life. Now your historical novel, sir, is not worth the paper it's written on.'

## How Not to Begin a Novel

As Dr. Thorne is our hero—or I should rather say my hero, a privilege of selecting for themselves in this respect being left to all my readers—and as Miss Mary Thorne is to be our heroine, a point on which no choice whatsoever is left to any one, it is necessary that they shall be introduced and explained and described in a proper, formal manner. I quite feel that an apology is due for beginning a novel with two long dull chapters full of description. I am perfectly aware of the danger of such a course. In so doing I sin against the golden rule which requires us all to put our best foot foremost, the wisdom of which is fully recognized by novelists, myself among the number. It can hardly be expected that any one will consent to go through with a fiction that offers so little of allurement in its first pages; but twist it as I will I cannot do otherwise. I find that I cannot make poor Mr. Gresham hem and haw and turn himself uneasily in his armchair in a natural manner till I have said why he is uneasy. I cannot bring in my doctor speaking his mind freely among the bigwigs till I have explained that it is in accordance with his usual character to do so. This is unartistic on my part, and shows want of imagination as well as want of skill. Whether or not I can atone for these faults by straightforward, simple, plain story-telling—that, indeed, is very doubtful.

## Lady Eustace's Reading

Those ten first days of August went very slowly with Lady Eustace. 'Queen Mab' got itself poked away, and was heard of no more. But there were other books. A huge box full of novels had come down, and Miss Macnulty was a great devourer of novels. If Lady Eustace would talk to her about the sorrows of the poorest heroine that ever saw her lover murdered before her eyes, and then come to life again with ten thousand pounds a year,—for a period of three weeks, or till another heroine, who had herself been murdered, obliterated the former horrors from her plastic mind,—Miss Macnulty could discuss the catastrophe with the keenest interest. And Lizzie, finding herself to be, as she told herself, unstrung, fell also into novel-reading. She had intended during this vacant time to master the 'Fairy Queen'; but the 'Fairy Queen' fared even worse than 'Queen Mab';—and the studies of Portray Castle were confined to novels. For poor Macnulty, if she could only be left alone, this was well enough. To have her meals, and her daily walk, and her fill of novels, and to be left alone, was all that she asked of the gods. But it was not so with Lady Eustace. She asked much more than that, and was now thoroughly discontented with her own idleness. She was sure that she could have read Spenser from sunrise to sundown, with no other break than an hour or two given to Shelley,—if only there had been some one to sympathise with her in her readings. But there was no one, and she was very cross.

## Realism vs. the Heroic

And so also has the reading world taught itself to like best the characters of all but divine men and women. Let the man who paints with pen and ink give the gaslight, and the flesh-pots, the passions and pains, the prurient prudence and the rouge-pots and pounce-boxes of the world as it is, and he will be told that no one can care a straw for his creations. With whom are we to sympathise? says the reader, who not unnaturally imagines that a hero should be heroic. Oh, thou, my reader, whose sympathies are in truth the great and only aim of my work, when you have called the dearest of your friends round you to your hospitable table, how many heroes are there sitting at the board? Your bosom friend,—even if he be a knight without fear, is he a knight without reproach? The Ivanhoe that you know, did he not press Rebecca's hand? Your Lord Evandale,—did he not bring his coronet into play when he strove to win his Edith Bellenden? Was your Tresilian still true and still forbearing when truth and forbearance could avail him nothing? And those sweet girls whom you know, do they never doubt between the poor man they think they love, and the rich man whose riches they know they covet?

Go into the market, either to buy or sell, and name the thing you desire to part with or to get, as it is, and the market is closed against you. Middling oats are the sweepings of the granaries. A useful horse is a jade gone at every point. Good sound port is sloe juice. No assurance short of A 1. betokens even a pretence to merit. And yet in real life we are content with oats that are really middling, are very glad to have a useful horse, and know that if we drink port at all we must drink some that is neither good nor sound. In those delineations of life and character which we call novels a similarly superlative vein is desired. Our own friends around us are not always merry and wise, nor, alas! always honest and true. They are often cross and foolish, and sometimes treacherous and false. They are so, and we are angry. Then we forgive them, not without a consciousness of imperfection on our own part. And we know—or, at least, believe—that though they be sometimes treacherous and false, there is a balance of good. We cannot have heroes to dine with us. There are none. And were these heroes to be had, we should not like them. But neither are our friends villains,—whose every aspiration is for evil, and whose every moment is a struggle for some achievement worthy of the devil.

The persons whom you cannot care for in a novel, because they are so bad, are the very same that you so dearly love in your life, because they are so good. To make them and ourselves somewhat better,—not by one spring heavenwards to perfection, because we cannot so use our legs,—but by slow climbing, is, we may presume, the object of all teachers, leaders, legislators, spiritual pastors, and masters. He who writes tales such as this, probably also has, very humbly, some such object distantly before him. A picture of surpassing god-like nobleness,—a picture of a King Arthur among men, may perhaps do much. But such pictures cannot do all. When such a picture is painted, as intending to show what a man should be, it is true. If painted to show what men are, it is false. The true picture of life as it is, if it could be adequately painted, would show men what they are, and how they might rise, not, indeed, to perfection, but one step first, and then another on the ladder.

## Unread Books

SHE OFTEN LOVED, if the truth is to be spoken, to be idle, and to spend hours with an unread book in her hand under the shade of the deanery trees, and among the flowers of the deanery garden. The Dean never questioned her as to those idle hours. But at Cross Hall not a half-hour would be allowed to pass without enquiry as to its purpose. At Cross Hall there would be no novels,—except those of Miss Edgeworth, which were sickening to her. She might have all Mudie down to the deanery if she chose to ask for it.

## Reader's Taste

'I DON'T LIKE being idle. I read a good deal. Do you read?'

'I have but few books here. I have read more perhaps than

most young women of my age. I came away in such a hurry that I have almost nothing with me.'

'Can I lend you books?'

'If you will. I will promise to take care of them.'

'I have "The Heartbroken One," by Spratt, you know. It is very absurd, but full of life from beginning to end. All that Spratt writes is very lively.'

'I don't think I care for Spratt. He may be lively, but he's not life-like.'

'And "Michael Bamfold." It is hard work, perhaps, but very thoughtful, if you can digest that sort of thing.'

'I hate thought.'

'What do you say to Miss Bouverie's last;—"Ridden to a Standstill"; a little loud, perhaps, but very interesting? Or "Green Grow the Rushes O," by Mrs. Tremaine? None of Mrs. Tremaine's people do anything that anybody would do, but they all talk well.'

'I hate novels written by women. Their girls are so unlovely, and their men such absurdly fine fellows!'

'I have William Coxe's "Lock Picked at Last," of which I will defy you to find the secret till you have got to the end of it.'

'I am a great deal too impatient.'

'And Thompson's "Four Marquises." That won't give you any trouble, because you will know it all from the first chapter.'

'And never have a moment of excitement from the beginning to the end. I don't think I care very much for novels. Have you nothing else?'

Caldigate had many other books, a Shakespeare, some lighter poetry, and sundry heavier works of which he did not wish specially to speak, lest he should seem to be boasting of his own literary taste; but at last it was settled that on the next morning he should supply her with what choice he had among the poets.

## Reader's Understanding

'All the books have got to be so stupid! I think I'll read Pilgrim's Progress again.'

'What do you say to Robinson Crusoe?' said Bell.

'Or Paul and Virginia?' said Lily. 'But I believe I'll have Pilgrim's Progress. I never can understand it, but I rather think that makes it nicer.'

'I hate books I can't understand,' said Bell. 'I like a book to be clear as running water, so that the whole meaning may be seen at once.'

'The quick seeing of the meaning must depend a little on the reader, must it not?' said Mrs. Dale.

'The reader mustn't be a fool, of course,' said Bell.

'But then so many readers are fools,' said Lily. 'And yet they get something out of their reading. Mrs. Crump is always poring over the Revelations, and nearly knows them by heart. I don't think she could interpret a single image, but she has a hazy, misty idea of the truth. That's why she likes it,—because it's too beautiful to be understood; and that's why I like Pilgrim's Progress.'

## Would-be Author

'You are just like some of those men who for years past have been going to write a book on some new subject. The intention has been sincere at first, and it never altogether dies away. But the would-be author, though he still talks of his work, knows that it will never be executed, and is very patient under the disappointment. All enthusiasm about the thing is gone, but he is still known as the man who is going to do it some day.'

## At the Royal Academy

One morning, early, Gregory and Ralph from Norfolk were together at the Royal Academy. Although it was not yet ten when they entered the gallery, the rooms were already so crowded that it was difficult to get near the line, and almost impossible either to get into or to get out of a corner. Gregory had been there before, and knew the pictures. He also was supposed by his friends to understand something of the subject; whereas Ralph did not know a Cooke from a Hook, and possessed no more than a dim idea that Landseer painted all the wild beasts, and Millais all the little children. 'That's a fine picture,' he said, pointing up at an enormous portrait of the Master of the B.B., in a red coat, seated square on a seventeen-hand high horse, with his hat off, and the favourite hounds of his pack around him. 'That's by Grant,' said Gregory. 'I don't know that I care for that kind of thing.' 'It's as like as it can stare,' said Ralph, who appreciated the red coat, and the well-groomed horse, and the finely-shaped hounds. He backed a few steps to see the picture better, and found himself encroaching upon a lady's dress.

## Thackeray

He [Thackeray] had been taught to regard the Civil Service as easy, and had counted upon himself to be able to add to it his novels, and his work with his *Punch* brethren, and to his contributions generally to the literature of the day. He might have done so, could he have risen at five, and have sat at his private desk for three hours before he began his official routine at the public one. A capability for grinding, an aptitude for continuous task work, a disposition to sit in one's chair as though fixed to it by cobbler's wax, will enable a man in the prime of life to go through the tedium of a second day's work every day; but of all men Thackeray was the last to bear the wearisome perseverance of such a life.

## Editor's Requirements

Now THERE WERE THOSE who had found out that Charley Tudor, in spite of his wretched, idle, vagabond mode of life, was no fool; indeed, that there was that talent within him which, if turned to good account, might perhaps redeem him from ruin and set him on his legs again; at least so thought some of his friends, among whom Mrs. Woodward was the most prominent. She insisted that if he would make use of his genius he might employ his spare time to great profit by writing for magazines or periodicals; and, inspirited by so flattering a proposition, Charley had got himself introduced to the editor of a newly-projected publication. At his instance he was to write a tale for approval, and 'Crinoline and Macassar' was the name selected for his first attempt.

The affair had been fully talked over at Hampton, and it had been arranged that the young author should submit his story, when completed, to the friendly criticism of the party assembled at Surbiton Cottage, before he sent it to the editor. He had undertaken to have 'Crinoline and Macassar' ready for perusal on the next Saturday, and in spite of Mr. M'Ruen and Norah Geraghty, he had really been at work.

'Will it be finished by Saturday, Charley?' said Norman.

'Yes—at least I hope so; but if that's not done, I have another all complete.'

'Another! and what is that called?'

'Oh, that's a very short one,' said Charley, modestly.

'But, short as it is, it must have a name, I suppose. What's the name of the short one?'

'Why, the name is long enough; it's the longest part about it. The editor gave me the name, you know, and then I had to write the story. It's to be called "Sir Anthony Allan-a-dale and the Baron of Ballyporeen."'

'Oh! two rival knights in love with the same lady, of course,' and Harry gave a gentle sigh as he thought of his own still unhealed grief. 'The scene is laid in Ireland, I presume?'

'No, not in Ireland; at least not exactly. I don't think the scene is laid anywhere in particular; it's up in a mountain, near a castle. There isn't any lady in it—at least, not alive.'

'Heavens, Charley! I hope you are not dealing with dead women.'

'No—that is, I have to bring them to life again. I'll tell you how it is. In the first paragraph, Sir Anthony Allan-a-dale is lying dead, and the Baron of Ballyporeen is standing over him with a bloody sword. You must always begin with an incident now, and then hark back for your explanation and description; that's what the editor says is the great secret of the present day, and where we beat all the old fellows that wrote twenty years ago.'

'Oh!—yes—I see. They used to begin at the beginning; that was very humdrum.'

'A devilish bore, you know, for a fellow who takes up a novel because he's dull. Of course he wants his fun at once. If you begin with a long history of who's who and all that, why, he won't read three pages; but if you touch him up with a startling incident or two at the first go off, then give him a chapter of horrors, then another of fun, then a little love or a little slang, or something of that sort, why, you know, about the end of the first volume, you may describe as much as you like, and tell everything about everybody's father and mother for just as many pages as you want to fill. At least that's what the editor says.'

'*Meleager ab ovo* may be introduced with safety when you get as far as that,' suggested Norman.

'Yes, you may bring him in too, if you like,' said Charley, who was somewhat oblivious of his classicalities. 'Well, Sir Anthony is lying dead and the Baron is standing over him, when out come Sir Anthony's retainers—'

'Out—out of what?'

'Out of the castle: that's all explained afterwards. Out come the retainers, and pitch into the Baron till they make mincemeat of him.'

'They don't kill him, too?'

'Don't they though? I rather think they do, and no mistake.'

'And so both your heroes are dead in the first chapter.'

'First chapter! why, that's only the second paragraph. I'm only to be allowed ten paragraphs for each number, and I am expected to have an incident for every other paragraph for the first four days.'

'That's twenty incidents.'

'Yes—it's a great bother finding so many.—I'm obliged to make the retainers come by all manner of accidents; and I should never have finished the job if I hadn't thought of setting the castle on fire. "And now forked tongues of liquid fire, and greedy lambent flames burst forth from every window of the devoted edifice. The devouring element—." That's the best passage in the whole affair.'

'This is for the *Daily Delight,* isn't it?'

'Yes, for the *Daily Delight.* It is to begin on the 1st of September with the partridges. We expect a most tremendous sale. It will be the first halfpenny publication in the market, and as the retailers will get them for sixpence a score—twenty-four to the score—they'll go off like wildfire.'

'Well, Charley, and what do you do with the dead bodies of your two heroes?'

'Of course I needn't tell you that it was not the Baron who killed Sir Anthony at all.'

'Oh! wasn't it? O dear—that was a dreadful mistake on the part of the retainers.'

'But as natural as life. You see these two grandees were next-door neighbours, and there had been a feud between the families for seven centuries—a sort of Capulet and Montague affair. One Adelgitha, the daughter of the Thane of Allan-a-dale—there were Thanes in those days, you know—was betrothed to the eldest son of Sir Waldemar de Ballyporeen. This gives me an opportunity of bringing in a succinct little account of the Conquest, which will be beneficial to the lower classes. The editor peremptorily insists upon that kind of thing.'

'*Omne tulit punctum,*' said Norman.

'Yes, I dare say,' said Charley, who was now too intent on his own new profession to attend much to his friend's quotation. 'Well, where was I?—Oh! the eldest son of Sir Waldemar went off with another lady and so the feud began. There is a very pretty scene between Adelgitha and her lady's-maid.'

'What, seven centuries before the story begins?'

'Why not? The editor says that the unities are altogether thrown over now, and that they are regular bosh—our game is to stick in a good bit whenever we can get it—I got to be so fond of Adelgitha that I rather think she's the heroine.'

'But doesn't that take off the interest from your dead grandees?'

'Not a bit; I take it chapter and chapter about. Well, you see, the retainers had no sooner made mincemeat of the Baron —a very elegant young man was the Baron, just returned from the Continent, where he had learnt to throw aside all prejudices about family feuds and everything else, and he had just come over in a friendly way, to say as much to Sir Anthony, when, as he crossed the drawbridge, he stumbled over the corpse of his ancient enemy—well, the retainers had no sooner made mincemeat of him, than they perceived that Sir Anthony was lying with an open bottle in his hand, and that he had taken poison.'

'Having committed suicide?' asked Norman.

'No, not at all. The editor says that we must always have a slap at some of the iniquities of the times. He gave me three or four to choose from; there was the adulteration of food, and the want of education for the poor, and street music, and the miscellaneous sale of poisons.'

'And so you chose poisons and killed the knight?'

'Exactly; at least I didn't kill him, for he comes all right again after a bit. He had gone out to get something to do him good after a hard night, a Seidlitz powder, or something of that sort, and an apothecary's apprentice had given him prussic acid in mistake.'

'And how is it possible he should have come to life after taking prussic acid?'

'Why, there I have a double rap at the trade. The prussic acid is so bad of its kind, that it only puts him into a kind of torpor for a week. Then we have the trial of the apothecary's boy; that is an excellent episode, and gives me a grand hit at the absurdity of our criminal code.'

'Why, Charley, it seems to me that you are hitting at everything.'

'Oh! ah! right and left, that's the game for us authors. The press is the only *censor morum* going now—and who so fit? Set a thief to catch a thief, you know. Well, I have my hit at the criminal code, and then Sir Anthony comes out of his torpor.'

'But how did it come to pass that the Baron's sword was all bloody?'

'Ah, there was the difficulty; I saw that at once. It was necessary to bring in something to be killed, you know. I thought of a stray tiger out of Wombwell's menagerie; but the editor says that we must not trespass against the probabilities; so I have introduced a big dog. The Baron had come across a big dog, and seeing that the brute had a wooden log tied to his throat, thought he must be mad, and so he killed him.'

'And what's the end of it, Charley?'

'Why, the end is rather melancholy. Sir Anthony reforms, leaves off drinking, and takes to going to church every day.

He becomes a Puseyite, puts up a memorial window to the Baron, and reads the Tracts. At last he goes over to the Pope, walks about in nasty dirty clothes all full of vermin, and gives over his estate to Cardinal Wiseman. Then there are the retainers; they all come to grief, some one way and some another. I do that for the sake of the Nemesis.'

'I would not have condescended to notice them, I think,' said Norman.

'Oh! I must; there must be a Nemesis. The editor specially insists on a Nemesis.'

## Writing as a Career

'Perhaps I may do something by writing,' said Charley, very bashfully.

'By writing! ha, ha, ha,' and Alaric laughed somewhat cruelly at the poor navvy—'do something by writing! what will you do by writing? will you make £20,000—or 20,000 pence? Of all trades going, that, I should say, is likely to be the poorest for a poor man—the poorest and the most heartbreaking. What have you made already to encourage you?'

'The editor says that "Crinoline and Macassar" will come to £4 10s.'

'And when will you get it?'

'The editor says that the rule is to pay six months after the date of publication. The *Daily Delight* is only a new thing, you know. The editor says that, if the sale comes up to his expectations, he will increase the scale of pay.'

'A prospect of £4 10s. for a fortnight's hard work! That's a bad look-out, my boy; you had better take the heiress.'

'It may be a bad look-out,' said Charley, whose spirit was raised by his cousin's sneers—'but at any rate it's honest. And I'll tell you what, Alaric, I'd sooner earn £50 by writing for the press, than get £1,000 in any other way you can think of. It may be a poor trade in one way; and authors, I believe, are poor; but I am sure it has its consolations.'

## ART AND LETTERS

### The Art Tourist

As regards the first object,—that of knowing the painter from his work,—the art tourist soon obtains many very useful guides to his memory. Indeed, it is on guides to his memory that he depends altogether. When he has progressed so far that he can depend on his judgment instead of his memory, he has ceased to be an art tourist, and has become a connoisseur. The first guide to memory is the locality of the picture. He knows that Raphaels are rife at Florence, Titians at Venice, Vandykes at Genoa, Guidos at Bologna, Van Eykes and Memlings in Flanders, and Rembrandts and Paul Potters in Holland. Pictures have been too much scattered about to make this knowledge alone good for much; but joined to other similar aids, it is a powerful assistance, and prevents mistakes which in an old art tourist would be disgraceful. Next to this, probably, he acquires a certain, though not very accurate idea of dates, which supplies him with information from the method and manner of the picture. If he is placed before a work of some early Tuscan painter,—Orcagne, or the like,—he will know that it is not the work of some comparatively modern painter of the same country,—such as Andrea del Sarto;—and so he progresses. Then the old masters themselves were very liberal in the aids which they gave to memory by repeating their own work,—as, indeed, are some of their modern followers, who love to produce the same faces year after year upon their canvas,—I will not say *usque ad nauseam*, for how can we look on a pretty face too often? The old masters delighted to paint their own wives or their own mistresses,—the women, in short, whom they loved best and were most within their reach, guided perhaps by some idea of economy in saving the cost of a model; and this peculiarity on their part is a great assistance to art tourists. He or she must be a very young art tourist who does not know the Murillo face, or the two Rubens faces, or the special Raphael face, or the Leonardo da Vinci face, or the Titian head and neck, or the Parmigianino bunch of hair, or the Correggio forehead and fingers. All this is a great assistance, and gives hope to an art tourist in a field of inquiry so wide that there could hardly be any hope without such aid. And then these good-natured artists had peculiar tricks with them, which give further most valuable help to the art tourist in his work. Jacobo Bassano paints people ever cringing toward the ground, and consequently a Jacobo Bassano can be read by a young art tourist in an instant. Claude Lorraine delighted to insert a man carrying a box. That vilest of painters, Guercino, rejoices in turbans. Schalken painted even scenes by candlelight, so that he was called Della Notte. Jan Steen usually greets us with a portrait of himself in a state of drunkenness. Adrian van Ostade seldom omits a conical-shaped hat, or Teniers a red cap and a peculiar figure, for which the art tourist always looks immediately when he thinks of discovering this artist. All these little tricks of the artist, and many more of the same kind, the art tourist soon learns, much to his own comfort.

## Country-House Scholar

GREGORY MARRABLE THE YOUNGER was a man somewhat over forty, but he looked as though he were sixty. He was very tall and thin, narrow in the chest, and so round in the shoulders as to appear to be almost humpbacked. He was so short-sighted as to be nearly blind, and was quite bald. He carried his head so forward that it looked as though it were going to fall off. He shambled with his legs, which seemed never to be strong enough to carry him from one room to another; and he tried them by no other exercise, for he never went outside the house except when, on Sundays and some other very rare occasions, he would trust himself to be driven in a low pony-phaeton. But in one respect he was altogether unlike his father. His whole time was spent among his books, and he was at this moment engaged in revising and editing a very long and altogether unreadable old English chronicle in rhyme, for publication by one of those learned societies which are rife in London. Of Robert of Gloucester, and William Langland, of Andrew of Wyntown and the Lady Juliana Berners, he could discourse, if not with eloquence, at least with enthusiasm. Chaucer was his favourite poet, and he was supposed to have read the works of Gower in English, French, and Latin. But he was himself apparently as old as one of his own black-letter volumes, and as unfit for general use.

## On the Pre-Raphaelites

OUR MODERN ARTISTS, whom we style Pre-Raphaelites, have delighted to go back, not only to the finish and peculiar manner, but also to the subjects of the early painters. It is impossible to give them too much praise for the elaborate perseverance with which they have equalled the minute perfections of the masters from whom they take their inspiration: nothing probably can exceed the painting of some of these latter-day pictures. It is, however, singular into what faults they fall as regards their subjects: they are not quite content to take the old stock groups—a Sebastian with his arrows, a Lucia with her eyes in a dish, a Lorenzo with a gridiron, or the Virgin with two children. But they are anything but happy in their change. As a rule, no figure should be drawn in a position which it is impossible to suppose any figure should maintain. The patient endurance of St. Sebastian, the wild ecstasy of St. John in the Wilderness, the maternal love of the Virgin, are feelings naturally portrayed by a fixed posture; but the lady with the stiff back and bent neck, who looks at her flower, and is still looking from hour to hour, gives us an idea of pain without grace, and abstraction without a cause.

## Mr. Popular Sentiment

Passing into the Strand, he saw in a bookseller's window an announcement of the first number of *The Almshouse;* so he purchased a copy, and hurrying back to his lodgings, proceeded to ascertain what Mr. Popular Sentiment had to say to the public on the subject which had lately occupied so much of his own attention.

In former times great objects were attained by great work. When evils were to be reformed, reformers set about their heavy task with grave decorum and laborious argument. An age was occupied in proving a grievance, and philosophical researches were printed in folio pages, which it took a life to write, and an eternity to read. We get on now with a lighter step, and quicker: ridicule is found to be more convincing than argument, imaginary agonies touch more than true sorrows, and monthly novels convince, when learned quartos fail to do so. If the world is to be set right, the work will be done by shilling numbers.

Of all such reformers Mr. Sentiment is the most powerful. It is incredible the number of evil practices he has put down: it is to be feared he will soon lack subjects, and that when he has made the working classes comfortable, and got bitter beer put into proper-sized pint bottles, there will be nothing further for him left to do. Mr. Sentiment is certainly a very powerful man, and perhaps not the less so that his good poor people are so very good; his hard rich people so very hard; and the genuinely honest so very honest. Namby-pamby in these days is not thrown away if it be introduced in the proper quarters. Divine peeresses are no longer interesting, though possessed of every virtue; but a pattern peasant or an immaculate manufacturing hero may talk as much twaddle as one of Mrs. Ratcliffe's heroines, and still be listened to. Perhaps, however, Mr. Sentiment's great attraction is in his second-rate characters. If his heroes and heroines walk upon

ART AND LETTERS

stilts, as heroes and heroines, I fear, ever must, their attendant satellites are as natural as though one met them in the street: they walk and talk like men and women, and live among our friends a rattling, lively life; yes, live, and will live till the names of their calling shall be forgotten in their own, and Buckett and Mrs. Gamp will be the only words left to us to signify a detective police officer or a monthly nurse.

*The Almshouse* opened with a scene in a clergyman's house. Every luxury to be purchased by wealth was described as being there: all the appearances of household indulgence generally found amongst the most self-indulgent of the rich were crowded into this abode. Here the reader was introduced to the demon of the book, the Mephistopheles of the drama. What story was ever written without a demon? What novel, what history, what work of any sort, what world, would be perfect without existing principles both of good and evil? The demon of *The Almshouse* was the clerical owner of this comfortable abode. He was a man well stricken in years, but still strong to do evil: he was one who looked cruelly out of a hot, passionate, bloodshot eye; who had a huge red nose with a carbuncle, thick lips, and a great double, flabby chin, which swelled out into solid substance, like a turkey cock's comb, when sudden anger inspired him: he had a hot, furrowed, low brow, from which a few grizzled hairs were not yet rubbed off by the friction of his handkerchief: he wore a loose unstarched white handkerchief, black loose ill-made clothes, and huge loose shoes, adapted to many corns and various bunions: his husky voice told tales of much daily port wine, and his language was not so decorous as became a clergyman. Such was the master of Mr. Sentiment's *Almshouse*. He was a widower, but at present accompanied by two daughters, and a thin and somewhat insipid curate. One of the young ladies was devoted to her father and the fashionable world, and she of course was the favourite; the other was equally addicted to Puseyism and the curate.

[ 379 ]

## HE DISTILLS ITS IDEAS AND THEORIES

The second chapter of course introduced the reader to the more especial inmates of the hospital. Here was discovered eight old men; and it was given to be understood that four vacancies remained unfilled, through the perverse ill-nature of the clerical gentleman with the double chin. The state of these eight paupers was touchingly dreadful: sixpence-farthing a day had been sufficient for their diet when the almshouse was founded; and on sixpence-farthing a day were they still doomed to starve, though food was four times as dear, and money four times as plentiful. It was shocking to find how the conversation of these eight starved old men in their dormitory shamed that of the clergyman's family in his rich drawing-room. The absolute words they uttered were not perhaps spoken in the purest English, and it might be difficult to distinguish from their dialect to what part of the country they belonged; the beauty of the sentiment, however, amply atoned for the imperfection of the language; and it was really a pity that these eight old men could not be sent through the country as moral missionaries, instead of being immured and starved in that wretched almshouse...

The artist who paints for the million must use glaring colours, as no one knew better than Mr. Sentiment when he described the inhabitants of his almshouse; and the radical reform which has now swept over such establishments has owed more to the twenty numbers of Mr. Sentiment's novel, than to all the true complaints which have escaped from the public for the last half century.

### Literary Hack

Mr. Booker, of the 'Literary Chronicle' ... was a hardworking professor of literature, by no means without talent, by no means without influence, and by no means without a conscience. But, from the nature of the struggles in which he had been engaged, by compromises which had gradually been

## ART AND LETTERS

driven upon him by the encroachment of brother authors on the one side and by the demands on the other of employers who looked only to their profits, he had fallen into a routine of work in which it was very difficult to be scrupulous, and almost impossible to maintain the delicacies of a literary conscience. He was now a bald-headed old man of sixty, with a large family of daughters, one of whom was a widow dependent on him with two little children. He had five hundred a year for editing the 'Literary Chronicle,' which, through his energy, had become a valuable property. He wrote for magazines, and brought out some book of his own almost annually. He kept his head above water, and was regarded by those who knew about him, but did not know him, as a successful man. He always kept up his spirits, and was able in literary circles to show that he could hold his own. But he was driven by the stress of circumstances to take such good things as came in his way, and could hardly afford to be independent. It must be confessed that literary scruple had long departed from his mind.

### REVIEWERS' COURTESIES

'Welbeck Street, 25th February, 187-.

'DEAR MR. BOOKER,

'I have told Mr. Leadham'—Mr. Leadham was senior partner in the enterprising firm of publishers known as Messrs. Leadham and Loiter—'to send you an early copy of my "Criminal Queens." I have already settled with my friend Mr. Broune that I am to do your "New Tale of a Tub" in the "Breakfast Table." Indeed, I am about it now, and am taking great pains with it. If there is anything you wish to have specially said as to your view of the Protestantism of the time, let me know. I should like you to say a word as to the accuracy of my historical details, which I know you can safely do. Don't put it off, as the sale does so much depend

## HE DISTILLS ITS IDEAS AND THEORIES

on early notices. I am only getting a royalty, which does not commence till the first four hundred are sold.

'Yours sincerely,
'MATILDA CARBURY.'

'ALFRED BOOKER, ESQ.,
'"Literary Chronicle" Office, Strand.'

There was nothing in this which shocked Mr. Booker. He laughed inwardly, with a pleasantly reticent chuckle, as he thought of Lady Carbury dealing with his views of Protestantism,—as he thought also of the numerous historical errors into which that clever lady must inevitably fall in writing about matters of which he believed her to know nothing. But he was quite alive to the fact that a favourable notice in the 'Breakfast Table' of his very thoughtful work, called the 'New Tale of a Tub,' would serve him, even though written by the hand of a female literary charlatan, and he would have no compunction as to repaying the service by fulsome praise in the 'Literary Chronicle.' He would not probably say that the book was accurate, but he would be able to declare that it was delightful reading, that the feminine characteristics of the queens had been touched with a masterly hand, and that the work was one which would certainly make its way into all drawing-rooms. He was an adept at this sort of work, and knew well how to review such a book as Lady Carbury's 'Criminal Queens,' without bestowing much trouble on the reading. He could almost do it without cutting the book, so that its value for purposes of after sale might not be injured. And yet Mr. Booker was an honest man, and had set his face persistently against many literary malpractices.

## THE 'CRUSHING' REVIEW

THERE IS THE REVIEW intended to sell a book,—which comes out immediately after the appearance of the book, or sometimes before it; the review which gives reputation, but does not affect the sale, and which comes a little later; the review which snuffs a book out quietly; the review which is to raise or lower the author a single peg, or two pegs, as the case may be; the review which is suddenly to make an author, and the review which is to crush him. An exuberant Jones has been known before now to declare aloud that he would crush a man, and a self-confident Jones has been known to declare that he has accomplished the deed. Of all reviews, the crushing review is the most popular, as being the most readable. When the rumour goes abroad that some notable man has been actually crushed,—been positively driven over by an entire Juggernaut's car of criticism till his literary body be a mere amorphous mass,—then a real success has been achieved, and the Alf of the day has done a great thing; but even the crushing of a poor Lady Carbury, if it be absolute, is effective. Such a review will not make all the world call for the 'Evening Pulpit,' but it will cause those who do take the paper to be satisfied with their bargain. Whenever the circulation of such a paper begins to slacken, the proprietors should, as a matter of course, admonish their Alf to add a little power to the crushing department...

'Anything is better than indifference, Lady Carbury. A great many people remember simply that the book has been noticed, but carry away nothing as to the purport of the review. It's a very good advertisement.'

'But to be told that I have got to learn the A B C of history,—after working as I have worked!'

'That's a mere form of speech, Lady Carbury.'

'You think the book has done pretty well?'

'Pretty well;—just about what we hoped, you know.'

'There'll be something coming to me, Mr. Leadham?'

Mr. Leadham sent for a ledger, and turned over a few pages and ran up a few figures, and then scratched his head. There would be something, but Lady Carbury was not to imagine that it could be very much. It did not often happen that a great deal could be made by a first book. Nevertheless, Lady

Carbury, when she left the publisher's shop, did carry a cheque with her. She was smartly dressed and looked very well, and had smiled on Mr. Leadham. Mr. Leadham, too, was no more than man, and had written—a small cheque.

## Publisher's View of Manuscripts

ON THE FOLLOWING MORNING she herself took the manuscript to Messrs. Leadham and Loiter, and was hurt again by the small amount of respect which seemed to be paid to the collected sheets. There was the work of six months; her very blood and brains,—the concentrated essence of her mind,—as she would say herself when talking with energy of her own performances; and Mr. Leadham pitched it across to a clerk, apparently perhaps sixteen years of age, and the lad chucked the parcel unceremoniously under the counter. An author feels that his work should be taken from him with fast-clutching but reverential hands, and held thoughtfully, out of harm's way, till it be deposited within the very sanctum of an absolutely fireproof safe. Oh, heavens, if it should be lost!—or burned!—or stolen! Those scraps of paper, so easily destroyed, apparently so little respected, may hereafter be acknowledged to have had a value greater, so far greater, than their weight in gold! If 'Robinson Crusoe' had been lost! If 'Tom Jones' had been consumed by flames! And who knows but that this may be another 'Robinson Crusoe,'—a better than 'Tom Jones'? 'Will it be safe there?' asked Lady Carbury.

'Quite safe,—quite safe,' said Mr. Leadham, who was rather busy, and perhaps saw Lady Carbury more frequently than the nature and amount of her authorship seemed to him to require.

'It seemed to be,—put down there,—under the counter!'

'That's quite right, Lady Carbury. They're left there till they're packed.'

'Packed!'

'There are two or three dozen going to our reader this

week. He's down in Skye, and we keep them till there's enough to fill the sack.'

'Do they go by post, Mr. Leadham?'

'Not by post, Lady Carbury. There are not many of them would pay the expense. We send them by long sea to Glasgow, because just at this time of the year there is not much hurry. We can't publish before the winter.' Oh, heavens! If that ship should be lost on its journey by long sea to Glasgow!

# Life's Vagaries

### No. 10 and No. 11

How LITTLE DO WE KNOW how other people live in the houses close to us! We see the houses looking like our own, and we see the people come out of them looking like ourselves. But a Chinaman is not more different from the English John Bull than is No. 10 from No. 11. Here there are books, paintings, music, wine, a little dilettanti getting-up of subjects of the day, a little dilettanti thinking on great affairs, perhaps a little dilettanti religion; few domestic laws, and those easily broken; few domestic duties, and those easily evaded; breakfast when you will, with dinner almost as little binding, with much company and acknowledged aptitude for idle luxury. That is life at No. 10. At No. 11 everything is cased in iron. There shall be equal plenty, but at No. 11 even plenty is a bondage. Duty rules everything, and it has come to be acknowledged that duty is to be hard. So many hours of needlework, so many hours of books, so many hours of prayer! That all the household shall shiver before daylight, is a law, the breach of which by any member either augurs sickness or requires condign punishment. To be comfortable is a sin; to laugh is almost equal to bad language. Such and so various is life at No. 10 and at No. 11.

### An Inferior Bottle

THE EVENING PASSED between them not without much enjoyment. On the opening of that third cork the wine was declared to be less excellent than what had gone before, and

Signor Bolivia was evoked in person. A gentleman named Walker, who looked after the establishment, made his appearance, and with many smiles, having been induced to swallow a bumper of the compound himself, declared, with a knowing shake of the head and an astute twinkle of the eye, that the wine was not equal to the last. He took a great deal of trouble, he assured them, to import an article which could not be surpassed, if it could be equalled, in London, always visiting Epernay himself once a year for the purpose of going through the wine-vaults. Let him do what he would an inferior bottle,—or, rather, a bottle somewhat inferior,— would sometimes make its way into his cellar. Would Mr. Tringle let him have the honour of drawing another cork, so that the exact amount of difference might be ascertained? Tom gave his sanction; the fourth cork was drawn; and Mr. Walker, sitting down and consuming the wine with his customers, was enabled to point out to a hair's breadth the nature and the extent of the variation. Tringle still thought that the difference was considerable. Faddle was, on the whole, inclined to agree with Signor Bolivia. It need hardly be said that the four bottles were paid for,—or rather scored against Tringle, who at the present time had a little account at the establishment.

## Drafts on the Train

Then the last final bustle was made by the guard; the Colonel got in, the door was shut, and Mrs. Dosett, standing on the platform, nodded her head for the last time.

There were only four persons in the carriage. In the opposite corner there were two old persons, probably a husband and wife, who had been very careful as to a foot-warming apparatus, and were muffled up very closely in woollen and furs. 'If you don't mind shutting the door, Sir,' said the old gentleman, rather testily, 'because my wife has a pain in her face.' The door absolutely was shut when the words were spoken, but the Colonel made some sign of closing all the apertures. But there was a ventilator above, which the old lady spied. 'If you don't mind shutting that hole up there, Sir, because my husband is very bad with neuralgia.' The Colonel at once got up and found that the ventilator was fast closed, so as not to admit a breath of air. 'There are draughts come in everywhere,' said the old gentleman. 'The Company ought to be prosecuted.' 'I believe the more people they kill the better they like it,' said the old lady. Then the Colonel looked at Ayala with a very grave face, with no hint at a smile, with a face which must have gratified even the old lady and gentleman. But Ayala understood the face, and could not refrain from a little laugh. She laughed only with her eyes,—but the Colonel saw it.

'The weather has been very severe all day,' said the Colonel, in a severe voice.

Ayala protested that she had not found it cold at all. 'Then, Miss, I think you must be made of granite,' said the old lady. 'I hope you'll remember that other people are not so fortunate.' Ayala again smiled, and the Colonel made another effort as though to prevent any possible breath of air from making its way into the interior of the vehicle.

## The 'Nipping Frost'

YEARS DO NOT MAKE A MAN OLD gradually and at an even pace. Look through the world and see if this is not so always, except in those rare cases in which the human being lives and dies without joys and without sorrows, like a vegetable. A man shall be possessed of florid youthful blooming health till, it matters not what age. Thirty—forty—fifty, then comes some nipping frost, some period of agony, that robs the fibres of the body of their succulence, and the hale and hearty man is counted among the old.

## The Painful Pleasure of Entertaining

The trouble in civilised life of entertaining company, as it is called too generally without much regard to strict veracity, is so great that it cannot but be matter of wonder that people are so fond of attempting it. It is difficult to ascertain what is the *quid pro quo*. If they who give such laborious parties, and who endure such toil and turmoil in the vain hope of giving them successfully, really enjoyed the parties given by others, the matter could be understood. A sense of justice would induce men and women to undergo, in behalf of others, those miseries which others had undergone in their behalf. But they all profess that going out is as great a bore as receiving; and to look at them when they are out, one cannot but believe them.

Entertain! Who shall have sufficient self-assurance, who shall feel sufficient confidence in his own powers to dare to boast that he can entertain his company? A clown can sometimes do so, and sometimes a dancer in short petticoats and stuffed pink legs; occasionally, perhaps, a singer. But beyond these, success in this art of entertaining is not often achieved. Young men and girls linking themselves kind with kind, pairing like birds in spring because nature wills it, they, after a simple fashion, do entertain each other. Few others even try.

Ladies, when they open their houses, modestly confessing, it may be presumed, their own incapacity, mainly trust to wax candles and upholstery. Gentlemen seem to rely on their white waistcoats. To these are added, for the delight of the more sensual, champagne and such good things of the table as fashion allows to be still considered as comestible. Even in this respect the world is deteriorating.

## Carrying It Off

Wise people, when they are in the wrong, always put themselves right by finding fault with the people against whom they have sinned. Lady De Courcy was a wise woman; and therefore, having treated Miss Thorne very badly by staying away till three o'clock, she assumed the offensive and attacked Mr. Thorne's roads. Her daughter, not less wise, attacked Miss Thorne's early hours. The art of doing this is among the most precious of those usually cultivated by persons who know how to live. There is no withstanding it. Who can go systematically to work, and having done battle with the primary accusation and settled that, then bring forward a counter-charge and support that also? Life is not long enough for such labours. A man in the right relies easily on his rectitude, and therefore goes about unarmed. His very strength is his weakness. A man in the wrong knows that he must look to his weapons; his very weakness is his strength. The one is never prepared for combat, the other is always ready. Therefore it is that in this world the man that is in the wrong almost invariably conquers the man that is in the right, and invariably despises him.

## Love at Middle Age

It is, we believe, common with young men of five and twenty to look on their seniors—on men of, say, double their own age—as so many stocks and stones,—stocks and stones, that is, in regard to feminine beauty. There never was a greater mistake. Women, indeed, generally know better; but on this subject men of one age are thoroughly ignorant of what is the very nature of mankind of other ages. No experience of what goes on in the world, no reading of history, no observation of life, has any effect in teaching the truth. Men of fifty don't dance mazurkas, being generally too fat and wheezy; nor do they sit for the hour together on river banks at their mistresses' feet, being somewhat afraid of rheumatism. But for real true love, love at first sight, love to devotion, love that robs a man of his sleep, love that 'will gaze an eagle blind,' love that 'will hear the lowest sound when the suspicious tread of theft is stopped,' love that is 'like a Hercules, still climbing trees in the Hesperides,'—we believe the best age is from forty-five to seventy; up to that, men are generally given to mere flirting.

## On Talking of Oneself

SHE WAS, MOREOVER, one of those few persons—for they are very few—who are contented to go on with their existence without making themselves the centre of any special outward circle. To the ordinary run of minds it is impossible not to do this. A man's own dinner is to himself so important that he cannot bring himself to believe that it is a matter utterly indifferent to every one else. A lady's collection of baby-clothes, in early years, and of house linen and curtain-fringes in later life, is so very interesting to her own eyes, that she cannot believe but what other people will rejoice to behold it. I would not, however, be held as regarding this tendency as evil. It leads to conversation of some sort among people, and perhaps to a kind of sympathy. Mrs. Jones will look at Mrs. White's linen chest, hoping that Mrs. White may be induced to look at hers. One can only pour out of a jug that which is in it. For the most of us, if we do not talk of ourselves, or at any rate of the individual circles of which we are the centres, we can talk of nothing.

## Gentlemen's Amusement

'HAVE YOU EVER OBSERVED, Grace,' said Miss Dale, 'how much amusement gentlemen require, and how imperative it is that some other game should be provided when one game fails?'

'Not particularly,' said Grace.

'Oh, but it is so. Now, with women, it is supposed that they can amuse themselves or live without amusement. Once or twice in a year, perhaps something is done for them. There is an arrow-shooting party, or a ball, or a picnic. But the catering for men's sport is never ending, and is always paramount to everything else. And yet the pet game of the day never goes off properly. In partridge time, the partridges are wild, and won't come to be killed. In hunting time the foxes won't run straight,—the wretches. They show no spirit, and will take to ground to save their brushes. Then comes a nipping frost, and skating is proclaimed; but the ice is always rough, and the woodcocks have deserted the country. And as for salmon,—when the summer comes round I do really believe that they suffer a great deal about the salmon. I'm sure they never catch any. So they go back to their clubs and their cards, and their billiards, and abuse their cooks and blackball their friends.'

## Chemist's Bill

It's PAINFUL—that bill for £15, with nothing to show for it but old scars, rheumatic twinges, and the memory of sick headaches. You have revelled in your beef and mutton; you have still the tailor's good things within your drawers; you have appreciated your wine merchant; and your plumber, whom I regard as the worst enemy of the human race, has served at least to keep the rain out. There is still a doubt in your bosom whether the chemist has really done anything for you. The contents of very few of the numerous little pots have been applied to your own body. It is on this account that the feelings of paterfamilias as to the exorbitant nature of his account have been so strong, and that we have been reminded from time to time that the 1s. 6d. which we have paid for the small bottles recently sent in has been charged at the rate of 500 per cent. on the original cost of the drug which has been used. Nevertheless, if there be a cheap chemist in the neighbourhood, you will hardly trust your stomach or those of your wife and offspring to his tender mercies.

## Your Plumber

THE PLUMBER, PAINTER, AND GLAZIER of our youth has disappeared, and in lieu of him has come up the man who mends our kitchen furniture and destroys our roofs. Such, at least, is the reputation which our friend the plumber enjoys. We do not say that of our own knowledge it is deserved. We do not profess to declare that he plans the perforation of our leads. We cannot so far condemn the man who continually haunts our premises, and whose half-yearly bill is of all our torments the most regular, bearing a proportion to our rent which we should have regarded as formidable had we anticipated the necessity of these periodical visits. The plumber should be put down with the tax-gatherer as being as certain as fate and as inexorable,—almost as serious. You shall put your house into excellent order and think to have seen the last of him for years; but he will be there again till the sight of him is a perpetual eyesore to you. You will come to have an unnatural hatred for the man and his myrmidons.

## The London Season

JUNE PASSED AWAY,—as Junes do pass in London,—very gaily in appearance, very quickly in reality, with a huge outlay of money and an enormous amount of disappointment. Young ladies would not accept, and young men would not propose. Papas became cross and stingy, and mammas insinuated that daughters were misbehaving. The daughters fought their own battles, and became tired in the fighting of them, and many a one had declared to herself before July had come to an end that it was all vanity and vexation of spirit.

## The Earl's '20 Port

'Dale, I know you drink port,' said the earl when Lady Julia left them. 'If you say you don't like that, I shall say you know nothing about it.'

'Ah! that's the '20,' said the squire, tasting it.

'I should rather think it is,' said the earl. 'I was lucky enough to get it early, and it hasn't been moved for thirty years. I like to give it to a man who knows it, as you do, at the first glance. Now there's my friend Johnny, there; it's thrown away upon him.'

'No, my lord, it is not. I think it's uncommonly nice.'

'Uncommonly nice! So is champagne, or ginger-beer, or lollipops,—for those who like them. Do you mean to tell me you can taste wine with half a pickled orange in your mouth?'

'It'll come to him soon enough,' said the squire.

'Twenty port won't come to him when he is as old as we are,' said the earl, forgetting that by that time sixty port will be as wonderful to the then living seniors of the age as was his own pet vintage to him.

## Picnics

Picnics are, I think, in general, rather tedious for the elderly people who accompany them. When the joints become a little stiff, dinners are eaten most comfortably with the accompaniment of chairs and tables, and a roof overhead is an *agrément de plus*. But, nevertheless, picnics cannot exist without a certain allowance of elderly people. The Miss Marians and Captains Ewing cannot go out to dine on the grass without some one to look after them. So the elderly people go to picnics, in a dull tame way, doing their duty, and wishing the day over.

'INDIGGESTION'

'Thursday morning,—July, 185-.

'MY DEAR SIR,

'I write from my bed where I am suffering a most tremendous indiggestion, last night I eat a stunning supper off pork chopps and never remembered that pork chopps always does disagree with me, but I was very indiscrete and am now teetotally unable to rise my throbing head from off my pillar, I have took four blu pills and some salts and sena, plenty of that, and shall be the thing to-morrow morning no doubt, just at present I feel just as if I had a mill stone inside my stomac— Pray be so kind as to make it all right with Mr. Oldeschole and believe me to remain,

'Your faithful and obedient servant,
'VERAX CORKSCREW.

'Thomas Snape, Esq., &c.,
'Internal Navigation Office, Somerset House.'

SAYING GOODBYE

THEY GOT TO THE DOCKS in time, and got on board that fast-sailing, clipper-built, never-beaten, always-healthy ship, the *Flash of Lightning,* 5,500 tons, A 1...

The world, we think, makes a great mistake on the subject of saying, or acting, farewell. The word or deed should partake of the suddenness of electricity; but we all drawl through it at a snail's pace. We are supposed to tear ourselves from our friends; but tearing is a process which should be done quickly... Who has not seen his dearest friends standing round the window of a railway carriage, while the train would not start, and has not longed to say to them, 'Stand not upon the order of your going, but go at once!' And of all such farewells, the ship's farewell is the longest and the most dreary. One sits on a damp bench, snuffing up the odour of oil and ropes, cudgelling one's brains to think what further word of increased tenderness can be spoken. No tenderer word can be spoken. One returns again and again to the weather, to coats and cloaks, perhaps even to sandwiches and the sherry flask. All effect is thus destroyed, and a trespass is made even on the domain of feeling.

## Ambitions

HE WAS AT THE CHANCERY BAR, and after the usual years of hard and almost profitless struggling, had worked himself up into a position in which his income was very large, and his labours never ending. Since the days in which he had begun to have before his eyes some idea of a future career for himself, he had always been struggling hard for a certain goal, struggling successfully, and yet never getting nearer to the thing he desired. A scholarship had been all in all to him when he left school; and, as he got it, a distant fellowship already loomed before his eyes. That attained was only a step towards his life in London. His first brief, anxiously as it had been desired, had given no real satisfaction. As soon as it came to him it was a rung of the ladder already out of sight. And so it had been all through his life, as he advanced upwards, making a business, taking a wife to himself, and becoming the father of many children. There was always something before him which was to make him happy when he reached it. His gown was of silk, and his income almost greater than his desires; but he would fain sit upon the Bench, and have at any-rate his evenings for his own enjoyment. He firmly believed now, that that had been the object of his constant ambition; though could he retrace his thoughts as a young man, he would find that in the early days of his forensic toils, the silent, heavy, unillumined solemnity of the judge had appeared to him to be nothing in comparison with the glittering audacity of the successful advocate. He had tried the one, and might probably soon try the other. And when that time shall have come, and Mr. Quickenham shall sit upon his seat of honour in the new Law Courts, passing long, long hours in the tedious labours of conscientious painful listening; then he will look forward again to the happy ease of dignified retirement, to the coming time in which all his hours will be his own. And then, again, when those unfurnished hours are there, and with them shall have come the infirmities which years and toil shall have brought, his mind will run on once more to that eternal rest in which fees and salary, honours and dignity, wife and children, with all the joys of satisfied success, shall be brought together for him in one perfect amalgam which he will call by the name of Heaven.

*HE VISITS THE UNITED STATES*

# He Visits the United States[*]

## Prefatory Note

THIRTY YEARS AGO my mother wrote a book about the Americans, to which I believe I may allude as a well known and successful work without being guilty of any undue family conceit. That was essentially a woman's book. She saw with a woman's keen eye, and described with a woman's light but graphic pen, the social defects and absurdities which our near relatives had adopted into their domestic life. All that she told was worth the telling, and the telling, if done successfully, was sure to produce a good result. I am satisfied that it did so. But she did not regard it as a part of her work to dilate on the nature and operation of those political arrangements which had produced the social absurdities which she saw, or to explain that though such absurdities were the natural result of those arrangements in their newness, the defects would certainly pass away, while the political arrangements, if good, would remain. Such a work is fitter for a man than for a woman. I am very far from thinking that it is a task which I can perform with satisfaction either to myself or to others. It is a work which some man will do who has earned a right by education, study, and success to rank himself among the political sages of his age. But I may perhaps be able to add something to the familiarity of Englishmen with Americans. The writings which have been most popular in England on the subject of the United States have hitherto

[*] Excerpts from *North America* except one from *The Tireless Traveler*.

dealt chiefly with social details; and though in most cases true and useful, have created laughter on one side of the Atlantic, and soreness on the other. If I could do anything to mitigate the soreness, if I could in any small degree add to the good feeling which should exist between two nations which ought to love each other so well, and which do hang upon each other so constantly, I should think that I had cause to be proud of my work.

## Boston

In September we did not stay above a week in Boston, having been fairly driven out of it by the mosquitoes. I had been told that I should find nobody in Boston whom I cared to see, as everybody was habitually out of town during the heat of the latter summer and early autumn; but this was not so. The war and attendant turmoils of war had made the season of vacation shorter than usual, and most of those for whom I asked were back at their posts. I know no place at which an Englishman may drop down suddenly among a pleasanter circle of acquaintance, or find himself with a more clever set of men, than he can do at Boston. I confess that in this respect I think that but few towns are at present more fortunately circumstanced than the capital of the Bay State, as Massachusetts is called, and that very few towns make a better use of their advantages. Boston has a right to be proud of what it has done for the world of letters. It is proud; but I have not found that its pride was carried too far.

Boston is not in itself a fine city, but it is a very pleasant city. They say that the harbour is very grand and very beautiful. It certainly is not so fine as that of Portland in a nautical point of view, and as certainly it is not as beautiful. It is the entrance from the sea into Boston of which people say so much; but I did not think it quite worthy of all I had heard. In such matters, however, much depends on the peculiar light in which scenery is seen. An evening light is generally the best for all landscapes; and I did not see the entrance to Boston harbour by an evening light. It was not the beauty of the harbour of which I thought the most; but of the tea that had been sunk there, and of all that came of that successful speculation. Few towns now standing have a right to be more proud of their antecedents than Boston.

## Newport

IT IS THE HABIT of Americans to go to some watering place every summer,—that is, to some place either of sea water or of inland waters. This is done much in England; more in Ireland than in England; but, I think, more in the States than even in Ireland. But of all such summer haunts, Newport is supposed to be in many ways the most captivating. In the first place it is certainly the most fashionable, and in the next place it is said to be the most beautiful. We decided on going to Newport,—led thither by the latter reputation rather than the former. As we were still in the early part of September we expected to find the place full, but in this we were disappointed;—disappointed, I say, rather than gratified, although a crowded house at such a place is certainly a nuisance. But a house which is prepared to make up six hundred beds, and which is called on to make up only twenty-five becomes, after a while, somewhat melancholy. The natural depression of the landlord communicates itself to his servants, and from the servants it descends to the twenty-five guests, who wander about the long passages and deserted balconies like the ghosts of those of the summer visitors, who cannot rest quietly in their graves at home.

In England we know nothing of hotels prepared for six hundred visitors, all of whom are expected to live in common. Domestic architects would be frightened at the dimensions which are needed, and at the number of apartments which are required to be clustered under one roof. We went to the Ocean Hotel at Newport, and fancied, as we first entered the hall under a verandah as high as the house, and made our way into the passage, that we had been taken to a well-arranged barrack. 'Have you rooms?' I asked, as a man always does ask on first reaching his inn. 'Rooms enough,' the clerk said. 'We have only fifty here.' But that fifty dwindled down to twenty-five during the next day or two.

We were a melancholy set, the ladies appearing to be afflicted in this way worse than the gentlemen, on account of their enforced abstinence from tobacco. What can twelve ladies do scattered about a drawing-room, so-called, intended for the accommodation of two hundred? The drawing-room at the Ocean Hotel, Newport, is not as big as Westminster Hall, but would, I should think, make a very good House of Commons for the British nation. Fancy the feelings of a lady when she walks into such a room intending to spend her evening there, and finds six or seven other ladies located on various sofas at terrible distances—all strangers to her. . .

And then the music? There is always a piano in an hotel drawing-room, on which, of course, some one of the forlorn ladies is generally employed. I do not suppose that these pianos are in fact, as a rule, louder and harsher, more violent and less musical, than other instruments of the kind. They seem to be so, but that, I take it, arises from the exceptional mental depression of those who have to listen to them. Then the ladies, or probably some one lady, will sing, and as she hears her own voice ring and echo through the lofty corners and round the empty walls, she is surprised at her own force, and with increased efforts sings louder and still louder. She is tempted to fancy that she is suddenly gifted with some power of vocal melody unknown to her before, and filled with the glory of her own performance shouts till the whole house rings. At such moments she at least is happy, if no one else is so. Looking at the general sadness of her position, who can grudge her such happiness? . . .

The hotels, too, are all built away from the sea; so that one cannot sit and watch the play of the waves from one's window. Nor are there pleasant rambling paths down among the rocks,

## HE VISITS THE UNITED STATES

and from one short strand to another. There is excellent bathing for those who like bathing on shelving sand. I don't. The spot is about half a mile from the hotels, and to this the bathers are carried in omnibuses. Till one o'clock ladies bathe; —which operation, however, does not at all militate against the bathing of men, but rather necessitates it as regards those men who have ladies with them. For here ladies and gentlemen bathe in decorous dresses, and are very polite to each other. I must say, that I think the ladies have the best of it. My idea of sea-bathing for my own gratification is not compatible with a full suit of clothing. I own that my tastes are vulgar and perhaps indecent; but I love to jump into the deep clear sea from off a rock, and I love to be hampered by no outward impediments as I do so. For ordinary bathers, for all ladies, and for men less savage in their instincts than I am, the bathing at Newport is very good.

The private houses—villa residences as they would be termed by an auctioneer in England—are excellent. Many of them are, in fact, large mansions, and are surrounded with grounds, which, as the shrubs grow up, will be very beautiful. Some have large, well-kept lawns, stretching down to the rocks, and these to my taste give the charm to Newport. They extend about two miles along the coast. Should my lot have made me a citizen of the United States, I should have had no objection to become the possessor of one of these 'villa residences,' but I do not think that I should have 'gone in' for hotel life at Newport.

### PORTLAND, MAINE

I DOUBT WHETHER I EVER SAW a town with more evident signs of prosperity. It has about it every mark of ample means, and no mark of poverty. It contains about 27,000 people, and for that population covers a very large space of ground. The streets are broad and well built, the main streets not running in those absolutely straight parallels which are so common in American towns, and are so distressing to English eyes and English feelings. All these, except the streets devoted exclusively to business, are shaded on both sides by trees—generally, if I remember rightly, by the beautiful American elm, whose drooping boughs have all the grace of the willow without its fantastic melancholy. What the poorer streets of Portland may be like I cannot say. I saw no poor street. But in no town of 30,000 inhabitants did I ever see so many houses which must require an expenditure of from six to eight hundred a year to maintain them.

The place too is beautifully situated. It is on a long promontory, which takes the shape of a peninsula;—for the neck which joins it to the mainland is not above half a mile across. But though the town thus stands out into the sea, it is not exposed and bleak. The harbour again is surrounded by land, or so guarded and locked by islands as to form a series of saltwater lakes running round the town. Of those islands there are, of course, 365. Travellers who write their travels are constantly called upon to record that number, so that it may now be considered as a superlative in local phraseology, signifying a very great many indeed. The town stands between two hills, the suburbs or outskirts running up on to each of them. The one looking out towards the sea is called Mountjoy— though the obstinate Americans will write it Munjoy on their maps. From thence the view out to the harbour and beyond the harbour to the islands is, I may not say unequalled, or I shall be guilty of running into superlatives myself; but it is, in its way, equal to anything I have seen. Perhaps it is more like Cork harbour, as seen from certain heights over Passage than anything else I can remember; but Portland harbour, though equally landlocked, is larger; and then from Portland harbour there is as it were a river outlet, running through delicious islands, most unalluring to the navigator, but delicious to the eyes of an uncommercial traveller. There are in all four outlets to the sea, one of which appears to have been made expressly for the Great Eastern. Then there is the hill

## HE VISITS THE UNITED STATES

looking inwards. If it has a name I forget it. The view from this hill is also over the water on each side, and though not so extensive is perhaps as pleasing as the other.

The ways of the people seemed to be quiet, smooth, orderly, and republican. There is nothing to drink in Portland of course, for, thanks to Mr. Neal Dow, the Father Mathew of the State of Maine, the Maine Liquor Law is still in force in that State. There is nothing to drink, I should say, in such orderly houses as that I selected. 'People do drink some in the town, they say,' said my hostess to me; 'and liquor is to be got. But I never venture to sell any. An ill-natured person might turn on me, and where should I be then?' I did not press her, and she was good enough to put a bottle of porter at my right hand at dinner, for which I observed she made no charge. 'But they advertise beer in the shop-windows,' I said to a man who was driving me—'Scotch ale, and bitter beer. A man can get drunk on them.' 'Wa'al, yes. If he goes to work hard, and drinks a bucketful,' said the driver, 'perhaps he may.' From which and other things I gathered that the men of Maine drank pottle deep before Mr. Neal Dow brought his exertions to a successful termination.

### THE WHITE MOUNTAINS

HE WILL THEN,—if he take my advice and follow my track,—go by Portland up into the White Mountains. At Gorham, a station on the Grand Trunk line, he will find an hotel as good as any of its kind, and from thence he will take a light waggon, so called in these countries;—and here let me presume that the traveller is not alone; he has his wife or friend, or perhaps a pair of sisters,—and in his waggon he will go up through primeval forests to the Glen House. When there he will ascend Mount Washington on a pony. That is *de rigueur,* and I do not, therefore, dare to recommend him to omit the ascent. I did not gain much myself by my labour. He will not stay at the Glen House, but will go on to—Jack-

## HE VISITS THE UNITED STATES

son's I think they call the next hotel; at which he will sleep. From thence he will take his waggon on through the Notch to the Crawford House, sleeping there again; and when here let him of all things remember to go up Mount Willard. It is but a walk of two hours, up and down, if so much. When reaching the top he will be startled to find that he looks down into the ravine without an inch of fore-ground. He will come out suddenly on a ledge of rock, from whence, as it seems, he might leap down at once into the valley below. Then going on from the Crawford House he will be driven through the woods of Cherry Mount, passing, I fear without toll of custom, the house of my excellent friend Mr. Plaistead, who keeps an hotel at Jefferson. 'Sir,' said Mr. Plaistead, 'I have everything here that a man ought to want; air, sir, that ain't to be got better nowhere; trout, chickens, beef, mutton, milk,—and all for a dollar a day. A-top of that hill, sir, there's a view that ain't to be beaten this side of the Atlantic, or I believe the other. And an echo, sir!—We've an echo that cames back to us six times, sir; floating on the light wind, and wafted about from rock to rock till you would think the angels were talking to you. If I could raise that echo, sir, every day at command I'd give a thousand dollars for it.'

### NEW YORK CITY

SPEAKING OF NEW YORK as a traveller I have two faults to find with it. In the first place there is nothing to see; and in the second place there is no mode of getting about to see anything. Nevertheless New York is a most interesting city. It is the third biggest city in the known world;—for those Chinese congregations of unwinged ants are not cities in the known world. In no other city is there a population so mixed and cosmopolitan in their modes of life. And yet in no other city that I have seen are there such strong and ever-visible characteristics of the social and political bearings of the nation to which it belongs. New York appears to me as infinitely more American than Boston, Chicago, or Washington. It has no peculiar attribute of its own, as have those three cities; Boston in its literature and accomplished intelligence, Chicago in its internal trade, and Washington in its congressional and State politics. New York has its literary aspirations, its commercial grandeur, and,—heaven knows,—it has its politics also. But these do not strike the visitor as being specially characteristic of the city. That it is pre-eminently American is its glory or its disgrace,—as men of different ways of thinking may decide upon it. Free institutions, general education, and the ascendancy of dollars are the words written on every paving-stone along Fifth Avenue, down Broadway, and up Wall Street. Every man can vote, and values the privilege. Every man can read, and uses the privilege. Every man worships the dollar, and is down before his shrine from morning to night.

As regards voting and reading no American will be angry with me for saying so much of him; and no Englishman, whatever may be his ideas as to the franchise in his own country, will conceive that I have said aught to the dishonour of an American. But as to that dollar-worshipping, it will of course seem that I am abusing the New Yorkers. We all know what a wretchedly wicked thing money is! How it stands between us and heaven! How it hardens our hearts, and makes vulgar our thoughts! Dives has ever gone to the devil, while Lazarus has been laid up in heavenly lavender. The hand that employs itself in compelling gold to enter the service of man has always been stigmatized as the ravisher of things sacred. The world is agreed about that, and therefore the New Yorker is in a bad way. There are very few citizens in any town known to me which under this dispensation are in a good way, but the New Yorker is in about the worst way of all. Other men, the world over, worship regularly at the shrine with matins and vespers, nones and complines, and whatever other daily services may be known to the religious houses; but the New Yorker is always on his knees.

## Baltimore

Baltimore is, or at any rate was, an aspiring city, proud of its commerce and proud of its society. It has regarded itself as the New York of the South, and to some extent has forced others so to regard it also. In many respects it is more like an English town than most of its transatlantic brethren, and the ways of its inhabitants are English. In old days a pack of fox-hounds was kept here,—or indeed in days that are not yet very old, for I was told of their doings by a gentleman who had long been a member of the hunt. The country looks as a hunting country should look, whereas no man that ever crossed a field after a pack of hounds would feel the slightest wish to attempt that process in New England or New York. There is in Baltimore an old inn with an old sign, standing at the corner of Eutaw and Franklin Streets, just such as may still be seen in the towns of Somersetshire, and before it are to be seen old wagons, covered, and soiled, and battered, about to return from the city to the country, just as the wagons do in our own agricultural counties. I have found nothing so thoroughly English in any other part of the Union.

But canvas-back ducks and terrapins are the great glories of Baltimore. Of the nature of the former bird I believe all the world knows something. It is a wild duck which obtains the peculiarity of its flavour from the wild celery on which it feeds. This celery grows on the Chesapeake Bay, and I believe on the Chesapeake Bay only. At any rate Baltimore is the head-quarters of the canvas-backs, and it is on the Chesapeake Bay that they are shot. I was kindly invited to go down on a shooting-party; but when I learned that I should have to ensconce myself alone for hours in a wet wooden box on the water's edge, waiting there for the chance of a duck to come to me, I declined. The fact of my never having as yet been successful in shooting a bird of any kind conduced somewhat perhaps to my decision. I must acknowledge that the canvas-

## HE VISITS THE UNITED STATES

back duck fully deserves all the reputation it has acquired. As to the terrapin, I have not so much to say. The terrapin is a small turtle, found on the shores of Maryland and Virginia, out of which a very rich soup is made. It is cooked with wines and spices, and is served in the shape of a hash, with heaps of little bones mixed through it. It is held in great repute, and the guest is expected as a matter of course to be helped twice. The man who did not eat twice of terrapin would be held in small repute, as the Londoner is held who at a city banquet does not partake of both thick and thin turtle. I must, however, confess that the terrapin for me had no surpassing charms.

### Washington, D. C.

Washington is but a ragged, unfinished collection of unbuilt broad streets, as to the completion of which there can now, I imagine, be but little hope.

Of all places that I know it is the most ungainly and most unsatisfactory;—I fear I must also say the most presumptuous in its pretensions. There is a map of Washington accurately laid down; and taking that map with him in his journeyings a man may lose himself in the streets, not as one loses oneself in London between Shoreditch and Russell Square, but as one does so in the deserts of the Holy Land, between Emmaus and Arimathea. In the first place no one knows where the places are, or is sure of their existence, and then between their presumed localities the country is wild, trackless, unbridged, uninhabited, and desolate. Massachusetts Avenue runs the whole length of the city, and is inserted on the maps as a full-blown street, about four miles in length. Go there, and you will find yourself not only out of town, away among the fields, but you will find yourself beyond the fields, in an uncultivated, undrained wilderness. Tucking your trousers up to your knees, you will wade through the bogs, you will lose yourself among rude hillocks, you will be out of the reach of humanity. The unfinished dome of the Capitol will loom before you in the distance, and you will think that you approach the ruins of some western Palmyra. If you are a sportsman, you will desire to shoot snipe within sight of the President's house. There is much unsettled land within the States of America, but I think none so desolate in its state of nature as three-fourths of the ground on which is supposed to stand the city of Washington.

## CINCINNATI

THE GREAT BUSINESS of Cincinnati is hog killing now, as it used to be in the old days of which I have so often heard. It seems to be an established fact, that in this portion of the world the porcine genus are all hogs. One never hears of a pig. With us a trade in hogs and pigs is subject to some little contumely. There is a feeling, which has perhaps never been expressed in words, but which certainly exists, that these animals are not so honourable in their bearings as sheep and oxen. It is a prejudice which by no means exists in Cincinnati. There hog killing and salting and packing are very honourable, and the great men in the trade are the merchant princes of the city. I went to see the performance, feeling it to be a duty to inspect everywhere that which I found to be of most importance; but I will not describe it. There were a crowd of men operating, and I was told that the point of honour was to 'put through' a hog a minute. It must be understood that the animal enters upon the ceremony alive, and comes out in that cleanly, disembowelled guise in which it may sometimes be seen hanging up previous to the operation of the pork-butcher's knife. To one special man was appointed a performance which seemed to be specially disagreeable, so that he appeared despicable in my eyes; but when on inquiry I learned that he earned five dollars, or a pound sterling, a day, my judgment as to his position was reversed. And after all what matters the ugly nature of such an occupation when a man is used to it?

Cincinnati is like all other American towns, with second,

## HE VISITS THE UNITED STATES

third, and fourth streets, seventh, eighth, and ninth streets, and so on. Then the cross-streets are named chiefly from trees. Chestnut, walnut, locust, &c. I do not know whence has come this fancy for naming streets after trees in the States, but it is very general. The town is well built, with good fronts to many of the houses, with large shops and larger stores;—of course also with an enormous hotel, which has never paid anything like a proper dividend to the speculator who built it. It is always the same story. But these towns shame our provincial towns by their breadth and grandeur. I am afraid that speculators with us are trammelled by an 'ignorant impatience of ruin.' I should not myself like to live in Cincinnati or in any of these towns. They are slow, dingy, and uninteresting; but they all possess an air of substantial, civic dignity. It must however be remembered that the Americans live much more in towns than we do. All with us that are rich and aristocratic and luxurious live in the country, frequenting the metropolis for only a portion of the year. But all that are rich and aristocratic and luxurious in the States live in the towns. Our provincial towns are not generally chosen as the residences of our higher classes.

## SAN FRANCISCO STOCK EXCHANGE

THE STOCK EXCHANGE BOARD in San Francisco is not open to strangers as it is in Paris, but may be visited with an order, and by the kindness of a friend I was admitted. Paris is more than six times as large as San Francisco; but the fury at San Francisco is even more demoniac than in Paris. I thought that the gentlemen employed were going to hit each other between the eyes, and that the apparent quarrels which I saw already demanded the interference of the police. But the uproarious throng were always obedient, after slight delays, to the ringing hammer of the chairman, and as each five minutes' period of internecine combat was brought to an end I found that a vast number of mining shares had been bought and sold. Perhaps a visit to this chamber when the stockbrokers are at work, between the hours of eleven and twelve, is, of all sights in San Francisco, the one best worth seeing.

## Sleeping Cars and Other Contrivances

In making this journey at night we introduced ourselves to the thoroughly American institution of sleeping cars;—that is, of cars in which beds are made up for travellers. The traveller may have a whole bed, or half a bed, or no bed at all as he pleases, paying a dollar or half a dollar extra should he choose the partial or full fruition of a couch. I confess I have always taken a delight in seeing these beds made up, and consider that the operations of the change are generally as well executed as the manœuvres of any pantomime at Drury Lane. The work is usually done by negroes or coloured men; and the domestic negroes of America are always light-handed and adroit. The nature of an American car is no doubt known to all men. It looks as far removed from all bedroom accommodation, as the baker's barrow does from the steam-engine into which it is to be converted by harlequin's wand. But the negro goes to work much more quietly than the harlequin, and for every four seats in the railway car he builds up four beds, almost as quickly as the hero of the pantomime goes through his performance. The great glory of the Americans is in their wondrous contrivances,—in their patent remedies for the usually troublous operations of life. In their huge hotels all the bell ropes of each house ring on one bell only, but a patent indicator discloses a number, and the whereabouts of the ringer is shown. One fire heats every room, passage, hall, and cupboard,—and does it so effectually that the inhabitants are all but stifled. Soda-water bottles open themselves without any trouble of wire or strings. Men and women go up and down stairs without motive power of their own. Hot and cold water are laid on to all the chambers;— though it sometimes happens that the water from both taps

## HE VISITS THE UNITED STATES

is boiling, and that when once turned on it cannot be turned off again by any human energy. Everything is done by a new and wonderful patent contrivance; and of all their wonderful contrivances that of their railroad beds is by no means the least. For every four seats the negro builds up four beds,—that is, four half-beds or accommodation for four persons. Two are supposed to be below on the level of the ordinary four seats, and two up above on shelves which are let down from the roof. Mattresses slip out from one nook and pillows from another. Blankets are added, and the bed is ready. Any overparticular individual—an islander, for instance, who hugs his chains—will generally prefer to pay the dollar for the double accommodation. Looking at the bed in the light of a bed,—taking as it were an abstract view of it,—or comparing it with some other bed or beds with which the occupant may have acquaintance, I cannot say that it is in all respects perfect. But distances are long in America; and he who declines to travel by night will lose very much time. He who does so travel will find the railway bed a great relief. I must confess that the feeling of dirt on the following morning is rather oppressive.

### The Horse Car

AND THEN THERE ARE STREET CARS—very long omnibuses—which run on rails but are dragged by horses. They are capable of holding forty passengers each, and as far as my experience goes carry an average load of sixty. The fare of the omnibus is six cents or three pence. That of the street car five cents or two pence half-penny. They run along the different avenues, taking the length of the city. In the upper or new part of the town their course is simple enough, but as they descend to the Bowery, Peckslip, and Pearl Street, nothing can be conceived more difficult or devious than their courses. The Broadway omnibus, on the other hand, is a straightforward honest vehicle in the lower part of the town, becoming,

## HE VISITS THE UNITED STATES

however, dangerous and miscellaneous when it ascends to Union Square and the vicinities of fashionable life.

The street cars are manned with conductors, and therefore are free from many of the perils of the omnibus, but they have perils of their own. They are always quite full. By that I mean that every seat is crowded, that there is a double row of men and women standing down the centre, and that the driver's platform in front is full, and also the conductor's platform behind. That is the normal condition of a street car in the Third Avenue. You, as a stranger in the middle of the car, wish to be put down at, let us say, 89th Street. In the map of New York now before me the cross streets running from east to west are numbered up northwards as far as 154th Street. It is quite useless for you to give the number as you enter. Even an American conductor, with brains all over him, and an anxious desire to accommodate, as is the case with all these men, cannot remember. You are left therefore in misery to calculate the number of the street as you move along, vainly endeavouring through the misty glass to decipher the small numbers which after a day or two you perceive to be written on the lamp posts.

But I soon gave up all attempts at keeping a seat in one of these cars. It became my practice to sit down on the outside iron rail behind, and as the conductor generally sat in my lap I was in a measure protected. As for the inside of these vehicles, the women of New York, were, I must confess, too much for me. I would no sooner place myself on a seat, than I would be called on by a mute, unexpressive, but still impressive stare into my face, to surrender my place. From cowardice if not from gallantry I would always obey; and as this led to discomfort and an irritated spirit, I preferred nursing the conductor on the hard bar in the rear.

## The Free Girls' School

I DO NOT KNOW any contrast that would be more surprising to an Englishman, up to that moment ignorant of the matter, than that which he would find by visiting first of all a free school in London, and then a free school in New York. If he would also learn the number of children that are educated gratuitously in each of the two cities, and also the number in each which altogether lack education, he would, if susceptible of statistics, be surprised also at that. But seeing and hearing are always more effective than mere figures. The female pupil at a free school in London is, as a rule, either a ragged pauper, or a charity girl, if not degraded at least stigmatized by the badges and dress of the Charity. We Englishmen know well the type of each, and have a fairly correct idea of the amount of education which is imparted to them. We see the result afterwards when the same girls become our servants, and the wives of our grooms and porters. The female pupil at a free school in New York is neither a pauper nor a charity girl. She is dressed with the utmost decency. She is perfectly cleanly. In speaking to her, you cannot in any degree guess whether her father has a dollar a day, or three thousand dollars a year. Nor will you be enabled to guess by the manner in which her associates treat her. As regards her own manner to you, it is always the same as though her father were in all respects your equal.

## Emerson in Boston

MR. EMERSON IS A MASSACHUSETTS MAN, very well known in Boston, and a great crowd was collected to hear him. I suppose there were some three thousand persons in the room. I confess that when he took his place before us my prejudices were against him. The matter in hand required no philosophy. It required common sense, and the very best of common sense.

## HE VISITS THE UNITED STATES

It demanded that he should be impassioned, for of what interest can any address be on a matter of public politics without passion? But it demanded that the passion should be winnowed, and free from all rhodomontade. I fancied what might be said on such a subject as to that overlauded star-spangled banner, and how the star-spangled flag would look when wrapped in a mist of mystic Platonism.

But from the beginning to the end there was nothing mystic —no Platonism; and, if I remember rightly, the star-spangled banner was altogether omitted. To the national eagle he did allude. 'Your American eagle,' he said, 'is very well. Protect it here and abroad. But beware of the American peacock.' He gave an account of the war from the beginning, showing how it had arisen, and how it had been conducted; and he did so with admirable simplicity and truth. He thought the North were right about the war; and as I thought so also, I was not called upon to disagree with him. He was terse and perspicuous in his sentences, practical in his advice, and above all things, true in what he said to his audience of themselves. They who know America will understand how hard it is for a public man in the States to practise such truth in his addresses. Fluid compliments and high-flown national eulogium are expected. In this instance none were forthcoming. The North had risen with patriotism to make this effort, and it was now warned that in doing so it was simply doing its national duty. And then came the subject of slavery. I had been told that Mr. Emerson was an abolitionist, and knew that I must disagree with him on that head, if on no other. To me it has always seemed that to mix up the question of general abolition with this war must be the work of a man too ignorant to understand the real subject of the war, or too false to his country to regard it. Throughout the whole lecture I was waiting for Mr. Emerson's abolition doctrine, but no abolition doctrine came. The words abolition and compensation were mentioned, and then there was an end of the subject. If Mr. Emerson be an abolitionist he expressed his views very mildly on that occasion. On the whole the lecture was excellent, and that little advice about the peacock was in itself worth an hour's attention.

## A Boston Public Library

I WENT TO SEE A PUBLIC LIBRARY in the city, which, if not founded by Mr. Bates, whose name is so well known in London as connected with the house of Messrs. Baring, has been greatly enriched by him. It is by his money that it has been enabled to do its work. In this library there is a certain number of thousands of volumes—a great many volumes, as there are in most public libraries. There are books of all classes, from ponderous unreadable folios, of which learned men know the title-pages, down to the lightest literature. Novels are by no means eschewed,—are rather, if I understood aright, considered as one of the staples of the library. From this library any book, excepting such rare volumes as in all libraries are considered holy, is given out to any inhabitant of Boston, without any payment, on presentation of a simple request on a prepared form. In point of fact it is a gratuitous circulating library open to all Boston, rich or poor, young or old. The books seemed in general to be confided to young children, who came as messengers from their fathers and mothers, or brothers and sisters. No question whatever is asked, if the applicant is known or the place of his residence undoubted. If there be no such knowledge, or there be any doubt as to the residence, the applicant is questioned, the object being to confine the use of the library to the *bona fide* inhabitants of the city. Practically the books are given to those who ask for them, whoever they may be. Boston contains over 200,000 inhabitants, and all those 200,000 are entitled to them. Some twenty men and women are kept employed from morning to night in carrying on this circulating library; and there is, moreover, attached to the establishment a large reading-room supplied with papers and magazines, open to the public of Boston on the same terms.

Of course I asked whether a great many of the books were not lost, stolen, and destroyed; and of course I was told that there were no losses, no thefts, and no destruction. As to thefts, the librarian did not seem to think that any instance of such an occurrence could be found. Among the poorer classes a book might sometimes be lost when they were changing their lodgings, but any thing so lost was more than replaced by the fines. A book is taken out for a week, and if not brought back at the end of that week, when the loan can be renewed if the reader wishes, a fine, I think of two cents, is incurred. The children, when too late with the books, bring in the two cents as a matter of course, and the sum so collected fully replaces all losses. It was all *couleur de rose;* the librarianesses looked very pretty and learned, and, if I remember aright, mostly wore spectacles; the head librarian was enthusiastic; the nice instructive books were properly dogs-eared; my own productions were in enormous demand; the call for books over the counter was brisk, and the reading-room was full of readers.

## Land

I HAVE SAID that those who are called on to labour in these States have their own hardships, and I have endeavoured to explain what are the sufferings to which the town labourer is subject. To escape from this is the labourer's great ambition, and his mode of doing so consists almost universally in the purchase of land. He saves up money in order that he may buy a section of an allotment, and thus become his own master. All his savings are made with a view to this independence. Seated on his land he will have to work probably harder than ever, but he will work for himself. No taskmaster can then stand over him and wound his pride with harsh words. He will be his own master; will eat the food which he himself has grown, and live in the cabin which his own hands have built. This is the object of his life; and to secure this position he is content to work late and early and to undergo the indignities of previous servitude. The Government price for land is about five shillings an acre—one dollar and a quarter—and the settler may get it for this price if he be contented to take it not only untouched as regards clearing, but also far removed from any completed road. The traffic in these lands has been the great speculating business of western men. Five or six years ago, when the rage for such purchases was at its height, land was becoming a scarce article in the market! Individuals or companies bought it up with the object of reselling it at a profit; and many no doubt did make money. Railway companies were, in fact, companies combined for the purchase of land. They purchased land, looking to increase the value of it five-fold by the opening of a railroad. It may easily be understood that a railway, which could not be in itself remunerative, might in this way become a lucrative speculation. No settler could dare to place himself absolutely at a distance from any thoroughfare. At first the margins of nature's highways, the navigable rivers and lakes, were cleared. But as the railway system grew and expanded itself, it became manifest that lands might be rendered quickly available which were not so circumstanced by nature. A company which had purchased an enormous territory from the United States Government at five shillings an acre might well repay itself all the cost of a railway through that territory, even though the receipts of the railway should do no more than maintain the current expenses. It is in this way that the thousands of miles of American railroads have been opened; and here again must be seen the immense advantages which the States as a new country have enjoyed. With us the purchase of valuable land for railways, together with the legal expenses which those compulsory purchases entailed, have been so great that with all our traffic railways are not remunerative. But in the States the railways have created the value of the land. The States have been able to

## HE VISITS THE UNITED STATES

begin at the right end, and to arrange that the districts which are benefited shall themselves pay for the benefit they receive.

### THE FRONTIERSMAN

VISIT HIM, AND YOU WILL FIND him without coat or waistcoat, unshorn, in ragged blue trousers and old flannel shirt, too often bearing on his lantern jaws the signs of ague and sickness; but he will stand upright before you and speak to you with all the ease of a lettered gentleman in his own library. All the odious incivility of the republican servant has been banished. He is his own master, standing on his own threshold, and finds no need to assert his equality by rudeness. He is delighted to see you, and bids you sit down on his battered bench without dreaming of any such apology as an English cottier offers to a Lady Bountiful when she calls. He has worked out his independence, and shows it in every easy movement of his body. He tells you of it unconsciously in every tone of his voice. You will always find in his cabin some newspaper, some book, some token of advance in education. When he questions you about the old country he astonishes you by the extent of his knowledge. I defy you not to feel that he is superior to the race from whence he has sprung in England or in Ireland. To me I confess that the manliness of such a man is very charming. He is dirty and perhaps squalid. His children are sick and he is without comforts. His wife is pale, and you think you see shortness of life written in the faces of all the family. But over and above it all there is an independence which sits gracefully on their shoulders, and teaches you at the first glance that the man has a right to assume himself to be your equal.

### FACTORY WORKERS AT LOWELL

THAT WHICH MOST SURPRISES an English visitor on going through the mills at Lowell is the personal appearance of the

## HE VISITS THE UNITED STATES

men and women who work at them. As there are twice as many women as there are men, it is to them that the attention is chiefly called. They are not only better dressed, cleaner, and better mounted in every respect than the girls employed at manufactories in England, but they are so infinitely superior as to make a stranger immediately perceive that some very strong cause must have created the difference. We all know the class of young women whom we generally see serving behind counters in the shops of our larger cities. They are neat, well dressed, careful, especially about their hair, composed in their manner, and sometimes a little supercilious in the propriety of their demeanour. It is exactly the same class of young women that one sees in the factories at Lowell. They are not sallow, nor dirty, nor ragged, nor rough. They have about them no signs of want, or of low culture. Many of us also know the appearance of those girls who work in the factories in England; and I think it will be allowed that a second glance at them is not wanting to show that they are in every respect inferior to the young women who attend our shops. The matter, indeed, requires no argument. Any young woman at a shop would be insulted by being asked whether she had worked at a factory. The difference with regard to the men at Lowell is quite as strong, though not so striking. Working men do not show their status in the world by their outward appearance as readily as women; and, as I have said before, the number of the women greatly exceeded that of the men.

One would of course be disposed to say that the superior condition of the workers must have been occasioned by superior wages; and this, to a certain extent, has been the cause. But the higher payment is not the chief cause. Women's wages, including all that they receive at the Lowell factories, average about 14*s*. a week, which is, I take it, fully a third more than women can earn in Manchester, or did earn before the loss of the American cotton began to tell upon them. But if wages at Manchester were raised to the Lowell standard, the Manchester women would not be clothed, fed, cared for, and educated like the Lowell women. The fact is, that the workmen and the workwomen at Lowell are not exposed to the chances of an open labour market. They are taken in, as it were, to a philanthropical manufacturing college, and then looked after and regulated more as girls and lads at a great seminary, than as hands by whose industry profit is to be made out of capital. This is all very nice and pretty at Lowell, but I am afraid it could not be done at Manchester.

## Reading Matter Everywhere

I DO NOT KNOW that anything impresses a visitor more strongly with the amount of books sold in the States, than the practice of selling them as it has been adopted in the railway cars. Personally the traveller will find the system very disagreeable, —as is everything connected with these cars. A young man enters during the journey,—for the trade is carried out while the cars are travelling, as is also a very brisk trade in lollipops, sugar-candy, apples, and ham sandwiches,—the young tradesman enters the car firstly with a pile of magazines or of novels bound like magazines. These are chiefly the 'Atlantic,' published at Boston, 'Harper's Magazine,' published at New York, and a cheap series of novels published at Philadelphia. As he walks along he flings one at every passenger. An Englishman, when he is first introduced to this manner of trade, becomes much astonished. He is probably reading, and on a sudden he finds a fat, fluffy magazine, very unattractive in its exterior, dropped on to the page he is perusing. I thought at first that it was a present from some crazed philanthropist, who was thus endeavouring to disseminate literature. But I was soon undeceived. The bookseller, having gone down the whole car and the next, returned, and beginning again where he had begun before, picked up either his magazine or else the price of it. Then, in some half-hour, he came again, with an armful or basket of books, and distributed them in the same way. They were generally novels, but not always. I do not think that any endeavour is made to assimilate the book to the expected customer. The object is to bring the book and the man together, and in this way a very large sale is effected. The same thing is done with illustrated newspapers. The sale of political newspapers goes on so quickly in these cars that no such enforced distribution is necessary. I should say that the average consumption of newspapers by an American must amount to about three a day. At Washington I begged the keeper of my lodgings to let me have a paper regularly,— one American newspaper being much the same to me as another,—and my host supplied me daily with four.

But the numbers of the popular books of the day, printed and sold, afford the most conclusive proof of the extent to which education is carried in the States. The readers of Tennyson, Thackeray, Dickens, Bulwer, Collins, Hughes, and— Martin Tupper, are to be counted by tens of thousands in the States, to the thousands by which they may be counted in our own islands. I do not doubt that I had fully fifteen copies of the 'Silver Cord' thrown at my head in different railway cars on the continent of America. Nor is the taste by any means confined to the literature of England. Longfellow, Curtis, Holmes, Hawthorne, Lowell, Emerson, and Mrs. Stowe, are almost as popular as their English rivals. I do not say whether or no the literature is well chosen, but there it is. It is printed, sold, and read. The disposal of ten thousand copies of a work is no large sale in America of a book published at a dollar; but in England it is a large sale of a book brought out at five shillings.

## Corruption in Public Life

It is not by foreign voices, by English newspapers or in French pamphlets, that the corruption of American politicians has been exposed, but by American voices and by the American press. It is to be heard on every side. Ministers of the cabinet, senators, representatives, State legislatures, officers of the army, officials of the navy, contractors of every grade,—all who are presumed to touch, or to have the power of touching public money, are thus accused. For years it has been so. The word politician has stunk in men's nostrils. When I first visited New York, some three years since, I was warned not to know a man, because he was a 'politician.' We in England define a man of a certain class as a black-leg. How has it come about that in American ears the word politician has come to bear a similar signification?

## American Men and Women

I CANNOT PART with the West without saying in its favour that there is a certain manliness about its men, which gives them a dignity of their own. It is shown in that very indifference of which I have spoken. Whatever turns up the man is still there,—still unsophisticated and still unbroken. It has seemed to me that no race of men requires less outward assistance than these pioneers of civilization. They rarely amuse themselves. Food, newspapers, and brandy-smashes suffice for life; and while these last, whatever may occur, the man is still there in his manhood. The fury of the mob does not shake him, nor the stern countenance of his present martial tyrant. Alas! I cannot stick to my text by calling him a just man. Intelligence, energy, and endurance are his virtues. Dirt, dishonesty, and morning drinks are his vices.

All native American women are intelligent. It seems to be their birthright. In the eastern cities they have, in their upper classes, superadded womanly grace to this intelligence, and consequently they are charming as companions. They are beautiful also, and, as I believe, lack nothing that a lover can desire in his love. But I cannot fancy myself much in love with a western lady, or rather with a lady in the West. They are as sharp as nails, but then they are also as hard. They know, doubtless, all that they ought to know, but then they know so much more than they ought to know. They are tyrants to their parents, and never practise the virtue of obedience till they have half-grown-up daughters of their own. They have faith in the destiny of their country, if in nothing else; but they believe that that destiny is to be worked out by the spirit and talent of the young women. I confess that for me Eve would have had no charms had she not recognized Adam as her lord. I can forgive her in that she tempted him to eat the apple. Had she come from the West country she would have ordered him to make his meal, and then I could not have forgiven her.

# Books on Trollope

AMONG a number of good books on Trollope, we recommend here a very short list. Michael Sadleir's *Trollope: A Commentary* (London, 1945) is an essential book for both background and interpretation of Trollope's work. L. T. and R. P. Stebbins' *The Trollopes: The Chronicle of a Writing Family* (New York, 1945) covers a wide range of critical and biographical interpretation, both of Trollope and his less famous brother and mother. J. H. Wildman's *Anthony Trollope's England* (Providence, 1940) offers an interesting analysis of social and intellectual elements in the Victorian England that underlies the Barchester novels. Interpretations by three critics who are themselves novelists, Henry James (writing in 1883), Hugh Walpole (writing in 1928), and Elizabeth Bowen (writing in 1945) are illuminating. Henry James's 'Anthony Trollope' appears in *Partial Portraits* (New York, 1899). Hugh Walpole devoted a book to *Anthony Trollope* (New York, 1928). Elizabeth Bowen's brief but stimulating comment for the B.B.C., in May 1945, appears as *Anthony Trollope: A New Judgment* (New York and London, 1946).

The increased interest in Trollope now is reflected in a new journal, *The Trollopian,* published quarterly at the University of California Press. It is 'Devoted to Studies in Anthony Trollope and His Contemporaries in Victorian Fiction,' under the able and spirited editorship of Bradford A. Booth of the University of California, with an impressive Advisory Board.

For Trollopians, new and old, there is a forthcoming event of great interest: the publication in the not too distant future at the Princeton University Press of *A Guide to Trollope* by

## BOOKS ON TROLLOPE

Winifred G. Gerould and James Thayer Gerould. The *Guide* will have an alphabetical record of characters and places having a significant role in the novels and stories and will list the precise whereabouts of scenes and persons.

So real was Trollope's imaginary county of Barsetshire that there have been three maps made of it. Trollope's own, Father Ronald Knox's, and Spencer van B. Nichols' are reproduced in Sadleir's *Trollope: A Commentary*. Father Knox's map is the basis for the one that forms the lovely endpapers of the World's Classics edition of Trollope. And Mr. Nichols in his *The Significance of Anthony Trollope* (New York, 1925) reproduces a version of his own map, done in colors by George F. Muendal.

# Index

The arrangement of the book makes an index of subjects unnecessary. The index to sources follows. The numbers in brackets are those of the pages in the volume from which the excerpt was taken; the figure following refers to the page in *The Trollope Reader*. Unless another publisher is indicated, all references in brackets are to the World's Classics Edition, Oxford University Press.

American Senator, The [51-3] 53, [327] 163, [504-5] 176, [76-9] 210, [194-8] 279, [349-50] 283, [471-3] 283, [253-4] 317

Ayala's Angel [193] 105, [132-3] 141, [243-4] 142, [126] 163, [464-5] 164, [31] 318, [295-6] 319, [11-12] 386, [346-7] 386, [446-7] 387

Barchester Towers (Modern Library) [383-4] 3, [408-10] 4, [682] 5, [416-20] 26, [743] 105, [559] 123, [566] 123, [288-9] 142, [632] 143, [224-5] 213, [228-9] 213, [245-6] 214, [560-61] 285, [705] 286, [357-8] 319, [593-4] 320, [656] 344, [659] 344, [302] 350, [554-5] 350, [555-6] 352, [525] 388, [568] 389, [582] 390, [589] 390

Belton Estate, The [211-16] 106, [88] 124, [224] 165, [412] 287

Bertrams, The (Harper, N. Y. 1871) [64-5] 28, [294] 110, [155] 143, [163] 165, [54-7] 235, [183-5] 329, [14] 352, [150] 360, [210-11] 360

Can You Forgive Her? [I 82-3] 5, [I 171-2] 6, [II 324-5] 7, [I 509-11] 8, [I 124-5] 30, [II 508-9] 31, [II 353-9] 55, [I 484-5] 111, [I 200-203] 177, [I 292-3] 287, [I 323] 288, [I 291-2] 321, [294] 361

Castle Richmond (Harper, N. Y. 1860) [9-11] 32, [372] 60, [7] 288, [107-8] 353, [7-8] 361

Claverings, The [284] 9, [14-16] 215, [85] 354

Dr. Thorne [20] 10, [1-2] 33, [331] 111, [410] 112, [436-7] 112, [8] 144, [380-85] 217, [29-36] 237, [375-8] 240, [402-3] 243, [532-5] 245, [472-3] 289, [526] 289, [194-6] 329, [266-7] 331, [17] 362

Dr. Wortle's School [151-4] 345, [5-7] 354

Duke's Children, The [I 369-70] 34, [I 161-8] 180, [I 276] 321, [II 148-52] 332

Eustace Diamonds, The [3-4] 10, [269-70] 11, [430-32] 35, [543-

[ 431 ]

## INDEX

Eustace Diamonds, The (Cont.)
6] 61, [155] 124, [331] 125, [279-84] 185, [357] 290, [165] 363, [262-3] 363
Eye for an Eye, An (Ward Lock, London n.d.) [24] 166, [270-71] 322

Framley Parsonage [21-2] 37, [413-14] 113, [184-5] 126, [184] 147, [120-22] 166, [163] 222, [15] 290, [261-2] 346, [112] 391

He Knew He Was Right (Strahan, London 1869) [II 100-101] 38, [I 62-3] 113, [I 248-9] 114, [I 49-51] 148, [I 274] 290, [I 360] 291, [I 200] 322, [I 293-4] 323
Hunting Sketches (E. V. Mitchell, Hartford 1929) [16] 189

Is He Popenjoy? (Ward Lock, London n.d.) [28-9] 38, [410] 151, [15-16] 168, [101-2] 292, [106-12] 324, [238-9] 358, [294] 365

John Caldigate [38-40] 41, [52-3] 365

Kellys and O'Kellys, The [53-5] 42, [6-7] 127
Kept in the Dark (Chatto, London 1891) [72-3] 169

Lady Anna [35] 293
Land Leaguers, The (Chatto, London 1884) [56-7] 190, [283] 293
Last Chronicle of Barset, The [I 436] 13, [I 172-6] 65, [II 282-6] 69, [II 419-25] 73, [I 149] 114, [I 157-8] 115, [I 148] 127, [I 433-5] 128, [II 451-2] 209, [I 224-5] 222, [I 440] 247, [I 361-2] 294, [I 53] 358, [I 260] 367, [I 95-6] 391
Linda Tressel (Blackwood, 1868, 2 vols.) [I 16-17] 43

London Tradesmen (Scribner's, N. Y. 1927) [75-6] 13, [13] 392, [32-3] 393

MacDermots of Ballycloran (T. B. Peterson, Phila. n.d.) [108-9] 44
Miss Mackenzie [217-18] 45
Mr. Scarborough's Family [572] 169, [575-6] 170, [264-5] 192, [127-8] 247, [148-50] 325

North America (Harper, N. Y. 1862) [1-2] 401, [16-17] 402, [20-25] 403, [32-4] 405, [36-7] 407, [182-3] 408, [299-300] 410, [301-2] 411, [369-70] 412, [111-12] 414, [188-9] 415, [220] 417, [220-21] 417, [230-31] 419, [126-7] 420, [128-9] 422, [245-6] 422, [270-71] 424, [385] 425, [395-6] 426

Old Man's Love, An [46-7] 130, [180-81] 131, [94] 224
Orley Farm [I 237-42] 79, [I 218-19] 116, [I 328-39] 171, [I 94-100] 249, [I 58-62] 258, [I 48-56] 262, [I 106-7] 295, [I 165-73] 295, [II 88] 300, [I 31-3] 356

Phineas Finn [II 159-60] 47, [II 253-7] 84, [I 253-6] 171, [I 266-75] 193, [I 81-2] 300, [II 128] 301, [II 196-8] 301, [II 34] 333, [II 57-8] 333, [II 61-2] 334
Phineas Redux [II 162-4] 87, [I 40] 335, [I 241] 346
Prime Minister, The [II 230-35] 89, [II 86-7] 131, [II 37-8] 270, [II 74] 271, [II 143] 272, [II 161-3] 272, [I 16-18] 303, [I 173-5] 303, [II 313-14] 304, [II 407] 305, [I 11-13] 335, [II 4-5] 336, [II 186-7] 337, [II 319-24] 338, [II 443-4] 340

Rachel Ray (Tauchnitz Collection of British Authors, vol. 680, Leipzig n.d.) [36] 274

# INDEX

Ralph the Heir [I 49-54] 14, [II 67-70] 132, [II 24-36] 201, [I 168-72] 225, [I 194-201] 305, [II 7-15] 341, [II 256] 368

Sir Harry Hotspur [40-41] 151, [62] 393
Small House at Allington, The [I 317-19] 17, [II 13-14] 19, [II 139-40] 20, [I 9] 48, [I 287-91] 93, [I 331-2] 116, [II 109-10] 117, [II 261-2] 118, [II 411-18] 134, [I 19] 151, [II 134-7] 152, [II 201-2] 154, [II 353] 155, [II 207-9] 174, [II 40-41] 250, [I 298-9] 311, [II 194] 367, [II 40] 394
Struggles of Brown, Jones and Robinson, The (Cornhill Magazine, vol. 4, August 1861) [182-4] 275

Tales of All Countries, 1st Series [135] 49, [203-4] 49, [243] 49, [234-5] 96, [122-3] 394
Thackeray (Harper, N. Y. 1901) [35] 368
Three Clerks, The [295-7] 21, [110-16] 97, [188-9] 156, [10-12] 251, [479-83] 252, [361] 275, [476] 347, [215-19] 369, [311] 374, [210] 395, [537-8] 395

Tireless Traveler, The (University of California Press, 1941) [217] 413
Travelling Sketches (Chapman and Hall, London 1866) [48-51] 23, [60-63] 375

Vicar of Bullhampton, The [330] 24, [43] 119, [302-3] 227, [59] 327, [305-6] 312, [310-11] 376, [292-3] 396

Warden, The (Modern Library) [7] 50, [130-31] 50, [75-6] 104, [73-4] 120, [148-9] 121, [57-60] 157, [8] 228, [15-16] 228, [31] 229, [47-8] 229, [112-13] 229, [152-4] 230, [157-9] 232, [66-7] 347, [142-3] 348, [131-2] 377, [143-5] 378
Way We Live Now, The [I 23-4] 160, [I 299-300] 161, [I 47-50] 312, [I 109-10] 327, [I 7-8] 349, [I 5-6] 380, [I 6-7] 381, [I 96-8] 382, [II 372-3] 384
Why Frau Frohmann Raised Her Prices (Chatto, London 1892) [342-3] 24, [110] 122, [270-71] 328

A153 2.50